ONLY T[...] ARE FREE

THE STORY OF A WAR CHILD IN GREECE

ANNA CHRISTAKE CORNWELL

To Mary,
Best wishes
Anna Christake Cornwell
5/20/2006

Royal Fireworks Press
Unionville, New York

English translation by Anna Christake Cornwell
Cover: Allen M. Hart
Cover Design: Adam J. Hart
Published under the title: *Mono Ta Poulia Einai Leftera*
in Athens, Greece in 1996

Royal Fireworks Press
First Avenue, PO Box 399
Unionville, NY 10988
(845) 726-4444
FAX: (845) 726-3824
email: rfpress@frontiernet.net

ISBN: 0-88092-571-X Library Binding; 0-88092-572-8 Paperback

Printed in the United States of America using vegetable-based inks on
acid-free, recycled paper by the Royal Fireworks Printing Co. of Unionville, New York.

DEDICATION

To the memory of Anne Frank and to the children of
all the world who were lost in the war.

TABLE OF CONTENTS

1 FAREWELL

The world is at the doorstep of a holocaust.

It is early May 1940, and all around me so much is happening every day. Swept up by events that surge forward like an avalanche, I search with terror for some meaning to the storm that has swallowed me up.

At the railroad station of a small Balkan country, a little girl still, dressed in my Sunday best, I'm saying good-bye to my father. The train is nearing the station. It will take him away, far, far away—perhaps forever. I stand there quietly... Only my heart can't be silenced. It pounds without stopping, inside my chest which has just begun to sprout tiny buds, pressing it, swelling until I can feel the beat inside me mounting to a crescendo, to the brink of an explosion. I wait for the time to pass, for an end to that thumping, that echo of some primitive rhythm being perpetuated in my heartbeat. Maybe my arms folded tightly across my chest can hold it still.

All around me, other sounds, other voices seem to be taking the shape of words. Something like a conversation. What can they be saying? My head is buzzing. I turn and notice, dimly at first, then more distinctly in the brilliant clarity of the azure spring sky, the silhouettes of relatives and friends. All are well dressed, deeply immersed in discussion, waiting to say farewell.

"The inviolate Maginot Line at the French border collapsed without anyone firing a single shot at the German invaders. Just one blow shattered untold hopes for the defense of France. The old world is falling apart. One country after another capitulates to the overpowering force of

1

the Nazis," claims Uncle John, the oldest and most learned among the relatives standing around.

As usual, he commands everyone's respectful attention, straining to his full height, which is not so impressive, gaining in admiration what he lacks in feet and inches. Besides his reputation as a *roué* who charms all the ladies that constantly swarm around him, he is generous to a fault. At every gathering he is the life of the party, distributing largesse left and right, singing, though he has no voice to speak of, telling *risqué* jokes, as the party brims with *kefi*, that indefinable *joie de vivre*. That's just when he slips off quietly to a corner to enjoy the festivities from a distance. Then the whole bunch of us kids milling around looking for some mischief, runs over to him, hoping he'll give us a treat.

"Off you go now, you little rascals, and get yourselves some candy. Remember now, be good." He tweaks everyone's ear "to make you grow faster," he says, laughing, as we try to squirm out of his reach.

"What concerns me," interjects Mr. Karayiannis, an aging lawyer, puffing on his old meerschaum pipe, "is that every European and Scandinavian country is capitulating to the superior maneuvering skills of the Nazis..." He pauses to scratch his balding head. "I don't know how they do it. Such an overpowering force..." He returns to his contemplative stance, gazing into the distance over the top of everyone's head.

"When will we see an end to this awful mess?" My mother sighs and turns her head furtively to wipe the tears from her reddened eyes. On her thin, carefully powdered, sensitive face, a dark stain marks the crease where the tears flowed, a dry riverbed after the rain has stopped.

"Don't you see?" says Mrs. Pezmazoglou, a refugee from Asia Minor who is my mother's close friend. "Those Germans attack one country after another, and the poor people don't even have a chance to do anything about it! They just crumble. It's terrible." Her black, almond-shaped eyes glance tearfully at my mother, looking for approval.

My father noiselessly moves his lips when a sudden gust of wind swallows his words. Or did he ever say them?

Holding my brother Tasio in his arms, he starts playing peek-a-boo. One of his favorite games. Now you see me, now you don't. He slides over to the other side of the platform, away from the clamor that abruptly stops before he has a chance to finish what he is secretly saying.

"Son..." His voice bounces back loud and clear. "You'll be the man of the house now, right? Now that daddy will be gone..." He can be heard laughing, a dry humorless laugh, but no one joins in. He moves closer to the company gathered around and starts cracking his stale jokes that no longer amuse me. His black eyes aren't smiling. Nor are my mother's.

"Can't you stop that nonsense now? Is this a time for jesting?"

"Oh, just leave us alone to have some fun, for Pete's sake."

"Ouf, *aman*." She sighs. "If I hear one more of your silly jingles, I'll scream."

"I scream, you scream, we all scream for ice cream." He starts joking around again, reciting one of his jingles, to weasel his way out.

Ice cream was his specialty. Homemade in his own ice cream parlor, the "Sugar Bowl." A few years before my parents decided to come back to their homeland, my father bought a store in Freeland, in the remote, small Pennsyl-

3

vania coal mining town where we lived. The winters were long and cold, and it snowed and snowed, covering every inch of land with snow so high I could jump over our porch, a full story above the ground, and land right in a great big white heap without getting hurt. Spring came late, ushered in by a country fair to chase away those winter doldrums. It featured merry-go-round rides, popcorn, cotton candy, and all the fun you could wish for. At night, the huge Ferris wheel glowed—all lit up, bigger than life. It stood right in front of my father's store that was next door to the only movie house in town. They let me in for free, so I got to see a lot of movies with my friends, who loved stopping afterward at my father's store for ice cream and candy.

Hopping on board the Ferris wheel, I watched, mesmerized, as the huge spokes of the wheel turned, swinging the seats loosely back and forth at each upward motion, pausing to take on more passengers, and then starting up again. Way up high, the twinkling machine came to a complete standstill once, I remember so well. Perched at the very top, that much closer to the dark sky, the chair dangled precariously in midair. The world below, packed with a festive crowd, resembled a marionette theater. My parents—two tiny people, heads upturned—gaped and gestured, watching me sit there all alone at the tippy top, and I not even five yet. Not a sound came through to me. Maybe they were saying what they had often whispered hush-hush before.

"Can't you see? She's a wild one." *'Agrimi'* was the word they used, figuring they could hide their meaning from me. "We should go back to our homeland before she runs away some day and just disappears. You never know in this country. Such strange things happen. Children run away from their parents, never to be seen again." Their words come back to me now, with all the bitterness I felt a long time ago.

I waved to them, thrilled to the core, hoping the machine would jam and stay there forever. I was in my element. Fearless and free, so high up in the air where I couldn't hear their hurtful words, glorying in my triumphant solitude.

Daring and brave, "like your grandfather," my mother often said. Unafraid, except of chickens. We bought them fresh killed at the chicken farm. Once, the beheaded beast escaped. I watched in horror as it ran around the yard, thrashing from side to side. The blood spattered in every direction. Sometimes it came menacingly close, mindlessly flailing its wings, totally out of control, yet it was still full of life. I was petrified. My mother paid the farmer, and we rushed home before it got dark. We only made a quick stop on the way at my father's store for some ice cream. Maybe that could cool my feverish head.

Suddenly the train reaches the station. The shrill, deafening wail sweeps aside all thoughts in its path, leaving in its wake a sense of raw, relentless pain.

An inhuman crashing noise bursts out close by, and the enormous machine-driven snake slithers past me, blocking out the sun. A cold chill envelops me.

The train screeches to a halt. Mr. Georgakas, a family friend and my father's business partner is standing next to me. Perhaps he sees my body trembling—or do I imagine he does—and says with indifference, his voice cold and distant, "You mustn't cry, you're a big girl." I feel orphaned. The whole world as I've known it until now is collapsing before me, and my own cry can't be heard.

Irrational absurdities are forbidden! Neither cries nor tears. Nothing. Silence. Drown your sobs; they're out of place.

He pulls away from me, adding. "It's embarrassing. You're a big girl now, you shouldn't cry," he says, moving away from the pile of crushed cigarette stubs that are gathered in front of his well-polished shoes. As he withdraws, a distance, an abyss separates me from the people around me. I feel fragmented, like a castaway. It's as though the ground underneath my feet is splitting in two, leaving me suspended between two opposed worlds. Unable to bear the rift, I feel a double separation. One, tangible, happening right here: parting from my father. Another, intangible: something being torn from the core of my being by the supposedly well intentioned who are indifferent to my existence. They won't let me lament openly, in my own way, the sorrow of parting.

Parting. Arms join, bodies separate, eyes tear; a lonely hand awkwardly waves a handkerchief in the air. The train whistles. "Don't cry, don't cry." Wrench yourself from your deepest feelings. No one stirs. They can't or they don't want to? Who knows? Your world doesn't exist. It doesn't matter who you really are. "You're a big girl now." Even while a deeply rooted part of you is fragmenting, the aloof bystanders, unknowingly perhaps, snatch you away from the most vital part of your being. They're only aware of the outer shell, the moth's cocoon, not the butterfly shuddering inside. They don't see the flame burning. Put it out, but not with your tears. "You don't cry." Not now. It's forbidden.

Those tears will remain until they dry. Forever. Burning.

Now, only a small hand shyly waves a wispy white handkerchief without uttering a single cry. Without a sob, as it should be. Eyes bone dry remain riveted on the huge metal machine moving away...running...running...running.... The wheels whirl against the edge of the platform, rapidly disappearing in the horizon. A dear face framed in the window of the train makes one final fleeting impression before the last turn, and every trace is lost.

That small, fluttering white bird quivering in my hand returns countless times in my dreams. Only my tears witness the ache in my heart. Only they bridge the void of my loneliness.

The next day on the way home from school, my friend Barbara asks me out of the blue, "how come your father left alone?" I look at her puzzled.

"You told me," she goes on, "that the American Consulate sent two official notices to your family about the threatening danger of a world war."

How true! It's strange! I really hadn't thought about it like that before, even though we talked about the war all the time at home.

"Why didn't you leave with him?" she insists while I try to find an answer.

"He went ahead to take care of his business first," I answer, sounding glum. "We'll join him later."

She makes a face, as if to say, "Don't take me for a fool," and we walk home side by side, without either of us exchanging another word. I vividly recall the time before my father went to America, and try to put the pieces of the puzzle together to make some sense of it all.

Barbara's question hounds me. *Why, why, why did he do it?* I ask myself, climbing slowly up the stairs.

For months I had been going back and forth to the consulate with my father to get his papers ready before leaving. At the same time, our papers also had to be prepared for our departure when he sent for us. As an American citizen, I had to accompany him everywhere to straighten out all the endless bureaucratic red tape, to get the official stamps, and, of course, the necessary signatures.

The American Consulate issued a warning. "War is impending. If you do not take your family with you now, their lives are endangered."

"Sir, my mother-in-law is deathly ill. My wife can't leave her in this state," he said, without blinking an eyelid. "How can I ask her to do that?" His voice was obsequious, without a trace of guilt, although he knew full well my grandmother had been dead for months! He wouldn't let anything stand in his way.

My grandmother, Theodora, was truly a gift of the gods. The whole village where she was born, married, and raised a family of eight children worshiped her. In reverence, the villagers called her an "Evangelio," The Holy Book. They rushed to her bedside where she lay incurably ill to receive her blessing, to have one last parting word to remember her by. Forever to be guided by her wisdom.

She died as she had lived all of her life: with the simplicity she was known for and the serenity that set her apart, a source of comfort and strength to everyone. Death didn't frighten her. Nor pain. After all, she knew it so well. "Tall mountains have no fear of snow," as the saying goes. And she dwelt a lifetime near one the tallest of them all, the perennially snow-capped Mt. Olympos, that never feared the snow it knew so well.

Her funeral—a pious worship, an offering honoring life—I wasn't allowed to attend. I who loved her probably more than anyone, could not go.

"The trip might do you harm," as though that mattered. "Maybe you'll even get sick again." Excuses. "And the cost," my father stressed the point, closing the matter. That was probably it. What else did he care about?

She had died and with her, a part of me. She who had nurtured me to health all summer, sharing her tranquility, helping me follow the doctor's strict orders, giving me sustenance beyond food, most of which was off-limits anyway: no meat, no milk, no fish, no egg, not even a hint of that poison that could make the yellowness come back.

"Stick out your tongue, open your eyes wide," my mother issued daily orders (as though I was going through military inspection) to look for telltale signs of the sickness, making me choke back my tears and wish for an end to this torment.

She peered without looking at me; she touched without stroking me. She examined me without healing me. I, alone, a vessel of ill health. As though it was an artificial body where you could study every detail of the human organism without it feeling anything.

Only my *nene* didn't judge, didn't raise her voice, but simply held my hand, taking me to her tiny room—the only one in the house with glass doors. She sat there knitting, patiently unraveling yarn, and undoing the tightest knots left by others. In the same way she knew how to quietly untangle worries, just like yarn that she handled deftly with her soft brown hands that I loved so dearly. Hands that amazingly knew the ways of tailoring and dressmaking by the time she was married at the age of sixteen.

"Everybody else is going to the picnic, except me," I complained. All summer everybody had gone on excursions, to have fun while I kept the yellow monster at bay.

"Never mind, child, they'll be back soon. You take care now and get well soon. That's the most important thing. Come near me and let me tell you a story, now," my *nene* said to me. Her words eased the pain and were a solace for little-understood, tender wounds.

"Worry, that's what gave her jaundice." My mother knew for sure. "After what we went through when we first came back to our homeland, the poor girl," she added, wiping her tears. "No wonder, she couldn't take it any more. She understood what was going on. She could hear my in-laws' accusations and snide comments that my husband had returned to his country too soon, without sufficient funds. Stinging wounds. They knew how to hurt, my in-laws. She could tell, so sensible."

Always that word. Thrown at me like an affliction, expecting me to understand their problems. "Sensible." Just hearing it made me feel as though I was carrying a heavy load and my back was permanently fitted with a saddle.

"Pray for us," I was told whenever things didn't go right.

"Why me?" I dared ask once.

"You're innocent and your prayers will be heard."

I knelt dutifully, thinking that by doing that I could make my family's worries disappear. Until the yellowness attacked me.

My grandmother was truly a *nene* who never said no, only yes, "ne." Not once, but twice, "ne, ne," and so she was forever christened "Nene."

Only I couldn't accompany her to her last domain, to be near her for one last time, to touch her hands, to know for myself that this was the end.

"Revered in life, her death should have been just as fittingly honored," I thought to myself, watching my mother and brother leave to attend my Nene's funeral, pleading, crying, knowing surely that if worrying could cause sickness, it would do so again, spreading to my eyes and liver and beyond for I was heartbroken. All to no avail, I had to stay in Thessaloniki with my father.

And yet, that sad event in my life didn't hinder my father, a few months later, from "resurrecting" her right before my very eyes when he applied to the American Consulate for his papers. To accomplish his goals, he even produced a certificate to prove that my grandmother was gravely ill.

Intent on getting his way, he went ahead following his own plan and dragged me from one office to another. He brushed off my mother's feeble objections by saying, "I know what I'm doing. If you don't like it, you know what you can do."

At every visit we had to satisfy the whims of one petty consular clerk or tax official or another. And it never failed that each one of them found some new excuse to send us to another official, often miles away, who then proceeded to send us somewhere else.

There was always something to do. Off we went as he held on to my hand, tickling my wrist with his pinky every so often, like he did when I was a little girl, to complete the 'procedures' that went on and on, without rhyme or reason. Constant delays stretched out from weeks to months. By the end of each day, we would tramp out of the office, fed up with the whole mess, but with one big difference. The officious petty clerk suddenly bowed down low as he started to close the door, full of promises:

"I assure you tomorrow everything will be O.K. Don't worry, all you need is one more official stamp,"

How odd! All the time we waited for hours to be taken care of he never raised his head to look at us. Now he gave glib assurances with an unctuous smile pasted on his corpulent face as he peered at us through his thick eye-glasses.

"Tomorrow everything will be taken care of without any delay. I assure you, everything will be O.K. Be patient. Tomorrow. Tomorrow, sir."

Armed with the endless enthusiasm of my few years, I bounced outside, running to tell my mother the good news.

"...The Sudan was attacked in the northern strip of the Maginot line..." The radio voice droned. I paid no attention. I had something else on my mind.

"Listen Mommy?" I cut in with my latest information, "I have good news. Tomorrow..."

"Aman! There's no end to that tomorrow. Every day they tell you the same story. I'm tired of hearing it," she snapped back one day and brushed me aside to turn the fish frying in the pan before they burned to a crisp. The tomato and chopped onion salad was already on the table. When we sat down to eat, my father turned on the radio to listen to the daily war report and the talking stopped.

"Parachutists invaded Belgium and Holland..." the dreary voice announced on the radio.

"Such terrible news from the European front. I thought we might have some relief, but instead I'm getting totally discouraged" my mother grumbled in a low voice, sounding exasperated.

"Are you kidding? It's nothing, I tell you. They just carry on; we don't have a thing to worry about. We're miles away from the fighting," my father answered, putting another fried fish on his plate.

One point was for sure. My father's decision was final. No one could change his mind. He was sure of himself and wouldn't listen to anybody. One day I overheard them talking.

"Other families that came here like us to educate their children in our mother tongue and visit our homeland are catching the next boat out because they see the mounting danger of war ahead," my mother said.

"Who said I wanted to come back? We could have stayed put." My father snapped back.

"For heaven's sake! What are you saying, Petro, wasn't that your wish as much as mine? Arguing like that in front of the children..."

"Woman, will you let me have some peace of mind?" he barked.

"Can you tell me what we'll live on? What can I collect from your debtors? You know what they're like. Don't leave me to shoulder the whole burden all by myself with two small children to feed," she pleaded in a broken voice. Hearing this always made me scared. What would we live on?

"All you do is worry," he shot back.

"All you care about is money," she fumed.

Arguments like that got started and before long, old conflicts resurfaced. Relatives and friends dropped in all the time and joined in the political discussions that usually ended up in more heated quarrels. Everybody had a pet theory.

"There's no danger of a world war," some maintained.

"Hopeless optimism," insisted others.

"Can't you see what's happening?" Uncle Demetrios' passionate voice bellowed and his deep-set blue eyes flamed with anger. "What else can the outcome possibly be?"

"You're right," Uncle Yiannis added. "The Nazi Axis doesn't only threaten the Europeans, but everybody. Hitler has no intention of stopping at Danzig or anywhere else. He wants to conquer the whole world."

"Nonsense," insisted Uncle Niko, with just as much passion, "it's just a passing storm. You've got to look at the total picture from a historic standpoint. What does Hitler want with so many far-flung countries? What he cares about is protecting his own borders. Once he reaches his goal, he'll stop. Mark my words. In a couple of months this whole thing will blow over, just as though nothing happened..." His dark brown eyes flashed around the room gathering admiring glances.

"If you ask me," Uncle Niko started up again, "Petro is the luckiest one."

"You can say that again," chimed in Mr. Karayiannis, "he's leaving an old world collapsing in the throes of a terrifying onslaught. Who knows where it will lead?" He sprang to his feet, pontificating in his best legalese style.

"Listen," he tugged Uncle Niko's lapel in a conspiratorial stance, as though he was going to let him in on an important secret. Everyone knew, of course, it was all part of his showmanship. His voice blasted your ears. Always making a play for his audience, in and out of the courtroom. Part of his style.

While my mother listened, she ironed clothes and deftly mended socks. Her uncommon speed betrayed the turmoil she tried to keep under control. Pressing the iron even harder, she made the shirt collar look store-bought crisp. She hurried back and forth to the stove, quickly stirring the food in the large black pot she always used to make stew, fragrant with spices and herbs. Many times she said in despair: "Soon I'll have to face life alone with two little children and no husband to support me. How can I manage?"

It made me scared to hear her whisper in a trembling voice, "...How will we live?" What would become of us?

"It's hard enough now. From the time we got here your brother has been accusing you of returning to your homeland too soon, without enough money..." my mother rekindled old wounds.

"He should talk," he interrupts. "I sent a fortune to educate him, and today he's feathering his nest."

"All I know is when you leave, I'll have to face the music alone, but you can't hear out of that ear. You and your cronies refuse to face the facts."

"Fiddlesticks."

Then she changed to one of her more philosophical moods while my father dozed off on the sofa and I stood by idly. "The smell of gunpowder is everywhere. The German Stukas fly around looking like prehistoric dinosaurs that sprouted huge wings and threaten the world with death and destruction. It's a sinful world and maybe that's our punishment...but why do the innocent have to suffer?"

"Who are the innocent?"

"You, the children, are."

"Why?" I asked.

"Because you have not sinned," she stated emphatically.

"Have you?" I asked, burning with curiosity.

"Everybody has faults," she murmured.

"If it's not my fault, it's not yours either." That brought a faint smile to her lips.

My mother prepared suitcases and boxes, but as time went on the future appeared threatening to her.

"More and more I see the threat of war worsening rather than lessening. Whenever I listen to those German military marches, inspired by Wagnerian themes, I have the impression that they're getting closer to us. I hope I'll be proven wrong."

My father and his friends saw things in a different light. They envied him for having the good luck to be returning to paradise and he, in turn, had no doubts about his decision. He was set on his course of action. He proceeded, fully confident in himself, laughed, cracked jokes and on Sundays after church he took me with him to the local taverna to buy some *kokkineli* wine for dinner.

"After all," he beamed, flashing a set of perfect white teeth, "isn't that popular song, right? 'Drink another glass of wine; sing another song and you'll feel fine.'" Well, that's certainly the secret of the good life—to rest on a well founded decision that leaves no room for worry. We examine what lies ahead with open eyes. We're not heading toward a utopia, but toward a rosy future which we toast with another glass of *kokkineli* wine. He merrily twirled me and my brother around the table and raised his glass in the air chanting, "Happy Family, Happy Family, Happy Days are here again," the saying that was popular in the United States just before the depression in 1929 when all hell broke loose.

For days on end after my father left, I try to understand what happened in such a short time that suddenly completely changed my life. I watch other girls strolling with their father along the waterfront, the *paralia* in Thessaloniki, pausing to enjoy some luscious looking pastries at the Cafe de la Quay. I wonder how they can be so carefree.

I often see my mother writing to my father with tears in her eyes and sometimes she even reads parts of it to me.

Thessaloniki 24/5/40

Dear Petro,

After so much anxiety, it was a blessing to receive your letter from Lisbon and I thank God that you arrived there safely and hope that today you will arrive in that blessed land.

We spent your name day on the 21th with a few friends who didn't neglect us and came to greet us.

Life is the same, it rains every day. When I go shopping I think of you with all my heart. I'm fed up. Walking tires me out this year, I don't know why, but everything will pass as long as we and the children are healthy and we collect what we earned by the sweat of our brow.

I get dizzy trying to figure out what is happening with the promissory notes. I was so upset when you were telling me about them, and now it's even worse. My brother-in-law Pavlos has not come over to help me, and my brother Demetrios is away on a trip. I'm complaining because I don't have anyone to help me.

The children are well. Tasio sighs when he hears your name, but I take him out to play with his friend. Ioanna understands my position and feels sorry for me.

A few days later my mother receives another letter from America. At the bottom of the last page there is a message for us children. "Beloved offspring, I bestow a kiss upon your forehead."

What is he saying from that faraway land? Even his words sound foreign.

2 THE RED BALLERINA

From the time my father leaves, we're on the lookout for the mailman every day. The minute we spot him down the street, Tasio and I make a mad dash, taking the stairs two at a time, fighting over who will get there first. Will we get a letter from Daddy? Can we join him in America before war breaks out? Today we're in luck. Tasio clutches the letter in his hand, and we rush upstairs. My mother tears open the envelope in one swift motion. I watch her eyes dart back and forth on the page, holding my breath.

"Listen to this," she looks up at us. "He writes about setting up his business, the Sugar Bowl, that he found a place to live, and that he met some old friends. Not a word about our eagerly awaited trip.

"I don't see him rushing to get us out of here. What is he waiting for?" My mother bursts out. "When will he decide, when it's too late? Doesn't he listen to the news?" she wonders aloud.

"Don't worry, Mommy. Be a little patient," I say softly, not knowing what else to do.

"Can't you see, child, that the whole world is in turmoil? I just read that the Germans are taking over all of Europe. This...this not knowing what will happen is eating me up."

"Maybe we'll have better news in the next letter," I answer. As I hurry out the door, I see her sit down next to the little end table where she keeps her writing material and take a folded piece of lined paper and her pen to write:

My dear and good Petro,

Every day I wait for your letter, but unfortunately, again today I didn't get any—you are keeping us in great anguish. I'm saying that if you had written surely we would have received it because from there all the letters do come, even if they are delayed a little.

The papers for our trip didn't arrive yet, but also without any money what can we do?

The money that I am collecting is trickling in and it is barely enough for us—prices are so high—yesterday I paid almost 1,000 drachmas for some old school expenses for Ioanna, her graduation certificate, and registration fees for both children because Tasio is starting school soon, he is a lovable boy, it makes me sad that he misses being with you.

I hardly need to mention how hard our separation from you is for all of us.

With love and kisses,
Maria

A few weeks later, at Uncle Demetrios' house where I go to play with my cousin Niko, everybody is busy just twirling around the room, doing nothing. Only my uncle is sitting quietly next to the radio, waiting to hear the special news bulletin.

"Keep still, for heaven's sake! We have to find out what's going on in the world." He scowls, and only then do we obey and the room becomes silent.

"Beautiful Paris capitulated today to the deathly enemy blow," the radio announcer says in a grave tone, and then he goes on. "Paris no longer exists! It succumbed to the

German army." He slowly paces his words like a funeral dirge. "The surprise German invasion from the north forced the Allied troops to retreat from France. Only ten days ago, Dunkirk was evacuated under harrowing conditions and, miraculously, three-hundred-thousand men escaped."

It's obvious that these developments have shaken my uncle's usually serene manner. "They will eat us alive!" he fumes, and his ruddy face is flushed beet red, his blue eyes darkened to the color of a stormy sea under steel-gray clouds. His congenial expression has changed to irritation, as he alternately tenses and relaxes his face muscles. What catches my attention is how his tightly clenched fists blanch, and then redden, in step with his fury.

"Why are you getting all worked up? Let them fight it out, just as long as they leave us alone," his rotund wife, Aunt Aspasia, says as she munches on Kalamata figs stuffed with roasted walnuts.

"What are you talking about?" he roars, turning his fierce glance toward her. His face instantly turns to beet red. "Do you think for a moment that they'll just leave us alone?" he adds as his eyes flash with rage.

As soon as my aunt sees how upset he is, she becomes visibly alarmed, knowing that he suffers from hypertension, and she starts taking it out on the Germans.

"A curse on Hitler for getting us in this mess," she wails, raising her trembling hands toward the ceiling. After each outburst she brings her dimpled hands together, then quickly apart so as not to disturb the rhythmic chewing of one stuffed fig after another.

The differences between my aunt and uncle are clear: they are a pair of opposites. He, mercurial, expansive, suffers from chronic high blood pressure and hypertension; she, indolent, lethargic, unshakable, revels in her hypochondria.

Then she dips her plump hand to grab another handful of nuts, and in her absentmindedness, since she was still staring at the ceiling, knocks down the plate and they all spill on the floor.

"You're a real 'lefty,' you can't do anything right," her daughter Katina says, and everybody laughs, clearing the air a bit.

It's only when Niko asks me to play a game of Old Maid with him, that I suddenly realize how late it is.

"I have to go," I say, waving a hurried good-bye.

"Take care now." Uncle Demetrios walks me to the door with a warm smile on his genial face. "Everything will turn out all right."

At home I find my mother all worked up over the latest developments. The news had traveled all over Thessaloniki. Throngs of people gathered at street corners and storefronts talk of nothing else.

"We must leave as soon as possible." She catches her breath. "Look, other people are finding ways to go back," she adds, almost to herself. "Why can't we do the same thing?"

"We'll find some way soon, Mommy, don't worry," I answer, outwardly cheerful, to reassure her. I just can't bear to see her so upset. Time passes and my mother is constantly writing letters to my father.

Thessaloniki 20/9/40

Dearest Petro,

God took pity on me at last and blessed me with a letter from you after two months since your last card,

21

and I am comforted that you received a few of our letters.

I was so happy to read your letter over and over, I cannot tell you how many times. I am surprised though that you don't ask about anything since you left so many matters unsettled. Trying to collect some of the money that was owed to us has become a terrible nightmare.

These days I am trying to rent a room in our apartment. I am waiting for your reply with specific suggestions about matters that concern me so you can shed some light and help guide me about what to do.

I avoid every contact with people and pass my time with my daily housework and shopping. I don't go anywhere because I get upset when people ask me questions. Look what I've come to!

The separation seemed easy to you, you thought it was just a matter of months. Remember what I said to you? I asked about our papers at the consulate and they told me that they would let us know when they come from Athens. That's how time passed, it is so hard for us, but what can we do, what do we have in our hands?

Tasio says he wants to learn quickly how to write so that, "I can write to my good Daddy."

Ioanna's school will cost 2,500 drachmas, I don't think it will come to the point that we can't pay this, she is a wonderful girl with rare qualities and one day in our old age we will benefit. Besides, what she learns today also makes us proud and is like a jewel that she wears with pride and will also benefit her children some day. Now, of course, we have to make sacrifices...

Early one morning she sends me to find out on which boat the Makris family is leaving. They still live in our old neighborhood on Syngrou Street near the Dioikitirio, the municipal building with its tall columns. On the way, I go through the Dioikitirio plaza for a quick run up and down its tree-lined marble stairs, jumping them two at a time. I remember the games I often played there with my friends from the neighborhood. Among them I had many Jewish schoolmates; we often did our homework together, either at my house or theirs. That's how our families got to know one another and we were invited to weddings or other celebrations at the nearby synagogue, while on other occasions my parents invited them over for our holidays.

When Abraham Pelassof's daughter got married, I remember the splendid wedding ceremony at the synagogue. What impressed me was the vast, simple interior without any icons, the white embroidered woven canopy covering the bride and groom, the plaintive, sonorous voice of the rabbi, as though he was lamenting the woes of the centuries, and at the end, the smashing of the glass, a custom in Jewish weddings. Afterward there was a sumptuous feast in grand style at the father's house where they served so many different kinds of food, all new to me. I had an insatiable hunger to see and know more.

The next day my friends and I got together again to play. One of our favorite after-school games was to climb on the roof of a cackling old lady's house, just to hear her go into one of her tirades.

"You naughty rascals, get out of here!" she screamed at us. We danced and jumped on the corrugated aluminum roof of her house that she could only reach with a ladder, calling out in Ladino whatever silly things came to our head. How we teased her! "You're deafening me! You, you good-for-nothings," she yelled even louder. The old lady usually ended up chasing us.   She shook the huge broom that she used for sweeping the roof, grabbing it with her gnarled, wrinkled hands like an old witch's.   Finally, that drove us away.   We burst out laughing and ran off to continue our game of hide-and-go-seek on the sidewalk where she couldn't catch us.

I happened to meet Rebecca one day, a beautiful, lively Jewish girl a little older than I, and she joined us.   Rebecca was the daughter of a diplomat who traveled to many parts of the world, and she knew everything.   I couldn't stop listening to her.   She could tell you about places I had never even dreamed existed: Hawaii, Japan, Alaska...

"You know what they wear in Hawaii?" she asked, as I sat gaping at her.   "Grass skirts, and they do the hula- hula dance, like this."   She shook her hips until we both squealed with laughter.   "In Japan people bow down to the ground instead of shaking hands when they meet in the street."   She imitated the gesture.   "And the Eskimos don't kiss like we do, they rub noses."   We giggled till I thought I'd burst. She talked for hours about the clothes they wear, their food, and the curious things they do so differently from us.   How I longed to be there to see with my own eyes all those wonders she described so vividly.

Once, while we were running on the steps of the municipal building, Rebecca stopped suddenly and stared at me with her chestnut eyes.

"Do you know if the Red Ballerina arrived?" she asked.

"No," I answered, "I don't know anything about her performance."

She tossed her head back, letting her thick, reddish-gold hair shake, as she burst out laughing.   I looked at her, puzzled.

"She comes often," she said, sitting on a step.

"Where," I said, "and so what?" I was feeling uneasy, but I didn't want it to show.

Rebecca must have sensed my annoyance and whispered in my ear about the mysterious visitor.

"One day she'll also appear to you, very soon. You'll recognize her by her red outfit. Mark my words," she said, disappearing around the corner. She was in a hurry to be home before sundown.

I take my time going home thinking about what Rebecca had told me. It stirred up my curiosity. That image of the red ballerina dashing around is floating in front of me, creating an intense desire to enter that magic world of delirious dancing, to be enveloped by a transparent silken veil, to see the world in rosy hues fleeing hurriedly before me. I can hardly hold back my excitement, but I don't want anyone to know my secret. I want to glide in the aura of that mystique alone.

"What happened, what did you find out?" My mother rushes anxiously to the door as soon as she hears my footsteps.

"Hm?" I fumble for words. "I saw Rebecca and..."

"Never mind that... Tell me about the boat when can we go?" she asks insistently.

"Oh, yeah, I mean...no, it's all booked."

"Completely?" Her voice turns shrill.

"They said we'll have to wait for the next boat," I finally blurt out. Her hands drop to her side and she collapses in the chair.

Thessaloniki 9/10/40

What can I tell you Petro, you left me with a complicated financial situation, I have so many things to look after for the children, I don't have to tell you, at least if I had enough money for our daily expenses—rent, books, school uniform for Tasio, soles for their shoes, composition books, not counting food. I'm short of funds—yesterday they came for the rent and I didn't have money—you can imagine my position...

One day, when I least expect it, the "Red Ballerina" makes her appearance to me, just as Rebecca had told me. I'm overjoyed. I can't wait to share the good news with her, but she's nowhere to be found. I run all over looking for her, asking everybody who might know her whereabouts, but no one has a clue. Now when I need her most.

I expect the "Red Ballerina," to disappear just as suddenly as she came. That's why I'm baffled when after a little while she's not gone. Every night I think for sure the mysterious dance will end, but the next morning I wake up with a moist sensation in my loins, feeling her presence. Her dance lasts five whole days.

Rebecca hadn't prepared me for this continuous performance of the "Red Ballerina" and I search for her in vain to explain the mystery to me.

During the last few days, my mother must have suspected something and while she's braiding my hair she starts explaining what's happening. I'm shocked to find out how many women share my condition—even my mother.

"You can't take communion, of course," she advises.

"Why not?" I ask.

"You must be pure when you take the sacraments. You're accepting the body and blood of Christ, and they mustn't leave your body."

"How long will they stay in me?" I ask again.

26

"Oh, till the next time. Now, don't bother me with all that. Just remember what I told you because it's a sin."

At church on Sunday, I keep my promise. I don't take communion, just like some of my older cousins, all of them a full head or more taller than I, who stand next to me surprised.

"What are you doing here with us?" Katina asks.

"You know, I can't, Mommy said. You know why," I say, blushing.

They giggle, eyeing me in disbelief.

"Look at the little pip-squeak," they whisper, elbowing each other.

But I don't care. No one knows my secret about the "Red Ballerina." I can share that only with Rebecca. Perhaps she has gone from my life forever, but she left me a souvenir of the beautiful red dancer who periodically flows into my life.

3

WAR

Monday, October 28, 1940. Italy declares war on Greece.

In school my class is working on Latin exercises: "regina rosas amat," all the students read one by one from our old, well-thumbed textbooks. *Was she a beautiful queen?* I wonder. *What color were the roses in her garden? Probably red. Who took care of them, the gardener or the queen herself?* I can just picture her in a yellow taffeta gown, basket in hand, gathering roses for... Ding, ding, the recess bell rings while I'm still daydreaming.

"Class dismissed," our teacher calls out. We close our books, leaving the queen alone till next time. I walk out of the classroom, bumping elbows with all the other girls trying to get out first. When we reach the corridor of the apartment building that had been recently converted to a private school, Dolly sways her puny behind, as usual, then leans on the wooden balustrade. The minute she notices Aglaia coming over to join her, she commands in her saccharine voice, "Go down and get me a hot sesame *koulouri*. Here's a drachma," and she turns her back. Aglaia rushes down the stairs with Fifi and Rena at her heels to catch the pretzel street vendor who makes his customary rounds on school days. Some of the other girls are obviously annoyed that Dolly always gets her way.

"Who does she think she is, always expecting to be served?" says one of them.

"What do you care?" the next girl calls out.

"You're jealous," chimes in someone else, and before you know it they're in a heated argument.

I take my grease-stained lunch bag and leave them to enjoy my snack of bread and *kaseri* cheese far from the commotion caused by the imperious demands of the rich merchant's daughter.

I sit at one of the desks in an empty classroom down the hall, idly glancing at the names etched in the time-darkened wood—Meropi, Eleni, Nafsika, Agapi, Artemis—then gaze at the empty inkwell as it catches a ray of sunlight and glistens with a purple iridescence.

Every now and then sounds of laughter and teasing filter in and distract me for a moment, and then I return to my own thoughts.

Maybe I would also like to be part of that enchanting environment where friendship is bought, but something inside me fights against the thought of being humiliated like that. At the same time, I would like to be a "regina" who loves roses, is loved by one and all, unquestionably a ravishing beauty.

I catch a glimpse of Barbara as she moves away from the others and comes near me.

"Why are you sitting here by yourself? Were you upset about Dolly?" she asks, sitting at the edge of a desktop.

"O.K., she is who she is, but how can those girls stand being her servant?" I explode.

"Oh, well. It's not worth it," she says, laughing it off.

"You know, if I didn't attend this stupid private school, I wouldn't have to put up with all this nonsense," I complain.

"How can you be so sure?" she says, and her black eyes sparkle.

"One thing I do know," I tell her. "I would never go down five flights of stairs, or even a single step for that matter, to buy a *koulouri* on someone else's orders. I can do without such a friendship!"

"You're right," she agrees, sliding off the desk. "See you later. I better get those verbs done." She dashes out. I know that my mother was trying her best when she decided to send me to this school, as she explained in one of her letters to my father.

The children are going to school and I enrolled Ioanna in the Lyceum because in the other one the classes were too large and the students didn't have good supervision and the professors were too strict. She is a sensitive girl and these things upset her and now she is lively and the teachers treat them like their own children, especially Mrs. Deliou who told me that she is a reserved girl and she will be exemplary in class. I think she was lucky because I enrolled her two days before the registration closed and hope God helps her and keeps her in good health, she is precocious and needs extra care because the children's life is not very good—we are always economizing.

Tasio loves school, but he misses you and his sorrow is written all over his face. Whoever sees him notices it right away. Especially when he sees an uncle, I see how he reacts and how can I help being moved to tears.

I go back to reviewing French vocabulary for my next class, feeling a bit calmer. I close the door to shut out the giggling and teasing that had annoyed me earlier and concentrate on practicing the pronunciation of the new words on my list. I realize I don't have much time left, and I head for my French class.

One of my favorite poems is written on the blackboard, and I'm reminded of the vivid impression her voice made on me the first time I heard my French teacher chant: *"Sur le pont d' Avignon on y dance, on y dance..."* It must be so lovely to dance and sing on that Avignon bridge, the valley around it covered with fragrant spring flowers.

A solitary bird sitting on the dusty windowsill catches my attention and my mind races as I watch it flutter away. *Where is Avignon?* I wonder. *Near the Maginot line? I'll have to ask. We didn't cover that in class yet. What will happen to that bridge with all that shooting and bombing?* An abrupt noise makes me jump.

I dash to the door and see Mme. Belaire rushing into class dressed in her usual chic style, but flushed and agitated.

"What is she doing here before the bell rings?" I ask Barbara.

"I have no idea. She never comes in before everybody's seated." She says, glancing at me.

"That's right. I'm surprised," I whisper

"Why is she frantically waving her arms in the air?" I ponder while more girls stream in to take their seats in the old wooden school desks, and Mme. Belaire walks right past them without paying any attention.

What can be bothering her? I think, baffled.

A puzzled look is on everyone's face.

Finally, Mme. Belaire speaks. Her voice is abrupt, unnatural, without its usual melodious sound. She gestures, repeating over and over. "War, war was declared."

For a split second everyone is dumbfounded and a deep silence settles in the room, then there's bedlam. We all start yelling and asking questions:

"War?"

"Where? Here?"

"Here in Greece?"

"With whom?"

"Why?"

"What will we do now?"

"Silence!" Mme. Belair shrieks, "Don't you understand what I'm saying? We're at war with Italy." Then she adds more calmly. "All of you must go home, immediately. *Tout de suite. Ecoutez?*" Her French sounds hollow, but her voice is a little less strained. Barbara and I exchange a glance, too afraid to talk, but we're bursting with questions.

"Please, leave at once. The school is closing. *Au revoir,*" Mme. Belaire adds more quietly, dabbing the tiny sweat beads covering her upper lip.

The pushing and shouting that follows is wild! All the schoolgirls rush downstairs, trampling each other underfoot, taking two, three steps at a time, shoving and yelling to get out first. What a commotion! But without the high spirits that usually go along with an unexpected holiday.

What can all this mean? I wonder on the way down, then shrug my shoulders.

Oh, well, since we're getting off early I'll have to find out where I'm going to play. I didn't make any plans to meet my cousin Niko this early, of course, so I'll have to go looking for him. We can decide later how we'll spend our free afternoon. It's almost noon, though, and I have to go home for lunch first. Then I can go out again or maybe he'll come over to our house. We'll have fun, as we always do. Things are not so bad.

It's just annoying that I had to miss French because it's one of my favorite classes. I even took secret private lessons during recess from Marie, a captain's daughter. She speaks like a real Parisian and teaches me some risqué French.

"Ma cherie, I went to diplomatic receptions with my father and mother, and I met so many *extraordinaire* people. The ladies were *tres chic,* the way I'll be when I grow up."

I listened in awe.

Marie's flirtatiousness never fails to get the boys all excited, and after school they hang out on the sidewalk waiting for her.

"Hi, cutie," they shout. She just goes right past them, as though they don't even exist and casts sidelong glances with her bright brown eyes while we skip on the sidewalk saying some of the naughty French jingles we know:

> *Je vous aime, je vous adore,*
> *qu'est que voulez vous encore?*
> *Un baiser à la bouche.*

That thrilling kiss! Little did I know what meaning it would have for me some day. Only an occasional strange, imperceptible shiver betrayed a secret world vaguely appearing before me, akin to gazing, nose pressed against the windowpane, at a misty showcase full of exotic goodies no one has ever described before.

By the time we come downstairs the sidewalks are full of other girls and boys dismissed from neighboring schools and a huge crowd of people is reacting to the latest events.

"Can you beat that? They think we'll give up the minute they declare war on us," I hear someone yell in the middle of the street.

"What do they think we are? Sissies?" another passerby calls out, full of fury.

"Of course we had to say NO to our attackers. And we say it again." The raised fists of a bunch of screaming people standing on the sidewalk draws a lively crowd around them.

"We'll show those rascals, ha, ha ha." The red-haired butcher gets riled up and rushes outside his shop, waving his hatchet in the air.

The throngs of people with their loud, non-stop talking and lively gestures give the streets an almost festive appearance. I walk down the avenue half dragging my feet, not really knowing what to make of all this commotion. It doesn't feel like my usual after-school mood, but I can't get used to what just happened, either.

On my way home, just as I'm passing the office of Vasilios Anagnostopoulos, M.D., Otorhinolaryngologist, I catch sight of my mother at the other end of the block. Seeing that familiar sign feels good. What a marvelous word that is: o-to-rhi-no-la-ryn-go-lo-gist. Every time I see that imposing gilded sign I stare at it with an irresistible urge to spell it. It always does something to me, stirring up all kinds of curious sensations. Sometimes it tickles my nostrils, sometimes it fills my throat with saliva, and still other times it floods my ears with funny sounds. I look at that word, marvel at it, secretly spy on it like a modern detective, ready to pounce on it, if I have to.

This time though, I'm startled by my mother's voice from the opposite sidewalk. Surely, she heard about the war and came to find me.

"Why are you so late? What are you doing there? Daydreaming? Don't you realize there's a war? Come home right away!" I leave the otorhinolaryngologist's sign standing there unchanged, the same as ever. Only today the word is left unspelled.

I run across the street to catch up with my mother who walks at a clipped pace.

"Hurry up," she calls over her shoulder. "I left the pot on the stove."

"But Niko..." I start, but don't dare say another word. I can always tell when she takes a firm stand and won't give in. I obediently follow her home, feeling disappointed over my ruined plans.

Later that day the papers are full of enormous headlines. The whole front page is about the war, and the historic *"OHI,"* "NO" to the fascist invaders.

"In a single voice Greece declares a resounding 'NO' to Mussolini's Italian fascists who demand total surrender. This is a declaration of war on Greece. Our inexhaustible Greek heroism will defeat the enemy troops. We will never let the foreign invader set foot on our homeland! With God's help we will declare victory over our enemy who at this very hour is marching through Albania to try and conquer our land."

The Greek government issues decrees calling all men to arms, and the Defense Department mobilizes the whole country for wartime alert: strict curfew regulations, blackout at night, the closing of schools, etc. I hear that all citizens are cautioned against enemy air raids and notice people starting to protect their windows with black crisscrossed strips of cardboard.

I watch what's going on like it's something in the movies. My mind is really on Niko. *When will he show up?* I wonder. I can't wait to get together with him. *What's taking him so long?*

He arrives after lunch, and I'm thrilled. Now we can go out to play even earlier than usual.

"Only in front of the house," my mother cautions, "in case anything happens."

"Don't worry Mommy," I call out. Niko and I sneak a quick look at each other and muffle a giggle until the door closes behind us.

"What could possibly happen?" I say, laughing, and start skipping rope down the sidewalk.

4 THE BALCONY

The next day a brilliant autumn sun shines in the sky. I step out on the balcony, feel its warmth, and watch the gentle waves in the Thermaic harbor bouncing up and down in the sunlight, like children skipping merrily in the street. From our third floor apartment on Nikiforou Foka, a long, narrow street near the White Tower, I can clearly see the ocean. My heart tingles with joy, mixed with a feeling of deep calm and trust in the world as it unfolds before me. The blue, luminous sky gives me a sure feeling that all is going well. It's truly an idyllic day, a moment of harmonious stillness. There's something irresistible about it. It pulls like a magnetic, overpowering force that's crossing its infinitely travelled path for the first time, it seems. I surrender without resisting, floating on air. *So what if there's no school? So what if there's a war? Everything is beautiful and carefree.*

This perfect stillness is shattered by the piercing shriek of a siren that punctures the air. The sky begins to rain bombs that explode into a sudden cacophony, spreading death in every direction. Buildings crumble, sidewalks are shattered, and stores burst into flames, like dry kindling wood. Pedestrians, who were carefree a moment earlier, run panic-stricken to find shelter, but in vain. Unprepared as they are, they don't know which way to turn. Some are thrust into the air like puppets, while others stagger, mutilated, then fall in a pool of blood amidst the sound of cries, groans, and wails coming from everywhere.

Dark clouds of dust and gunpowder surround us. A flock of grey migrating birds is frightened in mid air. The sun disappears behind a cloud of black smoke. It is lost.

I stand transfixed by this horrible sight when all at once I feel myself swaying. The balcony I'm standing on starts to groan like an enormous rusty hinge. The floor creaks and shakes so hard, I can hardly hold on to the rail. Terrified, I turn my head around and what do I see—a deep crevice is splitting the balcony in two and the floor is coming loose from the wall. Frantic, I knock on the glass door. No answer. *Where can they be? Are they in the kitchen and can't hear me?* I knock harder and still no answer. I jump on the narrow ledge as quickly as I can and try opening the balcony door, but it won't budge. *What am I to do?* I press the doorknob and it just slides through my damp fingers. I try to jiggle it once more and finally it gives. The gap is so wide now, it can't be bridged.

My legs shake as I scramble inside, only to find the apartment empty. *What should I do? Should I wait or leave? Go where?* A crashing sound spurs me to run downstairs, and I head straight for the first floor entrance. No one is there. I run to the back looking for the basement door. *Not a soul in sight.* I swirl around like a blind bat looking for the cellar. In desperation I open a door and hear my mother's frantic voice calling me. "Come down here before you get killed!"

I grope around in the dark, blindly at first, then gradually begin to make out the figures of my mother and brother huddled together with other tenants against the damp-smelling basement wall. I make my way over there and slouch in a corner next to my mother.

"What happened to you? Where did you get lost, child?"

I can hardly catch my breath. "You feel so flushed. Why?" she asks me, insisting on an answer. My brother cowers next to her.

"I'm alright," I stammer to comfort her and lean against the cool wall. Just sitting still feels so good.

From the bowels of the earth we soon hear the continuous sound of the siren. *Not again,* I think, shivering all over.

"All clear, all clear," some people shout from the other side, and I realize the difference between this and the staccato air raid sound. Freed from my terror, the fierce wail sounds less menacing.

Upstairs, the balcony hangs there precariously. A wide gulf divides it from us. Like the one separating us from our old world.

Bombings become a regular part of our life. Air raid sirens no longer send people scurrying around in the streets. More and more, whenever they head for the nearest shelter, they act like wound-up mechanical toys. Any building gets turned into a shelter, and everyone piles in helter-skelter: pedestrians, store owners, office workers, bakers, seamstresses, tenants, whoever happens to be nearby. "Cursed hour," some people swear under their breath, but no one even pays attention to them. Whenever a building is hit by a bomb, it gets turned into a mass burial ground for the hapless creatures trapped in its concrete walls.

Gradually, the rhythm of the city also begins to change. The traffic in the streets slows almost to a standstill, people hurry every morning to work, heads bent down, collars turned up. Housewives dash anxiously to the nearest baker or grocer for their daily shopping—they don't dare go as far as the central marketplace unless they live nearby. Sundays have an air of gloom and despair.

Gone are the sounds of children's playful games in the streets and on the sidewalks. I'm not allowed to play outside either. My mother won't let me. "Only right in front of the house. Don't you dare forget, or you'll get it," she never stops reminding me. From time to time, though, Niko and I sneak off to play in the little park near the White Tower, down by the waterfront.

Before the war the two of us went there after school, taking along a snack of whole wheat bread sprinkled with sugar and water, so the sugar could melt and seep into the nooks and crannies by the time we reached the park. We enjoyed it so much, walking and chatting about every little thing that came to our heads. No wonder they called us Romeo and Juliet. We were inseparable.

In those days, the whole waterfront, the *paralia* buzzed with crowds of factory, tobacco, and office workers who spilled into the streets to stroll along the quay and relax after a day's hard work. Here and there, a young couple slipped away into a secret hideaway for a quick rendezvous in the park, far from ever watchful eyes of gossips and trouble makers. We followed them from a distance until they disappeared behind the thick foliage of acacia trees and shrubs lining the edge of the park. From time to time we'd sit unnoticed on a park bench next to a group of tourists poring over their little guidebooks. Occasionally we'd catch a familiar word or two, sprinkled into their foreign talk: Hagia Sophia, exposition, *Yedi Koulé,* Tsimiski, etc., as they figured out what famous sites they planned to visit.

Once, we pretended to be foreigners, too, and started making up our own "language." We hit on this wild idea while we tried to talk with our mouths full of bread and all the words came out sounding zany. Whenever anyone came to sit next to us, first we'd say all the words only using the vowel "A," then we changed it to "I" and it sounded like chalk screeching on a blackboard or like a basso profundo chorus when we just used "O." We tried to be convincing and put on fancy airs, pretending we were having a serious discussion. The unsuspecting pedestrians sitting on the bench to catch their breath listened for a few minutes and rolled up their eyes. Then they hurried away muttering and disappeared into the crowd, taking small steps without even glancing back, probably afraid they'd turn into pillars of salt. We could hardly wait till they were out of earshot before bursting into laughter, doubling over till the tears rolled down our cheeks. Then we transferred the "scene of action" to the next park bench where we got ready to snare another unsuspecting victim.

Now desolation is everywhere. The park benches stand there empty, the trees are bare skeletons in the chill autumnal air, harbinger of winter storms when the north Varthari wind stings and numbs. The oppressive air is even worse at night when total darkness descends. Black tape covers all the windows to protect them from enemy attacks, steeping the city in an air of gloom.

"I can't stand it. Sitting around doing nothing is so boring," I tell Niko.

"Let's go down to the park," he says, brightening up, "for a little excitement." His blue eyes twinkle. "Never mind, your mother won't even find out," he says, sensing my uneasiness and knowing her temper. "I'll race you..." We're off.

Niko and I start dragging our feet through the dry leaves piled in an enormous heap in one corner of the park, closest to the street where I live. Soon the wind starts blowing harder, and we run after the leaves, trying to catch them midair. The stronger it blows, the faster we run, twisting round and round, as though we were caught in a whirlwind.

Every gust of wind stirs up another pile of leaves; our arms sketch circles in the air until, dizzy from all the turning, we fall on the soft mound of leaves that crunch under us like dry walnut shells.

The demonic howling of an air raid siren stops us cold in the midst of our wind-driven intoxication. Before I know what's happening, we're being dragged in the direction of the shelter. It's my mother! How did she know where to find us? She races, breathless, clutching us tight, one in each hand, heading toward the basement. In the semi-darkness of the underworld, fear and confusion. Up above, the bombs—exploding too close for comfort. Each blast shakes the walls, sending a jolt of electricity through the crowd. Niko, never at a loss for words, lets himself get carried away by his lively imagination and starts telling his latest fairy tale, knowing my weakness for them.

"Once upon a time, some gigantic blind mice were grinding their dragon-sized teeth. Every time they gnashed their monstrous jaws they scared everybody and everything, living or not. One day the princess heard them and got so frightened, she went in tears to her father, the mighty king…"

"Let's go, children," my mother's voice interrupts just as I'm getting excited over the story, "the air raid's over. Hurry." She scoots us out the door and marches ahead holding my brother by the hand. Niko and I stand there staring at each other, mirroring each other's thoughts. When she's out of sight, we sneak away, curious to see what happened. At the park, we both stop in our tracks.

"Oh, my God." Niko looks at me aghast.

"I don't believe it," I gasp.

Our pile of dead leaves was buried in the gaping pit of the bomb that had just exploded.

A cold chill runs up and down my spine as I stare at what could have been the horrible ending of our mad dance amid the dead autumn leaves.

5 AUNT FANI

The nonstop bombing raids and the constant drain on her finances bring my mother to the edge of hopelessness. Old customers have stopped paying because, although they still owe my father a lot of money for goods they bought on credit, when war broke out war in Albania, most men were drafted, others enlisted and some found themselves in hard times of their own. She pours out her soul in her letters.

Dearest Petro,

God bless our children—they are exceptional and wherever they go, they are admired—you can be very proud of them—but with all their goodness their life is troubled. I have sacrificed myself, but no matter how much I suffer, I don't complain, but when I see that the children are living as though they are rejected, what do I want my life for? Don't leave us any longer in this condition, set up a plan, since we can't collect the money they owe us, send us a monthly amount so that you have peace of mind and we will be grateful to you—the children need both of us now. A time will come when they will be a comfort to us because God endowed them with rare qualities. Isn't it a pity, then, that we should become the cause of their suffering? I don't want you to worry about the things I write, but you know your brother is to blame for taking you away from the arms of your children leaving us alone like deserted birds.

We live with the hope that soon you will ease our pain and I hope that my letter will find you in good health and may the Holy Mother ease the anguish of our souls.

With love and sorrow,
Maria

"I'm at my wit's end! I have no money left to feed my children," I hear my mother talking to her brother, Uncle Demetrios. "What am I to do? A woman alone, with no means of support. How are we going to live? I sold some jewelry just to buy groceries. Now what?" She wrings her hands as she goes on confiding her worries to him.

He nods pensively and tells her that he'll see if there's any way he can figure to make some collections in the countryside. "Maybe things haven't changed so much there," he tries to reassure her.

"Do what you can, because I feel desperate," my mother sighs.

Uncle Demetrios leans with an effort on his knees and gets up to leave.

The next morning, my mother dashes downstairs to check the mailbox. I expect to hear her footsteps dragging, when she comes back empty handed, but this time there's a bounce in her step as she hurries up the three flights of stairs. When she enters the kitchen panting, she waves a letter in the air, and I notice that her cheeks are flushed and her eyes unusually bright.

"Did we get some money?" I ask impatiently.

"No," she says, catching her breath and my spirits sag. "I got a letter from your Aunt Anthoula who wants us to go and stay with her." She stands by the kitchen window and starts to read the letter.

"'Come to Katerini until the war is over. At most it will take a few weeks, I have a strong premonition.'" She pauses, smiling.

"You know, my sister's hunches always come true. Ever since I can remember," she muses. Then she continues reading.

"'We'll spend the holidays together and, God willing, the New Year will bring us glad tidings. In the meantime, you'll be in a more protected area away from those awful bombings, not like Thessaloniki which is a main target zone. It makes all kinds of sense. Think about it and let me know soon. Give the children a big hug and kiss from me. Best regards to Fani. How is she doing? With love, your sister, Anthoula.'"

My mother loses no time in deciding to go to Katerini until this brief storm blows over, as Aunt Anthoula confidently expects. "These bombings and my shaky financial situation are wearing me to a frazzle. I can't stand it any longer." My mother answers her right away: "We'll stay with you for a short while, and as soon as things calm down, we'll come back. I'm keeping the apartment ready for our speedy return. You'll hear from me again soon when I know the exact date of our departure. I have to check the train schedule because nowadays, as you probably know, all means of transportation have been confiscated for military duty, and you can never tell how quickly we'll get passage. Hugs and kisses to the children and my warm regards to Bill. Until we meet again, your loving sister."

I'm amazed how quickly my mother's mood changes when she makes up her mind to visit Aunt Anthoula. Her step quickens as she darts about, clearly relieved of her burden. Soon the date of the trip is set, and she is back to her old self again, moving nonstop to get ready. She washes, irons, straightens drawers, stores belongings in trunks, and cleans everything in sight. I'm enlisted to help, but no matter how much I do, there's no end to the work. I would love to find a chance to avoid it, but there's no hope. Whenever a job's finished and I crawl in a corner to read a scrap of newspaper, she quickly gives me another chore.

Housework has always been such a bore, I think; I'm fed up with it. Whenever she happens to catch me "red handed" reading instead of dusting, I really get it. Once she starts, there's no end. "You lazy bone, what are you doing there, wasting your time reading?" So I start humming a tune to take my mind off the drudgery, and she gets furious.

An endless tirade follows. "Have you forgotten what I just told you? Tell me, who do you take after? Just like your father's folks..." On and on until I can feel my head swell like a drum. It hurts to listen anymore. I can't imagine anyone with so many faults as I have. A worse creature doesn't exist. "Singing your head off as though nothing happened, eh?" She even complains about my singing. How can she think for a single moment I could ever forget the words that had caused me so much pain? Their bitter taste is still in my mouth.

When she carries the nagging too far and I can't stand it any longer, my only way out is to leave the house. I have no choice, so I start wandering. All alone I roam around strange neighborhoods, sometimes to *Yedi Koulé* way up the mountain, near the old prison fortress overlooking the city, sometimes to Upper or Lower Toumba, if that part of the city strikes my fancy. At other times I just walk around, looking for something exciting to do, wherever the road takes me.

I go window-shopping; I play with street urchins or just kick a stone along from one side of the road to the other and watch the dust settle back on the unpaved street. Soon I head for new venues, living in what grownups call "an ephemeral microcosm" of my own.

Once when I was hanging around with a bunch of kids, I overheard some noise on the other side of a stone wall, and we went closer to have a look. We thought it was a fight of some sort. So we sneaked up and peeked over the toppled stones and saw below us that a man had pushed down a woman and had her pinned to the ground. They were in someone's back yard. We started giggling, and before you knew it, a crowd had gathered and the first thing they did was chase us away. "Get out of here, you snoopy little brats," they yelled. We ran like blazes. I wondered for a long time about that. Why did they chase us away and not that mean man? It puzzled me.

By sundown, my spirits lift, and I return home starving, but calm. I push through the door and can tell right away that my mother's anger has cooled off.

"Where have you been all this time?" she asks. I give her some vague answers to avoid another heated tiff. Besides, what can I tell her? Will she even believe me?

I sit down to eat by myself, and go to bed tired out. Even sleep won't let me rest. New adventures enter my dreams—beckoning, challenging. The minute I fight off one demon, ten others sprout in its place. A never-ending battle. I can't win. No demigod Heracles I, to fend off the monster and chop off the head of the Lernaean beast to be rid of it for good. Only around dawn do I finally fall into a dreamless sleep that ends much too soon as the alarm clock rings.

Groggy, I start getting ready for school.

That's what happened in the "old days."

Now I don't dare stray far from our neighborhood. If I get scolded, I choke down that tight feeling in my throat or, at most, I softly murmur a forgotten old tune and once in a while run downstairs to the back yard to get the dust rag that "accidentally" fell while I was shaking it out the window.

I'm excited that soon we're leaving for Katerini. I love my Aunt Anthoula, and some people think I take after her. It will be fun spending the holidays with her and my cousin Paul. I'm sure we'll have a good time.

"The bombings are driving me crazy," Aunt Fani starts complaining as soon as she sits down in her customary seat for her afternoon coffee. Aunt Fani, one of my mother's cousins who is much older then she, is a widow for years now. She dresses in black from head to foot—a walking monument to mourning—except for her all-white handkerchief that she takes out to wipe the tears overflowing constantly from her eye, sealed forever in its shrunken pocket. Every now and then she tilts her head to one side and, with slow movements, takes the handkerchief from the pocket of her long black skirt, and sweeps her hand across the bad eye two or three times without once interrupting her conversation, a lifelong habit that lends added weight to her carefully uttered words. All attention is riveted on the minutest detail of each motion as she fixes her good, sideswiped eye on her listeners. She folds the handkerchief again, just as carefully, turns the clean side out, and puts it back in its usual place.

My mother serves the coffee on a tray, and the conversation turns to our trip to Katerini.

49

"What will befall us?" Aunt Fani exclaims and repeats over and over, wiping the slow, but steady stream of tears from her good eye.

"We'll go to Katerini to weather the storm, and as soon as things calm down again, we'll come back," my mother says in a decisive tone. Her spirits have lifted, and her voice sounds lively. Surely the talk is doing her good.

"I can see that you've definitely made up your mind," Aunt Fani gives her a toothless grin. "And you've perked up quite a bit."

"You're right, I feel relieved knowing that we'll spend the holidays at my sister's. What about you?" She all at once pauses. "How will you manage?"

"Well, I was just thinking." She brushes a bony hand across her high, protruding cheekbone to stem a tear before it even appears. "Maybe I could go with you. Anthoula said something about spending the holidays with them." She turns to look sideways at my mother, cocking her head like a parrot perched on a stick.

"So it's settled," my mother adds quickly, before Aunt Fani has a chance to change her mind.

The day of our departure arrives at last. I close the jalousies tight before we leave, and at the last minute I glance one more time at the sea from the window, hoping we'll be back soon. How could I know that so many years would pass before my wish would come true?

We pick up our clothes and a few other essentials bundled in the monogrammed white linen squares from my mother's dowry collection. She is the last one to leave the house and locks the door behind her. Everything in the apartment is in place waiting for our speedy return. It is Friday morning, December 20,1940.

"Oh, what have I done?" Aunt Fani cries out on the way.

"What, what? What happened to you?" my mother asks anxiously.

"Not to me, I forgot my medicine," she answers, "but let's go straight to the railroad station. We can't take any chances just because of my forgetfulness."

"Oh, no, we'll make a quick stop at your apartment to get it, after all you need it for your high blood pressure," my mother insists.

To save time, we detour through Nikiforou Foka Street to the Hippodrome.

I vividly remember the pre-war days. The farmers' open market livened up the whole neighborhood with the buzz, buzz, buzz of housewives who came to buy their fruit and vegetables every Thursday. On my way to school, I passed by the stalls full of farm fresh goods, watching the women dressed in their chintz cotton prints, hair freshly combed, carrying their net shopping bags, wend their way around the vendors' stands, picking over the produce, bargaining, gossiping. I hurried around the corner to the *Agia Paraskevi* church, and when I had a test, there was just enough time to say a quick prayer, half kneeling in front of the wrought iron church gate, to ask for the saint's blessing. I ran to get to class before the late bell, as I heard the din of the lively marketplace gradually vanish behind me.

Those past moments seem so far away! Fleeting feelings, like snowflakes melting on the tip of the tongue. The present is so much more intense, more vital, or is it just that the past has lost its immediacy and is no longer binding?

Now, I distance myself from the silent, empty marketplace at the Hippodrome followed by the hollow echo of our footsteps, heavy under the load we're carrying.

51

We reach Aunt Fani's house opposite the Syndrivani fountain with no difficulty. She takes out her house key from her secret bosom pocket where she keeps it for safety, picks up her long black skirt with her other hand, opens the door, and goes upstairs. We rest on the stoop and wait. No one is talking. The streets are deserted. The fountain is dry.

She returns almost immediately, and we head for the train station at a brisk pace. As we walk along Egnatias Street, near the Gallerian arch, the sky darkens, suddenly. I look up and see a convoy of enemy planes blocking the sun. We slither along the wall of the nearest house, running as fast as we can along the edge of the street, always mindful of the danger of becoming a target, as we've been instructed from the time the bombings began. The air raid siren starts blowing just as we reach the Kamara arch, all sweaty and tired. Where can we go now? Where can we hide?

"We're exposed here," Aunt Fani says, alarmed. "I heard that this is a target area."

"Maybe," my mother looks up, "but at least these columns give us some protection."

"We have to find a hiding place quickly." Aunt Fani turns to my mother. "Let's go. If a bomb falls here, we have no hope. We'll be crushed to bits," she insists. "Can't you see how dangerous it is, Maria?"

They are still arguing the pros and cons of staying or leaving when a blast of bombs hits nearby, and we're trapped. We freeze in our tracks.

I lean heavily against one of the columns and sink deeper into its huge frame, becoming one with it. The cold stone absorbs the warmth of my body, in turn offering me its protection and its immobility.

The air is raining explosions. If our end is near, at what a historic site we happen to be. "This Roman monument with its magnificent *bas relief* surrounding us may accompany us to our last domain," my mother whispers. I had never before stopped to marvel at this Gallerian work of art adorning Egnatias Street, hurrying past it, hardly paying any attention to it. Now I might be looking at it for the last time.

What a gloomy idea, I think, swiveling to the left to look at Aunt Fani, standing there straight as a rod. Who knows what's going on in her mind? She hasn't said anything for a long time.

Then, wiping the tears from her wrinkled face, she whispers anxiously, "Do you think my handkerchief will be a target?" I feel sorry for her. She's trying to bear up under the strain, poor thing, and doesn't complain, despite her age. My mother sighs as the ground shakes from another explosion. Aunt Fani directs her good eye upward, looking at the arch. I follow her gaze.

Wars are not new to her, of course. As she told us many times before, "I lived through the First World War in 1918, and what didn't I see!" On cold wintry nights, her face glowing from the coals that burned in the shiny three-legged brass brazier, she recounted many tales and recited her trials and tribulations, often spiced with amusing anecdotes about the allied French and English troops in Greece in those days. We could listen to her for hours. Now she'll certainly have new stories to tell.

Once in a while I catch a glimpse of my mother holding on tightly to Tasio, who is clutching her legs, pale and terrified. I start clowning around, trying to amuse him a bit, but he just looks at me. Not even a faint smile brightens his face.

A dark shadow falls on him, and he crouches closer to my mother.

"What's the matter?" she asks, as another cloud of planes darkens the sky.

"What does that mean?" Aunt Fani wonders aloud.

"A new attack," my mother's curt answer comes back.

"Maybe they're going away?" Tasio whispers timidly, gazing at the sky.

"I wish they were," I puff, "my legs are numb. We've turned into statues, like that game we used to play. Remember?" I ask him.

"Sure I remember," he says, "and we called it 'statues'. You used to get so excited, you could hardly stand still." His eyes brighten as he talks.

"I know, but I never got caught." We both smile. "Now we're standing here so long."

"Yeah, but we're scared stiff, there's no fun in that..." his voice trails off.

The all-clear siren puts an end to our cheerless game, and we start stretching our arms and legs, bending our bodies with slow movements.

"Looking at us you'd think we had been drugged or something," Aunt Fani observes.

I take a few steps to stretch my legs, and a chill runs up and down my spine. We must leave these hospitable pillars that we formed a bond with and which have been like companions in our moment of need. Who knows how much longer these columns will survive such brutal attacks?

"We must go now. The danger of another raid...we can't take a chance—" my mother says and leads the way. "Let's not delay."

On our way again, we follow her at a clipped pace, leaving behind familiar, friendly streets that pass us by quickly, one after another. We don't even pause to catch our breath, and reach the other end of town without any more trouble. At the station, the train is waiting.

"Oh, we're saved, it's a miracle," shouts Aunt Fani.

"You're right, after such an attack," my mother agrees. "It was a narrow escape. I still can't believe it."

"Saint Demetrios, our patron saint, came to our rescue." Aunt Fani pauses to put down her bundle and crosses herself three times, starting at the top of her wrinkled forehead and reaching all the way down to her toes.

6　THE TRAIN STATION

Thirsty and out of breath from so much running, we head straight for the train.   Inside, we find some empty seats and settle down, carrying our bundles in our laps. We are in a roomy second-class compartment with maroon velvet seat covers.

"Such luck!" Aunt Fani beams, overjoyed.

"Didn't I always tell you, luck has to follow you, you can't chase after it?" My mother says as she gives her a teasing nudge.

Aunt Fani settles into her seat.   "You're right, Maria. It's funny, I was just thinking the same thing."

A faint smile like a timid ray of sunshine appears on Tasio's thin lips.

The seats opposite us are already occupied by a military officer and his family: wife, son, a little younger than my brother, and a middle-aged woman who seems to be the lieutenant's mother, judging by their looks. They both have the same features—dark hair and eyes, aquiline nose, and a large, sensuous mouth.

The lieutenant's wife looks short, almost petite, and her features are delicate, like a china doll. It's plain to see that she had spent time carefully grooming her golden brown hair, except for a few wisps that aren't tucked under her trim blue hat and loosely cover her ears. Only the rimless glasses draw away from the girlish impression she creates, adding a few years and something of a school-marmish look to her neatly tailored appearance in her blue suit and matching silk shantung blouse. It's hard to distinguish the color of her eyes, reddened from crying. The curly-haired little boy, dressed in a smart brown outfit, sits quietly on his grandmother's lap and halfheartedly twists a toy car between his fingers.

"Would you like some fruit, perhaps?" my mother asks the strangers, out of a sense of politeness. She brings out a small basket with snacks for refreshment, but they courteously refuse.

Aunt Fani, in typical style, has taken pity on them and to cheer them up she starts regaling them with her favorite adventures from the war of 1918, telling the stories with liveliness and freshness, not a bit stale for wear. Soon, everyone, young and old, hangs on her every word. Before you know it she has everybody eating from the palm of her hand. She manages to raise their spirits that only moments ago were sagging.

"You were all too young to have lived through that war," she repeats. "But I was in my prime and remember what happened as though it was only yesterday." She raises her head with pride, encouraged by their attention.

"You know," she continues, "when the English and French troops came to my village up in the mountains, every soldier was called an 'Anglo-Frenchman'." Oh, I chuckle to myself; she loves telling that story whenever she gets a chance. "An *Angloyallo!*" she adds with a laugh that stretches her puckered mouth into a wide, toothless grin, and wipes her copiously tearing eye.

The vigorous motion of the train momentarily distracts me from the last whimsical episode of the 'Anglo-Frenchmen' and their escapades. The train makes a maneuver, it backs up and then surges forward fitfully. *At last, our trip is beginning,* I think, taking a deep breath.

Before I return to my listening mood, I notice someone in the distance who is just entering from the next compartment. His uniform gives the impression of an inspector. He is walking slowly through the aisle with an army officer who gesticulates as he bends over, clearly talking to some of the passengers while the inspector writes something on a pad, then tears off a page which he puts in a large manila envelope tightly clasped under his armpit. The officer watches in silence, waiting until he completes that small task before they proceed together to the next group of travelers.

Our turn is next. They can be heard talking a couple of seats behind us, but I can't make out clearly what they're saying. The lieutenant's wife stretches her neck in their direction and makes an effort to listen, then squirms in her seat and casts a hurried glance at her husband. He seems to pay no attention. She shrugs her shoulders slightly, and then leans again on the velvet headrest covered with a yellowed embroidered doily. She glances sideways at my mother—quickly, furtively—then rests her head against the windowpane and becomes engrossed in Aunt Fani's description of the latest heroic battle.

Something about her looks makes me uncomfortable. *What's the matter with me?* I wonder. *Am I getting cross with strangers for no good reason?*

In the meantime, the train comes to a standstill. Evidently I was fooled earlier when I thought we were leaving. I sink back in my seat and stretch my legs in time to get a kick in my foot from the lieutenant's wife who is just shifting her weight to the other side to whisper something to her husband. I move over and lift my head to watch her for a moment. He clears his throat a couple of times and tells my mother:

"Excuse me, madam," he says very politely, "but I must inform you that this train is reserved exclusively for the transport of military officers heading for the Albanian front and their families. I am obliged, therefore, to ask you to leave since you have not been joined by an officer."

One by one his words enclose us in a chilling silence.

I break into a cold sweat at the thought that we must go back "empty handed."

"After such an ordeal," my mother murmurs, pale and drawn. She takes a deep sigh and whispers to herself, "If there is another air raid...who knows what hardships we'll have to face," she adds to herself. Aunt Fani can't stop wiping her eye. It's her way of covering up her uneasiness.

The officer and his inspector are closing in. Their conversation can be heard clearly now. Time is running out. What can we do? There's no way out. The lieutenant's wife seems about to say something, but checks herself. Not a sound is heard. My mother looks at her imploringly, but directs her remarks to her husband.

"Please, sir, do us a great favor, don't let them send us away," my mother begs. "Surely you can understand how hard it is for a woman alone with two children..." she pleads, looking directly at him. "And you," she says, facing his wife, "you know how hard separation is, your husband is leaving soon for the Albanian front. My situation is so difficult..." Her voice, shattered, catches in her throat. "We're at your mercy. Would you please tell the officer we're with you...one family?" She joins her hands, as in prayer. "May God bless you," she whispers faintly.

Everyone's eyes are riveted on the lieutenant and his wife.

The inspector approaches first. He moves aside, and the officer asks for our papers. Not a sound is heard. My tongue is glued to my mouth, my breath trapped in my throat. I try to set it free, but it won't give. Not a single drop moistens my parched mouth. Speechless, I wait for the verdict. Our time is up.

Like an echo from a faraway cave, the lieutenant's wife can be heard talking. Motioning toward us, she is telling the inspector. "We're all together." Soundlessly, a breath that barely escapes from my dry lips expresses my gratitude to our benefactors. The inspector takes the papers, puts them in his envelope, tucks them under his left arm, and walks to the next group of passengers with his head bent.

The train shudders and changes tracks. It inches along, but instead of picking up speed, it heads in another direction one more time. With each new maneuver the train criss-crosses the network of parallel tracks at the station, then it diagrams new patterns, like a child doodling on a large sheet of paper. It shuttles back and forth, and then changes direction without going anywhere. It stops just as suddenly as it starts. I turn to face the empty platform, hypnotized by the to and fro motion. Finally, a jerky movement propels us forward and the train is off.

"At long last, our trip is beginning." The lieutenant's mother lets out a sleepy yawn with her mouth gaping wide open. She dozes and before long can be heard snoring. The train rocks from side to side, then just as suddenly stands absolutely still. She wakes up with such a cry, like she was having a nightmare.

"Oh, my, I dreamt that I was trapped in the belly of a monstrous beast," she says. "Mercifully, our blessed St. Demetrios came to the rescue and slew him just as he was ready to devour us."

"That's a good omen; our patron saint will protect us."
Aunt Fani offers a toothless grin.

No sooner do I lean against the window and close my
eyes, thinking maybe I can have an exciting dream, too,
than the sirens begin to howl. I can hear the roar of the
airplanes overhead. Before long they're sowing destruction.
A new jolt shakes the train as bombs begin to fall, and the
fury of explosions is all around us. Terrified, everyone
turns deathly pale. A new, stronger explosion brings the
train to the brink of overturning, and there is mayhem.
Suitcases, bags, baskets spill on the floor and into the aisles.

"The bombs are falling close by," the startled conductor
tells the lieutenant who is groping around, trying to find
his glasses. His son slithers under the seat and hands them
to him before he has to part with his military dignity.

"What's to be done now?" the conductor asks the lieutenant.

"We will maintain our positions and await further orders," the lieutenant orders in a crisp voice while brushing
the dust off his hat with his sleeve.

The all-clear signal whistles its way through the windows.

"No one is allowed on or off the train," the conductor
announces, "we don't want any unauthorized people
around." The conductor walks back and forth and every
now and then pauses to discuss something with the lieutenant. A cold chill runs up and down my spine. *What
are they saying? Will he chase us off the train?* I ponder,
and hastily look away to avoid his gaze. *Are they planning
to review our papers again? If they decide to do a more
detailed inspection, we're in trouble,* I think, and secretly
look at them sideways. I'm scared out of my wits and fold
my hands in my best schoolgirl manner to look as casual
as I can.

As soon as I notice my mother staring at me, I cast my eyes down, afraid that my movements will become suspicious, but there's no time left for her to try and figure out what I'm worried about, because the bombs start falling again—this time without any warning. It feels as if the train is splitting apart right under our feet, but somehow it's still whole. I can't even grasp what's happening. My mind, too, has been mercilessly bombarded, and it is shaken.

"The enemy attacks that were targeted at the railroad station have not succeeded," the lieutenant declares, with a note of triumph in his voice. "It is this lack of mathematical precision which has saved us," he adds with a grin on his clean-shaven face; his beaming mother watches him as she gently strokes her grandson. "But, mind you, they will keep coming back until they achieve their goal, I'm sure of that."

Later in the afternoon, the bombing stops.

"Do you have any news? What happened?" the lieutenant asks the conductor with feigned indifference.

"Oh, yes, we heard that they knocked down that factory building across the way," the conductor answers. "But you can be sure they were aiming at the railroad station, all right. Well, luckily they missed their target," he adds, and briskly walks away.

Just as I lose every hope of departing, the train makes an abrupt motion and pulls out of the main station. At last, we're leaving. I watch every move it makes, quickening its pace as it leaves behind the outskirts of the city to enter the countryside. Rows of houses and open fields stand motionless on the horizon and disappear as fast as they come into view. They disappear, like a flock of fast-moving migrating birds.

The passing scenery absorbs all of my attention. From my seat I can chase after the loosely scattered trees casting their late-afternoon, long autumn shadows on the quiet earth. I feel overcome by an irresistible urge to run without stopping through the fields, to weave in and out of the trees standing in rows like guards parallel to the railroad tracks. I don't know how soon my wish will come true.

I suddenly feel the brakes groan under the floor. The conductor runs up and down the aisle shouting "Military orders: everyone must get off the train. We must evacuate immediately. Enemy planes in sight!"

The enemy is still pursuing its earlier target.

We scramble out of the compartment with the rest of the crowd. I run free as a bird on the dry embankment. I feel my feet picking up speed, following the earlier rhythm of the train that is standing deserted on the hillock overlooking the tiny village just ahead of us.

That unexpected moment of freedom makes me forget for a second the danger of the planes coming toward us in droves, like menacing crows.

The villagers gather up their little ones and hurry into the shelter. A few eye us with guarded, but not unkind, looks.

"Come along, join us in our poor shelter," an older man urges us to follow him inside. The passage is so narrow we have to crawl one by one into the rough-hewn tunnel built as a shelter by the villagers themselves.

I lower my head to file in silent procession behind the others. The farther I go inside that deep underground hole, the more it seems like being plunged into a cavern of black tar where all of the sun's warm light has been sucked out and extinguished forever. *The damp earth gives off an eerie death-like smell akin to decaying bodies in a graveyard,* I think, remembering how my cousins and I roamed about the cemetery in my father's hometown, curious to find out if the bones of the dead were really phosphorescent, as we had been told. One time, I vividly recall, a damp autumnal wind was blowing and the dank, putrid odor—not so different from the one chocking the air right now—penetrated my nostrils.

The words of our national anthem spring to my mind *'From the sacred bones of the Hellenes.' Like the bones buried in this very soil, I think, just as ours will be if a bomb falls on us right now. Would our bones buried in this strange grave for the living ever become sacred and be remembered in a hymn?*

Imprisoned in this human dungeon, I start to tremble and search for the comforting touch of familiar hands. Where can I find them, bound as they are in that tightly woven knot of strangers, so many people packed together in one underground tomb? I quickly give up on even that faint glimmer of hope.

The acrid smell is suffocating. Human sweat mixed with the odor of babies' vomit and hot breaths that reek of garlic is too much. I can't stand it. I stand on tiptoe, struggling in vain to escape, or, at least, to catch a breath of clean air from somewhere. My body sinks in a mire, and every live thought is stifled. I try in vain to keep alive.

Someone standing next to me begins to move and heads in the direction of the exit. Voices are heard in the distance, but I can't make out what they're saying. All I can feel is sweaty palms pushing me, squeezing me between feverish bodies trying to get out of this catacomb. I move along without any effort which is a blessing because my legs are numb. I'm gasping for air and start crawling on my hands and knees to get out of this horrible place.

"Come on, let's get out of here, this is a living tomb," I hear a faint voice next to me. I crouch next to her and by the time I reach the exit I feel like fainting.

Finally, I get outside and stumble, blinded by the sun hovering over the horizon. I hobble along, enjoying the dry air scorching my lungs. I gulp it in deep breaths until my chest aches. A pain sweet and pleasant and full of life.

It is a relief to see my mother outside, and Aunt Fani is already heading for the train, scooping up her long black skirt without turning back to look over her shoulder once. By the time we reach the train, she looks dead tired and is clutching her chest, breathing with difficulty.

"Just a little bit farther," my mother calls out to her and skips like a kid, running playfully after Tasio, who's giggling, obviously enjoying the game.

"Don't worry about me, you take care of the boy. See how much good the fresh air did him?" Aunt Fani puffs. I rush over, and with the help of another passenger, I get her hoisted up.

The rest of us pile into our seats that look to me like home—familiar and friendly. We settle down and look forward to the rest of our trip like a new beginning.

"The remaining half hour will pass quickly," the lieutenant's wife addresses her mother-in-law, as the train picks up speed, and we pass by a succession of small villages scattered among the barren trees and fields lying fallow.

"We've already been so delayed," the older woman sighs. "We should have been halfway to Athens by now." She fans her perspired face.

"The only thing that matters now..." Aunt Fani wipes her eye, but her thought remains unfinished.

"Emergency, emergency!" the conductor yells, running up and down the aisle. Once more, the train comes to a halt after traveling only a short distance. "Immediate evacuation!" The sound of the approaching airplanes makes us realize that the enemy is in hot pursuit of his earlier goal.

So, we do it again: scramble out, run, and hide. This time for sure, though, I'm really afraid our luck won't hold out. Even if a bomb doesn't fall directly on our heads, a single explosion anywhere near us will bury us alive. A fate worse than death.

We approach a small village with a handful of houses. The people scamper around like field mice and crawl into the shelter that gives off that familiar awful stench. I stand for a moment reliving that torment of nausea and suffocation. *I can't go in. I'd rather die free than be buried alive in a grave,* I'm thinking and catch sight of my mother mirroring in her eyes my very own fear. We are not going in. No words have to be spoken.

The three of us lie down next to each other. Aunt Fani has already gone in. I press my ear to the ground. Maybe I can hear something. I try listening, but only an occasional sound that means nothing to me filters through. I almost doze off when all at once I feel the earth underneath me trembling. A long rumble and then, in the distance, the dull droning of the enemy planes rapidly fades away, and we're summoned back to the train. A huge crater lies gaping wide open not far from the deserted train. Once more, the enemy missed their target.

We reach the train feeling tipsy and cavort about in a festive mood that is almost like a celebration. Not a soul complains about the delay or our exhaustion. Howls of laughter have replaced our somber mood.

"They did it again. Ha, ha, ha, they missed their target." And instantly, as though responding to a signal, everyone bursts into laughter.

"We'll decorate the enemy bombers with military honors," the lieutenant chimes in. "They made fools of themselves," he exclaims, caught up in the spirit of the moment.

"Bulls eye, that's what we'll call them." A young officer bursts out laughing, and everyone joins in the commotion.

"They saved our lives," another woman giggles doubled over.

The last streak of light has long settled into the night and we approach our destination. We must hurry because the train is only making a whistle stop in Katerini. Choked with emotion, my mother turns to the lieutenant and his wife.

"Thank you," she can barely whisper, "and bless you." She clasps his wife's hand while tears stream down her face. The lieutenant's mother is holding her sleeping grandson to her bosom and barely raises her left hand to wave goodbye.

Aunt Fani's trembling lips force a wan smile. "May you go well, *sto kalo*," she bids them farewell, wiping her eye and we leave before the conductor shuts the door. There is no time left to express our feelings.

The train reduces its speed, slowly rounds a tight curve, and arrives in the small Katerini station that is deserted. Only the dense darkness greets us.

The night mysteriously swallows the train that is rapidly gaining distance from us. Like lost birds searching for sanctuary, we head toward Aunt Toula and Uncle Bill's house.

Will they be waiting for us at this late hour?

As Aunt Fani knocks on the door, a thin ray of light in the shuttered window cuts into the darkness.

7 CHARGE!

"Fierce fighting rages on the Albanian battlefront with no sign of letting up," the radio broadcasts the latest war developments. "Korytsa, Argyrokastro, Kleisoura, Tepeleni: glorious victories of our Greek soldiers matched only by the spirit of our people who muster every ounce of strength to help save their men from dying of cold and hunger on the rugged mountains of Albania. The whole country is marshaling its resources as one body, with a single-minded purpose."

From the day we reach Katerini, a few days before Christmas, Aunt Toula is on the go. She gets started early and takes me with her on her daily treks through the neighborhood to enlist people's help for the war effort.

"Let's get going." She springs into action. "Come on, come on. Household chores never end," she urges the housewives who are busily cleaning house in their cotton floral dusters. "This is war. Our boys are counting on us for warm clothes so they won't freeze in those godforsaken mountains of Albania. We owe it to them. They're fighting for us, for our freedom." She bounces from one house to another, full of the liveliness and humor she is known for. Her friendliness makes her welcome wherever she goes.

"Come in, come in, have a cup of coffee," the women insist.

"Next time we'll have a chat." She hurries away. "I have a long list." And off we go to the next house.

Our *tsoliades,* those brave fighters, need to stay warm. She forges onward with "charge" as her slogan. That's how she is pioneering in her efforts to help the brave soldiers who are giving up their lives for us at the Albanian front. She organizes women—young and old—into 'knitting bees' to provide woolens for the soldiers fighting in the front lines. Knitting is the wellspring of village life. Knitting and the hit songs of Sophia Vembo. Inseparable. One keeps the other going. The young women gather in the evenings around the fire while their hands dart back and forth faster and faster to the music of Vembo's top wartime tunes. "Duce dons his uniform..." or "How Ciano sighs when the *tsoliades* charge ahead," and similar boasts about our troops' exploits. Once in a while the young women like to listen to the romantic crooning of other pop singers, but that starts the newlyweds pining away for their sweethearts who are fighting miles away from home, and the knitting doesn't get done, so they quickly switch to other songs.

Uncle Bill has a weakness for reading newspapers. He puts aside his greasy bookkeeping pads to read the latest news out loud so everyone can listen. "Our air force has successfully completed extensive raids at the Albanian front. Enemy casualties far outnumber our own." His voice rises. "Our soldiers are the crowning glory of our nation—they honor our ancient Greek heritage."

"Do you hear what they say in the international press? A small country like Greece has managed to thwart the aggressive schemes of a gigantic military power," he bellows. "We have gained the admiration of the whole world." He beams.

"Especially of America," he never fails to mention, raising his voice.

He has a soft spot for the United States where he lived in Ohio many years back, until he got drafted and returned to his homeland. Afterward he went into business, got rich, then got a set of gold teeth, and diabetes. A semi-invalid now, he sweetens his coffee with tiny saccharine pellets.

"Come here, girl," He's fond of calling me from time to time to exercise a handful of rusty English words he learned while living in America as a young man. I always try to pay attention. "You hear me, eh? You hear me?" I dutifully comply to keep him happy. "The sacrifices and victories of our soldiers are adding new pages to our glorious history," he boasts and his green eyes take on a curious luster.

"Nothing can stop our *tsoliades* now on their path to final victory." His barrel chest thrusts out even further.

"We'll throw those fascists in the sea," Aunt Toula shouts from around the corner, giving the sweepings an extra push with her broom, halfway to doing the deed herself right then and there.

"The way our troops are fighting up there in those mountains, the hostilities will be over real soon," Uncle Bill assures us. "Just wait and see." He flashes a gold-toothed grin before taking off to tend to his dairy business, which he runs from an adjoining shed. "O.K.?" He looks at me for admiration and approval.

Day in, day out we expect to hear that our victorious army has succeeded in bringing about an end to the war, but that moment is yet to arrive. Instead, the situation becomes more complicated. There's talk that the Germans are making suspicious moves in Bulgaria and the latest report reveals disturbing news about Prime Minister Metaxa's health.

"What's going on?" Aunt Fani wonders aloud.

71

"I don't know. The war situation is getting worse instead of better," my mother says under her breath. "Danger lurks around every corner." I hear a note of quiet alarm in her voice. "I must go to Salonica."

"Why?" her sister asks.

"To take care of my apartment...I just abandoned it..." My mother says in a plaintive voice, and she frowns.

"Why not wait a little longer to see how things will work out? The war is almost over." Aunt Toula looks at her, trying to fathom her thoughts.

"I've waited long enough. It's already January, and the rent is due by the middle of the month. Why pay rent for nothing?"

"You want to go alone at a time like this?" Aunt Fani asks, casting a piercing glance in her direction.

"I'm going," my mother says decisively.

"Then I'm coming with you," Aunt Fani joins in.

"Oh, now why?" My mother sighs.

"I refuse to let you go alone," Aunt Fani sounds just as determined. "With all those bombings? It's like walking right into the hungry wolf's den."

"I can manage."

"How can you be so sure? These are not ordinary times," Aunt Fani insists, her eye copiously streaming.

"I have to go, there is no other choice."

"So do I. I want to be with you. At a time like this you might need the wisdom of the elderly." Aunt Fani sounds reassuring.

"Oh, well," my mother finally agrees, and gives in without further struggle, probably knowing it would do no good.

In the next few days while they're making arrangements to leave, we hear the announcement: "Prime Minister John Metaxas is dead. The man who has been a dictator since 1936 passed away, and the country is in mourning."

"You know, I never went along with his fascist phalangist ideas. He got them when he went to Germany for his training," comments Uncle Bill after hearing the news, "but who dared speak up? That was a bloody dictatorship. You'd go to jail in a flash. Remember, Toula?" he says, turning to his wife.

She nods. "How could I forget?"

"I was used to the American democratic system, and it was impossible for me to bow down to his fascist oppression."

"Nobody got used to that terrorism. But what do you expect? People were scared out of their wits and didn't dare say a word," Aunt Toula exclaims with passion.

"Yeah, sure," he says. "Where did he get all those fascist ideas about forced parades and everything? He got them from Germany, of course. Straight from the horse's mouth, so to speak," he adds, scowling.

"I wonder what kind of government they'll set up now. From one mess to another," Aunt Toula says, indignant.

"Who knows? It's anybody's guess," he says, scratching his head.

Not a day goes by without more disquieting reports. The latest is, according to well-informed unofficial sources, German armored units crossed the Danube River and entered Bulgaria.

"Do you think there's any chance they'll invade other Balkan countries?" Aunt Toula anxiously asks her husband.

He slowly raises his eyes from his favorite newspaper, *The Macedonian News,* to look directly at her and cocks his head to one side, quizzically.

"Why on earth would they do that?" He rolls his eyes in disbelief. "They have no interest in coming here. Bulgaria is their ally, that's why they went there. What's in it for them to go anywhere else?" He dismisses her point.

"Well, we're not so far away. You never know..." Her voice trails off.

"What would they gain by coming to this kingdom of lice-laden paupers?" He gives her a stern look that puts a halt to their conversation. Then he returns to his reading, but he can't sit still. He twists and turns, fidgety and restless.

"What's the matter with you? Stop whirling around like a spinning top. You're getting me all jittery and nervous. I don't need that," Aunt Toula complains. He rubs his eyes two or three times, and goes back to reading his paper without paying any attention to her.

"Toula, I'm afraid that's not good news, that's why he can't sit still," Aunt Fani whispers in her ear. "He knows full well that clashes always start in the Balkans, and then they flare up into full-fledged wars." She reaches for her handkerchief with jerky movements. "Isn't that how the First World War started? Prince... got killed. For heaven's sake, his name is on the tip of my tongue. How can I forget it, I know it so well. Anyhow. Who is to say it can't happen again?" She adjusts her black headscarf, pushing in the hairpin to hold it securely in place.

"Yeah, I know who you mean," Aunt Toula agrees. "After all, isn't that why they always called Greece 'The Apple of Discord'?" She busies herself with her knitting, looking up every now and then. "Because of our strategic location," she says, facing Aunt Fani. "They fight over who will take over the Mediterranean. Right?" Aunt Toula looks intently at her. "Why don't you answer me? You know I'm right."

"I hope your husband is right, but the way things look, it's definitely not good news, as you say. I think deep down he knows it too, that's what makes him so jumpy. Only he won't admit it, you know him," she goes on and tries to wink, but only manages a feeble one-eyed squint. "Just like all men. Don't meddle with their ego."

By nighttime heavy snow starts falling in big soft tufts. I watch it settle on the ground and start worrying about my mother's and Aunt Fani's trip. After leaving so late will they arrive safely in Thessaloniki in this weather?

The next morning a terrible snowstorm is blanketing the streets. For two days it keeps us indoors. By the third day I must go out for a while looking for something to do. I wander about without really knowing where I'm going and find myself in a half forgotten neighborhood. I pass by the house where, I remember, Uncle Lakis had his grocery store. I haven't seen him since the last time we came to Katerini to visit and feel overcome by a pang of longing. All at once, I realize I've missed him.

I walk inside shyly, like a stranger. What greets me are the familiar odors of packed sardines and olives and instantly I feel at home. Patched sacks full of rice, flour, and beans arranged side by side await me like trusty old friends. They're still lying on the same spot on the floor full of oil stains darkened with time right next to newer, damp ones.

The solid brass scale is sitting in its usual place on the counter. I feel drawn to it as though I'm looking at it for the first time. What is it about it that captures my attention? It's neither that shiny nor that unusual.

"Well, well, how are you, my child," Uncle Lakis' tremulous voice interrupts my reverie, startling me. "I haven't seen you in ages. What's become of you?" His genial eyes twinkle.

"Good, Uncle," I give him a half-hearted greeting, still lost in thought. I can't get that old scale out of my mind.

"Tell me, now, what's gotten into you? What are you staring at with your mouth wide open? Aren't you afraid you might swallow a fly?" We both laugh and start chatting. Uncle Lakis is boasting about his five new grandchildren, and I listen without getting a word in edgewise.

"That scale caught your fancy, eh?" he asks in a bit.

"I don't know," I answer, "something strange is bothering me."

"It's the same one I've always had. My cousin Vasilis, God rest his soul, brought it for me from Smyrna years ago. Remember how I used to weigh the candy before I gave it to you when you came shopping with your mother? You probably figured I was putting them on your account, but I wasn't even charging you for them. See?" He laughs again and winks at me mischievously.

"Oh, yeah, sure." I smile at the thought.

"Come on, take some, I know you like them."

As I reach out to accept his offer and thank him, my eyes fall on the scale gleaming in the path of a stray streak of dim afternoon light filtering in from the only window in the store. The glow settles on the brass weights arranged neatly according to size on the wooden counter.

"That's it. Eureka," I cry out.

"What is it, child?" he asks, confused.

"Something has been bothering me ever since I got here."

"Let's hear you. What have you drummed up now?" he muses.

"When I was a little girl and my mother sent me to the store to do shopping, she always warned me, 'Set your mind at four hundred,' as I left the door.

"Yes, Mommy, I would answer, but I didn't have a clue what she was driving at."

"Why didn't you ask?" His eyes twinkle.

"I was afraid she'd scold me," I admit, sheepishly. "Then all the way to the store I'd puzzle over it. What did she mean? Why four hundred? How could I reach that magic number? When I came back she never graded me. So how could she tell if my mind was set at four hundred or two hundred or seven hundred? See?"

"Not really. This is a deep mystery. Carry on, child, I'm listening." He leans forward and turns his head to the left to hear better with his good ear.

"Just before, when I was looking at the scale weights I finally realized what she meant."

"Yes, yes, go on. I'm listening." His gentle brown eyes are fixed on me.

"Now I know! One *oka* equals four hundred grams, so four hundred is a full measure," I say, thrilled to the core.

"So, she was telling you, keep your wits about you, be sharp." He taps his head with a good-natured smile.

"But how should I have known? She never explained it to me."

"So you just kept quiet." Uncle Lakis lights his hand-carved wooden pipe and puffs slowly two or three times. The smoke twirls silently, circling around the half-extinguished ray of sunlight disappearing into the dark ceiling.

"Well, it probably put the fear of God into you, so it served the same purpose," he says after a long silence, shaking his silvery head pensively. He looks at me steadily to be sure I got his message.

"Here, take this candy. And share it. It's not all for you. Run along now, before it gets dark."

"Thank you, Uncle Laki." I smile, feeling happy as I leave.

"Don't forget now, come and see me again. We might solve another mystery, eh?" he adds.

"Sure, I will," I promise.

I jump down the stairs and into the street. A heavy weight has been lifted from me.

Awakened by footsteps in the front yard the following morning, I dash barefoot to the window to see what's going on. It's too early for a train to be arriving, but I could never tell these days. I always had to count on the unexpected. Besides, how could I be so sure they were taking the train? All sorts of possibilities race through my mind, hopes rising and falling with the up and down beats of my heart. I blow on the frosted glass and use the sleeve of my nightgown to elbow a spot to look though, my own little porthole, like they have on ocean liners.

I imagine I'm sailing on a boat, like the one that brought us from America, the *Vesuvius,* part of the Italian line. No sooner were we on board than I was off running through long, narrow corridors, up and down stairs, to find the whereabouts of everything and learn the goings on. By the time I got back to our cabin, I knew half the crew and was expert at giving directions to anyone who showed even the slightest inclination to get a guide, mostly people who were confused and couldn't find their way.

Many passengers asked me. "Are you the captain's daughter?" or "Do you live on board?" While others mused out loud before I had even turned the next corner "How can she know her way around so soon after boarding?"

I blow on the window again, wiping off the mist gathered on the small clearing to peer at the goings on outside.

"Help the National Solidarity Fund." A neighbor is asking for a donation, all part of a big campaign advertised every day on the radio. I crawl back into bed, disappointed.

"We haven't had any news at all," I burst out crying the minute Aunt Toula walks in. "They were supposed to be here yesterday. Did something go wrong?" A hoarse whisper escapes from my throat.

"Now, now, be quiet. Do you know how much work they have to do? They have a whole apartment to pack up. It's not easy, especially in wartime with all those bombings."

"And if something happened to her?" I ask, scared, clasping my arms around my legs.

"Oh, my, that's all you can think about. Don't worry. They're only bombing military targets. It was different in the beginning," she tells me, taking my hand. *How she resembles my mother, I think, yet they're so different, in style, in manner, even in looks. Aunt Toula's fair complexion and light brown hair don't compare to my mother's dark hair and almost sun burnt-looking skin. I can talk to Aunt Toula, and she accepts whatever I say. I think we're more alike "You could be her daughter," people often say. Sometimes I wish I were. Right now it's good to feel her warmth close to me.* I snuggle up to her.

"Come down here," Uncle Bill calls out to her, "I need you to help with a customer." I'm left there alone, not knowing where to turn.

The next day, late in the afternoon, my mother arrives loaded with bundles looking wrinkled like Aunt Fani who walks behind her. She looks ten years older. At least she's safe; I sigh and dash out, fighting back a flood of tears.

"They're here, they're here," I shout, overjoyed.

We all rush to hug them and take their bundles. Aunt Toula ushers them inside and offers some ouzo. "To soothe your aching souls," as she's fond of saying to weary travelers.

"Welcome, welcome," she toasts.

"Thank you," two faint low voices are heard saying in unison.

"How did you manage?" Aunt Toula asks after a long, painful silence, but gets no reply. "Was there any trouble?" The silence is heavy.

"Oh, my god, how terrible," my mother bursts out like an explosion. "I can't even bear to think about it. For one horrible moment I felt like throwing everything out the window. If Fani hadn't been there to hold me back..."

Aunt Fani weeps quietly and slowly wipes the tears from her eyes, her head bowed low.

I picture my mother leaning out the window—the one facing the sea and the *paralia* along the waterfront, totally unmindful of its beauty—ready to throw away her household that she took so much pride in and tended so faithfully. In one frantic moment all of it would have been gone forever. And with it a part of her.

"I wouldn't wish such torment on my worst enemy."

My mother talks like that for a long time. Her words pour out like a waterfall. "My home is shut," my mother goes on. "I stored the furniture in a makeshift warehouse. I've exhausted my last savings. I have nothing more to give you for our upkeep. I can't impose on you any longer. We have to leave. I don't want to be a burden on you any more. Maybe I'll go to my hometown and find a piece of bread to live on. I don't know what to do—" she suddenly stops short.

No one utters a sound. A heavy, weary quiet falls.

8 TO MOUNT OLYMPOS

Winter is not over yet, but my mother is set on leaving to go to her hometown near Mount Olympos, way up in the mountains where it's even colder than it is here.

The thought that I'll be in that beautiful village perched high up on a mountain opposite Mount Olympos rekindled my desire to go there and revived memories of familiar places and the fragrance of pine trees mingled with the fresh mountain breezes.

"How can you go on your own, without a guide?" Aunt Anthoula asks, anxiously. "Don't you know they've been enlisted in the war effort?"

"What can I tell you? I'm worried. I don't know the road that well, and it's a long trip through the mountains. I can't take that kind of responsibility with two small children." She breathes a deep sigh.

"Of course not. Those winding roads can be treacherous, you can get lost, not to mention other dangers in that wilderness," Aunt Anthoula says.

By a stroke of good luck, my cousin Yiorgo arrives in town and gladly offers to accompany us. "Don't worry! I'll make all the necessary arrangements," he says to my mother. "As it happens, I have some family matters to attend to, and I don't mind leaving a little earlier."

"Bless you, my son." She smiles. "You're always so tactful and sensitive."

"Anything for you, aunt." His affection shines through.

The muleteer's wife lets us know that the following Thursday her son will bring the animals to Aunt Toula's house.

"Make sure you're ready very early," she says. My mother gets our few belongings ready for the trip and steals a few minutes from her chores to write to my father.

Katerini 2/2/41

Dear Petro,

I wait for your letter every day, I spent 47 days with that anxiety. I can't tell you how worried I am, but I know that I have to be patient.

These days I decided to go to my hometown in Livadi so we can spend a few months there and afterward, God will help us.

Ioanna and Tasio respectfully send you many kisses.

With much love and sorrow,
Maria

It's pitch black outside when we're awakened to set off that frosty early March morning. I rub my eyes and scramble out of bed to get ready. It's hard to leave the cozy warmth of Aunt Anthoula's home to face the brisk cold. We clasp each other in the darkness, shedding bitter tears. Aunt Fani is waiting at the top landing to say goodbye. She embraces me, and I'm startled when her thin, bony frame almost disappears in my slender arms. Her wet tears on my cheek sting like an open wound.

"Go with my blessing, children." Her tremulous voice reaches us through the pre-dawn sea mist. "And you, take care of yourself," she advises my mother, who shakes her head two or three times, unable to utter a word. Overcome by emotion, she holds on to Aunt Anthoula, who walks through the yard to see us off at the front gate.

"Are you ready, Yiorgo?" Aunt Anthoula checks that everything is in order.

"Yes, yes," he assures her.

"Of course, always punctual and efficient like your father. Remember to give brother John my best," she calls out to him.

He has already loaded the two mules with our few belongings and on the saddles piled the provisions that other people have given him for their folks back home because regular transport is so slow and unreliable.

"Now, now, my little pigeons." Aunt Anthoula's tearful voice catches in her throat. "May you go well."

She hugs Tasio and me, holding us tight, one on each side of her warm, soft bosom. We hang on to her neck and kiss her over and over.

"*Adio, adio, adio,* goodbye," she says and puts another fistful of goodies in our pockets.

The two sisters cry and kiss each other on both cheeks one more time before we leave.

The mule's footsteps echo through the shadowy back streets as we head for the uphill road. Near daybreak the valley of Katerini, stretching way out to the shimmering steel gray sea, is beginning to stir with life. The air coming from the sea tastes of salt.

We pass through the Drosopigi Narrows where the water, like its name, is fresh and cool. At the first wide curve in the road we are enveloped by a gossamer veil of mist that evaporates into nothingness with every gust of wind, letting us catch a fleeting glimpse of the mountains rising tall and proud before us. The biting cold wind digs deep into the marrow of our bones.

Cousin Yiorgos, polite and considerate as always—even under the most trying conditions—tries to cheer my mother with gentle banter or a sugar cube soaked in home-brewed ouzo.

"You know," Yiorgos says, "in the village you'll find the serenity you need among the people you know and have always loved. They're just as you remember them," he adds, poking the animal to pick up speed. "And the wonderful climate will do you a world of good." He smiles affectionately.

"Yes, yes, my son." He is her oldest brother's firstborn and a favorite nephew. "You're right," she says, sitting taller.

"Besides, Aunt Maria, the end of the war is just a matter of a couple of months, at the most. It's lasted longer than we expected, of course, but now we've practically kicked the enemy into the Adriatic Sea." He waves his arm in a general westward direction. "The songs are overdoing it when they say that our troops will even get into Rome. We have no business there."

We all chuckle and start singing one of the popular war songs.

About halfway there, at the village of St. Demetrios, we dismount to let the animals rest and have some water. At the fountain, we meet some shepherds and other travelers, mostly old men and a few beardless youths.

"Where are you going in this cold? Far?" a white-haired man asks Yiorgo.

"Far, far, and we must hurry before night falls and finds us on the road," he answers.

Another man perks up and ventures to speak to my mother.

"I know you, you come from quite a family, good stock." The shepherd leans on his staff.

"Yes, and how did you recognize me?" she replies.

"E!" He pulls his mule away from the fountain. "I took care of your father's flock once, for a short while."

"And you remember me after so many years? I must have been a little girl." A dreamy look clouds her eyes.

"You look like your father, your expression. He was a righteous man. Too bad he died so young," he says, shaking his head.

"Well, what can we do? Such is life," my mother answers. She mounts the mule, and Yiorgo lifts Tasio up to her lap.

"Kalo taxithi, a good voyage," the old shepherd wishes us.

We wave good-bye and head for the steep road. The farther uphill we go, the worse the cold gets. With only two animals, Yiorgo and I take turns riding. On foot, I get tired, but when I ride, the brutal cold air sinks its teeth in, and soon my legs feel numb. I'm afraid I might get frostbite.

The long and difficult road seems unending.

"Courage, my girl," my mother turns her head and calls out, "we don't have too far to go."

Kindled by these words, and the smell of pine in the air, I feel an overpowering desire to be transported to my mother's hometown, Livadi. Traveling through that rugged territory excites me so much, I hardly even feel the cold any longer. I just want to see that breathtaking mountaintop near Mount Olympos, to reach the beautiful village steeped in the pine-fragrant air. Every turn of the long road re-awakens the longing to be there, to reach it now.

Step by step the animals shorten the distance. The rhythmic tapping of their horseshoes carries my thoughts away to that irresistible place: to strolls in the pine-covered Kioski facing the imposing profile of Zeus reclining at the top of snow-capped Mount Olympos; in the distance, the fertile fields of Elassona stretched out like a gold-embroidered apron glistening in the sunlight as far as the eye can see, all the way to the Kamvounia mountain range; to Melet Bahtsé at Tirnaviti's open air cafe, eating homemade halvah beneath the swaying poplars that swoon gently in the wind; to summertime serenades in dimly lit cobblestone streets. As the crowds return home late at night, the scattered sounds of songs close in, fade away, and then surrender to the shadows of the night. The fast-clicking heels of the young girls, hurrying home before their fathers kick up a fuss, tap in tune with their anxiously beating hearts.

A sudden turn in the road jolts me from my daydreaming and my heart jumps at the sight of Olympos-town right in front of my eyes. At the same moment, the mule—sensing that home is near, shakes his head and takes quick, deep breaths, as though it is also deeply moved.

The clouds in the sky scatter like migrant birds heading for distant lands. The wind swirls

The light rushes into the transparent film of mist and brings into full view the titanic magnificence of Mount Olympos on one side, and the curved cliff resembling an aquiline-nosed high-flying eagle on the other. They say that in the days of the Turkish occupation of Greece, a re-nowned revolutionary hero, Yiankoulas, had his hideout not far from these parts. The road is no more than a hairline-thin white sliver, like a bird's beak. Just wide enough for an animal's hoof—a human foot can hardly make it. Below, the gorge. A deep ravine. The mules march on, continuing their rhythmic pace: persistent, cautious, intuitively sensing danger. Haste is their enemy.

We reach the Saltsi outpost, and a bunch of kids shriek the minute they get wind of us. "Here come the *gaganes,*" they yell.

"Listen to them, Yiorgo, they're calling me a *gagana,* an outsider, in my own hometown. Imagine that, as though I'm a stranger!" my mother exclaims, a bit troubled.

"Well, what do you expect? You've been away for so many years. How should they know you're not a *gagana?*" Yiorgo teases her.

The kids gather around, bursting with questions. "Where'd you come from? Where you going? How long you staying?" They call out, full of curiosity.

Then they vanish, only to reappear out of narrow alleys, rushing to be the first to tell the news to the womenfolk, who are peering from half-opened doors to find out what the commotion is all about. Then they run panting to spread the news around town.

The mules head straight for the rapidly gurgling Stournari fountain at the entrance to the village square to get their fill from the large circular stone basin which is used to water the animals. We must go to our landlady's house situated opposite the tall, age-old plane tree. It stands in the center of the village square—the hub of the town's activities—surrounded by a variety of stores. They are as much a landmark as the fountain, which is enclosed on three sides by a low stone wall, identical to the cobblestones lining the village streets.

The woman of the house opens the door to welcome us. She is a simple woman whose wide-eyed, trusting face framed by the traditional head-scarf, the *tsemberi,* is in harmony with her quick, restless movements.

"Hello, Lenko," my mother greets our landlady.

Trailing her by a few footsteps is her neighbor and my mother's distant cousin, Despo, who welcomes her with her loud voice.

"Tsia dar?" she inquires, *"tsi si fatsi?"*

"Gini, gini, coum hi?" answers my mother.

I can only understand a few words, like, "how are you, fine thank you." Besides that I didn't know what they were saying. I always wanted to learn that language because ever since I was a little girl, when my parents wanted to talk privately, it aroused my curiosity, and I wanted to find out what they were hiding from me. Were they talking about me?

The chatting in their own Vlach tongue sounds so melodious, like others in the Romance language family. My mother's talk is lively and animated, bubbling just like the crystal clear water from the fountain. After eating an oven-fresh leek pita, one of their local specialties, Tasio and I go to sleep by the fireside. The low frame beds along each side of the hearth, covered with handwoven, colorful dark red, blue and green *kilim* rugs, feel warm and inviting after the day's long trek. Soon the fireplace is aglow, sparkling bright. The dry pine branches crackle, pirouetting in mid-air, dancing amidst the crimson-red flames, scattering aromatic resin fragrance all around the tiny whitewashed room. Each burst of light gives a fleeting glimpse of Lenko's somber wedding picture—now shining on her, prim and proper, now on her unsmiling husband who stands straight as a reed in his black wool homespun suit. By and by my itching eyes are soothed, weariness leaves my aching legs, and my body surrenders to a feeling of drowsiness. Tasio and

I go upstairs to our room and sleep comes quickly, delivering me into the tranquil land of dreams.

Near daybreak, the cockcrow hour, I have terrifying dreams that don't let me rest. Walls that are collapsing from the bombings surround me, and gigantic prehistoric birds march into my room and go about unfastening enormous hinges in the crumbling walls. A cataract of molten cement mixed with red ashes and stone is discharged into the void the instant they turn each key in the cracks.

"Bombs, bombs!" I try to scream, but something clutching at my throat won't let the words come out. I feel paralyzed. Half-asleep still, I rub my eyes to beat off the horrors. But the torment only gets worse. With eyes wide open now I watch ceiling and walls cracking, windows crashing while the floor sways from side-to-side. Fully awakened, my mind staggers in terror.

"Earthquake, earthquake!" panic-stricken voices filter in from downstairs. On the far side of the bed Tasio's frail, thin body shakes and his teeth chatter.

"I'm shivering, Mommy, I'm shivering," he repeats over and over. I try to run over and comfort him, but I stumble like a drunkard and have to hold on to the bed. At the other end of the room my mother is crossing herself rapidly in front of the icon whose votive candle stands there without a flame. She grabs us by the hands, and we hurry downstairs before the earth starts shaking again. We gather on the first floor for greater safety, supposedly, but find the same devastation. The blood curdling wails of the sheep dogs reach us from the distance.

"*Mea culpa,* I have sinned, my Lord, save us," our landlady cries out.

"Armageddon is here," wails an ascetic bleary-eyed old man who sits cringing inside the door, a short distance from his usual lonely post in the central square.

"Ah, how have your faithful servants sinned, Almighty God," cries a hunchbacked old woman who lives alone next door. Her bony hands make the sign of the cross over and over. "Holy Mother of Christ, send us poor hapless souls your blessing. Don't forsake us in our hour of need."

The earth's rumblings and mournful prayers continue for a long time. Then they slow down, but the pause is short-lived.

"The fury of nature," murmurs my mother.

"The children must pay for the sins of their parents," Lenko's brother hisses between his teeth.

That sounds puzzling. I can't help glancing at my mother. It's impossible for me to believe she ever erred so grievously.

In that case, I figure, I should never have any children because who knows what they'll suffer for all my naughtiness that I get scolded for.

At noon the earth's trembling comes to a standstill. Only the terror remains along with the collapsed walls that gape wide open in our midst. I venture outside with cautious, hesitant steps. The sun appears strange to me, a mockery of our pitiful condition. And yet, I soon find its presence heart-warming and feel less alone. I muster the courage to go to the fountain for a drink. My legs feel like they're made of wax, and I lean on the stone wall to regain my sure-footedness. Its immobility is reassuring.

With the palms of my hands stretched open, my trembling fingers explore the stone's rough surface. The dampness draws me closer until my lips touch it, and I suck in two or three drops of water. The refreshing cool is liberating. I'm no longer a slave to my terror.

I grope my way home like a sleepwalker awakened from a nightmare. The aimless comings and goings of people are happening in a void. Soft scared voices are heard down below, as though they're afraid of awakening an enemy.

"What has befallen us?" cries Lenko.

"That's all we needed," complains Despo looking at the remains of her old house that collapsed in the earthquake like a deck of cards.

"God forbid, it could've been worse," my mother tries to reassure her. "Suppose you got hurt, then what? You'd really be in bad shape. Don't worry, we'll find a corner to hide our head."

Sure enough, her words come true.

"Come stay with me," offers Lenko's neighbor Opi, short for Kaliopi. "I don't have too much damage. You can all share the small room in the back."

Cousin Yiorgo comes by to see how we are and helps us move our belongings. "You're fine here," he says, "after all, it's only temporary. Didn't we say we're driving those fascists into the sea? In a matter of days the war will be over," he says, and dashes off in a hurry.

Hardly a month goes by before the first soldiers begin to return from the Albanian front. Unshaven, downhearted, hungry, a sad lot dragging their bloodied feet in torn army boots. The heroic victors of Korytsa, Tepeleni, and Kleisoura were at the very pinnacle of their glory and started retreating without knowing why. Suddenly, the army generals ordered them: "Cease fire!"

Those warriors who were in the front lines were the last ones to find out about the capitulation to the Germans by the Greek top brass.

"Our men were still shedding their blood for their motherland while the generals were betraying them behind their backs," my mother says with sadness.

Now they walk with heads downcast, like the scum of the earth. They can't figure out why they were fighting bloody battles in the rugged Albanian mountains when the German troops had already occupied our country.

"It's a disgrace," a villager says, shaking his head. "Shaming our men like that."

The retreating soldiers arrive at the village one or two, maybe three at a time looking thoroughly beaten. You can see how they drag their bodies from far away. The kids are the first to spot them. They run like the wind to the main highway to meet them, find out their names and bring the tidings to their families.

"Aunt, come," they yell. As soon as the women hear the calls, they shuffle downhill to greet the soldiers midway, the women's headscarves are tied loosely around their heads.

As the soldiers get closer, the women's eyes fill with tears.

"You left a big strong lad only two months ago, and now you come home on a pair of crutches," a mother laments seeing her son at the clearing down below.

"My God, what has become of my one and only, my pride and joy," wails another. It is only when a husky voice cries out, *"Mana,* mother," that the dark shadow disappears from the woman's face and she runs to embrace her son. Soon other mothers and sisters join in, coming to meet their men or to find out if anybody has any news of them. A young girl bursts into tears when she sets eyes on her brother holding his amputated arm in a dirty sling fastened with a rusty safety pin.

All along the streets villagers drop what they're doing and close their stores to greet the returning men. A woman shakes her head.

"Alas, my son, light of my eyes. You shed your blood on those godforsaken mountains and were almost eaten alive. You went to defend our country, but you were betrayed by our own, may their souls burn in perdition. Forgive me, God," she cries out, raising her head to the sky.

"At least you got your own back, it's better than some who are lying in the cold earth, on foreign land," her friend comforts her.

"Mmm, my soul, the truth is bitter. One is bad, and the other is even worse. We godforsaken mothers are to be pitied. We raise our children and may never see them again." She sighs.

"But you raise heroes for our country," the younger woman adds.

"I want living heroes, not dead." She raises her hand as she follows her son down the crooked lane.

The few remaining English soldiers who have been cut off from their units—no one knows how—are also in a pitiful state. They scramble up the rocks to reach this small village and avoid being taken hostage. About a dozen of them arrive one afternoon around sunset and sit down to rest in a corner of the town square. In the meantime a truck arrives from Elassona, and they bring out some canned goods and biscuits to eat together.

As soon as they see the English soldiers, a bunch of barefoot, hungry-looking, scruffy kids, wiping their runny noses on the back of their hands, dash over to the new arrivals. They drag me along to talk to them in English and ask them for something to eat. The soldiers don't need my halting English. They can tell just by the look in our eyes what we're there for. They smile at us when the weak voices plead, "Mister, plees, mister."

From then on they always give us something, a can of evaporated milk that tastes delicious on bread or marmalade in a beautiful gold-colored tin that comes in handy for a lot of things or some biscuits to fill our growling stomachs. We grab the goodies, calling out. "Thenk you, mister," and rush home to devour them.

Most of the Englishmen leave as soon as word gets around that enemy troops are coming. A truck arrives in town to transport the Englishmen, but two young soldiers are not leaving with the others. No one knows why. They take refuge in friendly homes until they can join the rest of their unit. People are worried about their fate, knowing that Italian occupation troops have already marched into nearby towns. For sure they'll come to our village, too. They arrive sooner than anyone expected.

The sudden invasion—enemy patrols, illegal searching of homes, and occupation of the town hall—stuns the towns-people.

The two Englishmen were discovered in their secret hiding place and captured before they had a chance to escape to the mountains.

"They're being taken away," Yiorgo calls out to us in a hushed voice. We run out to see them walking down the street bound in chains, on their way to the armory. Across the way, the children they had befriended stare at them wide-eyed.

"Mister," Pavlo, the littlest one puts out his hand, ready to reach up to them.

"Shush." His mother covers his mouth.

95

He looks at her, puzzled, with his eyes wide open.

"Not a word out of you, hear me?" she whispers. "They're hostages now." He keeps quiet, but his eyes follow the soldiers' movements until they disappear from sight at the bottom of the path.

Two days later the hostages still haven't been shipped out, causing all sorts of wild rumors. They're double agents, they were planted there to distract the enemy troops from top secret activities in other parts of Greece, they're not really English, no end to speculation. No one knows the truth.

Surprise raids by the Italian invaders have terrified everyone. The soldiers barge in at any time of night or day, demanding food and liquor for their entertainment. All night long they serenade in the streets with their guitars, singing, *"Mama son tanto felice."* In the daytime they tease the pretty girls, motioning to them in sign language. "Come hither, come hither, *señorita,"* while rubbing their forefingers against each other back and forth, to signal that they want to find out if the girls are married or not. They really don't seem to have their minds on war so much as on leaving. *"Go home to mama,"* that's their favorite song.

At daybreak when the first rays of sunlight crown the mountaintop, the Italians post a notice in the town square. "Today at 3 p.m. the two English captives will be burned alive as enemies of the state."

A traitor from Larisa has given them the gasoline for the deadly deed. The loathsome turncoat stands nearby, smoothing his bald head and rubbing his left hand on his fresh-shaven jowls. Two black, beady eyes peer from his obese, oily face, darting suspiciously back and forth.

The whole town is horrified.

"They can't do that," women exclaim, huddled together in solitary side streets.

"There are international laws, these are wartime hostages," the men argue, casting anxious glances about.

"You mean they're not being taken as prisoners to Athens?" they shout.

Only the young Englishmen remain calm. At least that's how they look; tight-lipped, closed in their shell, their eyes betray nothing. All the townspeople are in an uproar, unable to fathom how something so hideous could be happening in their midst. They're vehemently opposed, yet powerless to change it. Unrest is everywhere: in the air, in the light, in the mountains, on the earth.

The footsteps of the small procession of men condemned to die and their executioners echo on the cobblestone street. All sounds cease when they reach the curve at the end of the road leading to the highway below.

Soon, a thick black cloud fills the air. It smells of burnt flesh and gasoline. I get a violent attack of nausea. My whole body is protesting. I try to run to the street, but cousin Yiorgo holds me back. I can hardly control my indignation at such an inhuman death, even in a time of war.

The next day permission is given to some townspeople to bury the dead. That night the "little beggars," gather secretly at the gravesite to spread some wild flowers on the still-damp earth and to show our appreciation to those who sweetened our hunger with their kindness.

In front of the wooden cross, thin tremulous voices offer in prayer: "Thenk you, mister." I leave with the other kids in the dense darkness without saying a word. Hand-in-hand we return before anyone catches us and we get in trouble.

9 NIGHT PATROL

It's Shrove Monday, and the house is a beehive of activity. I'm dashing around to help with the traditional cleaning in preparation for Lent. In the midst of the clamor of pots and pans getting scrubbed, who should pop in out of the blue but cousin Niko from Thessaloniki.

"Oh, welcome. Look who's here," my mother gives him a big hug. "What brings you here?" she asks.

"We had to get away from the bombings. We couldn't bear it any more," he bursts out. "It's terrible!" His voice has that well known melodramatic sound.

"You did the right thing, my boy," she answers, wiping the perspiration from her forehead. "You'll see a lot of people here from different parts of Greece, some to escape the bombs, like yourselves, others to eke out an existence from the land, to keep from starving."

"Oh, Aunt Maria, you should see what it's like in the city. The cost of everything is sky high. It's awful. Unbearable. Everybody is fed up."

"What can people do? We're all trying to make ends meet, somehow, till this storm clears up. Then, God willing, we'll see..." she says, as she mops the beads from her brow and goes back to scrubbing the floor.

"I'm so glad you came!" I tell him, putting aside the cleaning rag. "I have no one to talk to. It's so boring here." I take Niko's hand and head for the Kioski Park where we can chat on our own.

We play tag and laugh as we run under the fragrant pine trees before heading down to the Daili Cliff to hunt for flint stones. We remember playing with them many times before. First we rub them together and watch the sparks fly, and then inhale their flinty smell deep inside our nostrils.

Our next stop is the Englishmen's grave, near the embankment on the downhill road to Elassona. I tell him what happened, and we cry together for a long time. An unexpected sound behind us sends us scurrying away. It's only a lonely shepherd boy, but we don't want to take any chances.

Heading back to town, we stroll along the stone wall that faces Mt. Olympos and gaze in awe at its snow-capped peaks. I listen to Niko's stories, captivated, as always, until I have to go home.

"See you later." I wave and can't wait till we meet again.

That evening we meet at the old golden-green plum tree behind our grandparent's house. Our younger cousins join us to decide what games we'll play.

Niko gets a bright idea. "Let's go on an expedition!"

"Yeah, yeah," Tasoula shouts with glee, "we can be spies."

"Why don't we head straight to the front," Byron blurts out in typical macho style.

"No, no. I have another idea," Niko whispers in a conspiratorial tone. "We'll start our own radio broadcasts that will send messages to the front line, to our secret operations, wherever we want. All over the world!"

"We'll call it 'Night Patrol,' and our theme will be jingling bells, like Tsingiridi's radio station in Salonika," I suggest, jumping up and down with enthusiasm.

"Ding, ding, ding," Niko mimics the sound perfectly to everyone's delight.

The thrill of unknown adventure beckons, and darkness is the perfect foil for our mysterious schemes.

First, we set out two-by-two on a patrol operation to investigate some areas of suspicious enemy activity. Our footsteps leave an echo among the deserted buildings that were ruined in the earthquake.

"Come, quick!" A cry is heard the dark. "We found a cache of cables hidden in the barbed wire."

"Shhh, be quiet, they'll hear us," someone complains.

There's a mad dash to seize the booty before the enemy floodlights spot us.

"New dramatic developments in the fight against enemy espionage," our radio bulletin announces, without giving away details about where and what.

"Our broadcasts rival the best radio stations in the world," Niko boasts.

At times, we find ourselves in the midst of fierce battles. The plaintive cries of the wounded, agonizing in their delirium, are heartrending.

"Oh, I'm dying!" Shrieks pierce the night air.

We move heaven and earth to find transport and to notify the Red Cross to assist them. Transferring the injured behind the firing line isn't easy.

"Help! Help! I can't stand it anymore." The cries come from a pitiful mound of sprawled bodies. In the dark it's hard to tell who needs emergency care.

"Oh, oh, the pain...is killing me," the wounded moan on the way to the makeshift, run-down clinics where first aid is administered. The needs are enormous, and we suffer from a terrible lack of medical supplies. Who should we take care of first?

The folks back home are waiting to hear the latest news about their loved ones. Loyal to our cause, we risk our own lives to complete our mission. Fear must not stand in our way.

From time to time our work meets unexpected obstacles from some phantom creatures that creep out of the walls of the buildings destroyed by the earthquake, terrifying us before we complete our mission.

As soon as Byron shouts: "Retreat!" we make a hasty escape, yelling and screaming at the top of our lungs.

"What are you doing there?" our mothers' strict voices cry out. "Come here, instantly. Didn't I tell you not to go roaming in those abandoned buildings? Do you want to break a leg or something?" We're shaken from our fantasy world to reality. That leaves that night's project unfinished.

At sundown the next day, we wait until the blackout plunges the town in total darkness again, so we can resume our search for our secret hideout.

On other evenings we must join our family to take part in all-night vigils—a time of prayer. We gather in the church of the Holy Virgin to invoke her help for salvation from the enemy and for a quick end to the war.

The black-clad village women come in, most of them in mourning for a relative, head bent down, half a dozen children in tow, to light their humble grayish-yellow candle, a murmured prayer on their lips. "Oh, Holy Mother, send a guiding light to help find an end to this affliction." They make the sign of the cross three times, genuflecting reverently in front of the icon of the Holy Mary.

"Mother of Christ, please bring back my son." A mother weeps on her knees. "Send a sign. Take pity on me, the woebegone, he's my one and only, just like yours," she laments, withdrawing pensively to the solitude of the women's section in the back of the church.

Gradually, by the time the old lamplighter puts in the oil and lights the votive lamps, the pews fill up with people, and the chanter begins the vesper hymns. The enormous hollow space fills with melodious sounds. They surround the brass candelabra, blend with the fragrant incense, then rise to the dome of the church and fall in a ceaseless ebb and flow that sends an electrifying shock through the air, heavy with warm breath and the burning of candles.

On these nightlong vigils, we sleep in the church. Blankets are spread on the shiny, time-worn stone floor, pockmarked here and there with big and little grooves that absorb the light, hiding it in dark hollow spaces. With each tremulous sputter of candlelight, bare shadows spring up, then soundlessly move away, lengthening like rubber bodies, spreading languorously on the walls, climbing on the windows, then abruptly fall to the floor. Occasionally, one of the shadows slithers past me, and Niko nudges me secretly under the covers. "It'll tickle you if you don't hold your breath," he needles me.

I gag my mouth with my hand, and the minute the grotesque shape moves away we both burst into laughter. Actually, we're supposed to be sound asleep, but who can sleep? And miss the best part when the women softly chant the ancient hymns from enormous gilded books covered with sparkling precious stones?

"Jacob wed Sarah," the women read, "Benjamin wed Esther…" and each time they mention the word 'wed'—that reads 'copulated' in the ancient text—they giggle like schoolgirls.

Niko and I synchronize our muffled laughter with theirs to keep our secret enjoyment unnoticed.

When they finish telling about the copulation of all the biblical pairs, the voices of the faithful rise to the dome of the high ceiling as they recite: "And all the generations were fourteen."

"How come fourteen?" I wonder out loud.

"That's anybody's guess," Niko whispers, and we break up in hysterics again.

"Hallelujah! Hallelujah!" A final rousing chorus bursts out with gigantic force and transforms the pale faces of the worshippers, lifting their spirits to the heavens above. Only an old lady, in the shadow of the pale candlelight, motions them to lower their voices, "lest the enemy hears us, and evil falls on our heads just when we're waiting for salvation."

10 OCCUPATION

Our Night Patrol mission comes to an abrupt halt when the Germans occupy Greece in April of 1941. The foreign invaders bring a heavy oppression to our country and a new form of terror: Stukas airplanes. Droves descend even on our village.

"Po, po. My, my, what kind of attack is this, again," people cry out in the streets. "The flying beasts will eat us alive," they shout, running for cover. But to no avail.

The Stukas circle around us like fierce hornets, fire at innocent folk, taking one steep plunge after another, their engines groaning, ready to siphon off every ounce of life. This is no longer a mass attack. It's individual extermination.

"To save our lives," the mayor declares, "we must go into hiding instantly, at the Sanctuary of the Holy Trinity Monastery." Panic-stricken, we scramble uphill and run down gorges to get out of harm's way. Helter-skelter, mothers and children scatter about in ravines. No matter what we do, we can't avoid their fury. Like going deeper into hell. My legs are about to buckle from fright; my body feels as if it's on fire. I can't move, and I stop on a path for a second to catch my breath, but it's impossible because in no time, a Stukas monster dives at me.

For sure they spotted the red stripes on my green sweater and they're attacking me, I think, trembling. *What should I do, before others get killed because of me,* I consider, stifling a scream.

In a flash, I grab a branch from a nearby bush and stick it inside my sweater using the leaves for camouflage. I start running again, charging down the path as fast as I can with the twig sticking out of my back.

"Over here even trees are on the run." An old woman lets out a bitter snicker when she sees me unexpectedly. Her surprse is even greater when she notices Niko a little farther away mimicing me by wearing two shoots of fern in his glasses so he wouldn't become a target.

"The world is going crazy!" the woman shrieks, crossing herself three times.

I'm dripping with sweat, and my back is on fire from the twig's scratchings, as though wings are sprouting from my back. I yank out the branch and throw it down. Just as I approach the monastery, I pause at the fountain to cool off. Now nothing looks like the picturesque place I once knew. The monastery grounds resemble a military encampment.

As I bend down for a drink of water, the sight of the fountain brings back a vivid image of the monastery as it was the first time I saw it, a sheltered glen surrounded by skyscraping walnut trees beside a tranquil valley. We visited it as newcomers from America for the holiday of the Annunciation of the Virgin Mary. According to the tradition, all the relatives who came from many parts of the country for the August 15th festivities were going to sleep in the monks' cells after the Vespers.

The village square was swarming with vacationers for the occasion, three whole days and nights of celebration. The town echoed with the sounds of lutes, violins, and the famous clarinet that Kalleas—renowned in east and west—played every year. Souls rejoiced to see the dance of the elders—men and women dancing and twirling their walking sticks in the air, next to the proud lads and girls with eyes cast down. The air was fragrant with barbecued lamb and other tender morsels being prepared for the merrymakers. The sweet-smelling Farsala-style baked almond halvah was tantalizing, and the children circled around it as bees to a honey pot.

"Ma, you said you'd get me some." Yiannis, the neighbor's ruddy-faced boy, complained.

No answer.

"I want halvah."

Total indifference.

"Pa, Yiorgos is eating halvah, gimme a drachma, I want some too."

Not a word.

"Eh, ma-a-a-a," Yiannis whined in the middle of the crowded town square.

So, his ma gave in to get him off her back. The boy wrapped his hands around the piece of crispy burnt-orange halvah nestled in a cone of wax paper, gobbling it up without even letting it cool off. As it got smaller, he slowed down, taking tiny nibbles first on one side of the paper, then the other, sticking his pudgy nose deeper and deeper into the cone until all I could see was a mop of red hair bobbing up and down. In the end, his face came out of the wrinkled paper covered with grease. He grinned from one ear to the other.

By nightfall, the hub of activity quickened, and the unnatural light of the 'lux' acetylene bulbs swaying on the plane tree cast a strange glow on the people milling around the square. Holidaymakers seated at the table clinked glasses as they welcomed each wave of newcomers.

"Hronia Polla! Long may you live! Welcome." Friends and relatives were warmly greeted.

"Same to you," came the rejoinder.

The merriment, feasting and dancing lasted till dawn.

The next day was devoted to visiting the Holy Trinity monastery. Uncle Yiangos and Aunt Anthoula were in charge of making all the arrangements.

"You'll bring this, you that, and we'll go on ahead to start the fire and start preparing the barbecue."

"My, my, the two of you are unsurpassed. You got everything under control," my mother cheerfully complimented them. "We're in good hands."

"Mark my word, we're going to have a good time, just wait and see," Uncle Xenophon added. "After all, it's our tradition."

The first group gathered at my mother's family home, under the plum tree that grew olive green plums. We set off on foot, taking the downhill cobblestone road, and by the time we reached the Byzantine Saint Anargyri church, our small *parea* had swelled to a large group. And what we didn't carry. Pots full of aromatic food, golden-crusted cheese pitas in round pewter pans, baskets of fruit, and lots more. All-night revelers ambled past us, and as soon as they saw us, they started serenading with their violins and guitars. Villagers opened wide their doors to see what's going on and started talking to my mother. They were surprised to see her again after so many years.

"Oulai, iasti Maria, oh, my, it's Maria!" they said. "You left a young woman and you came back with two kids up to here," they gestured to their waist. "Do you still remember our Vlach tongue?" There was laughter, chatter, and more pauses at every turn of the winding downhill cobblestone road.

We left them behind, and when we reached the monastery, we found the older folks who had come on mule-back to bring the lambs for the barbecue. They had already started the fire to grill the delectable *kokoretsi* appetizer, under the walnut trees.

While the grownups were carrying out the preparations for the feast, Niko motioned to me to go with him and my other cousins to see the sights.

"Let's go to the fountain," he said, and we all ran after him. They elbowed each other to be the first to show the newcomer Amerikana cousin the *vrisi*. The crystal clear water sparkled in the sunlight, as it filled the large stone trough. They let me take the first turn, and I just stood there. They all laughed.

"Go ahead, have a drink," Despo urged me, but I expected her to give me a cup. Instead, she cupped her hands and drank.

"Let me try." I bounced over, but the water just slipped through my fingers.

"Like this." She showed me and finally, proud of my accomplishment, I drank to my heart's content.

They were full of new ideas, even when we went to gather fresh walnuts that had just fallen from the trees.

"Now watch us clean our teeth," Panos said, peeling off the green outer skin covering the walnut shell.

Big deal, I thought. Anyhow, what did that have to do with cleaning teeth? But I kept quiet, waiting to see what he was up to. As soon as he rubbed his teeth with the peel, his lips turned a bright purple.

"See," he said, "better than your toothpaste, huh?"

"Amazing!" I marveled, taking a peel to give it a try as he turned toward me and gave me a triumphant smile that shows a set of sparkling white teeth like I had never seen before.

"Do you think Hollywood will take me?" He winked.

Soon we all ran around showing off a purplish grin that made us look like scarecrows. Then we gave the extra peels to our older cousins who didn't want to get their hands stained, and we munched on the fresh moist walnuts.

"Who's ready for appetizers?" Uncle Mitros, my mother's brother, called out. "The *kokkoretsi* is ready."

In no time, our whole crowd appeared out of nowhere and began nibbling on the scrumptious morsels of braided barbequed liver and intestines covered with herbs.

"Me too, me too." I joined in. I could hardly contain my curiosity after all I'd heard about this special delicacy. "Mm, mm, it's so tasty," I exclaimed as soon as I put it in my mouth.

"Bravo, bravo," others shouted. "Mitro, you've done it again, better than ever." The pungent aroma of the lamb roasting on the spit was tantalizing.

Some of my "cousins in waiting," as they called themselves, took over the job of setting the tables with white cloths on which they scattered branches of freshly cut fern and put the lamb on the branches to give it that special woodsy fragrance. They brought over the home brewed *tsipouro,* much stronger than ouzo, lots of wine and *retsina,* cheeses, and the rest of the food. We all gathered around the table and Uncle Gianko, the eldest brother, officiated.

"Lord, bless this food and drink," he intoned, as everyone made the sign of the cross. "Now let's see what the lamb bones tell us about the future." He carefully "studied" the large shoulder blade for special omens, as was the custom on such occasions, and felt its bony edge bit-by-bit for portents. Lastly, he tugged at the tough sinew, the unmistakable 'financial indicator,' to size up how hefty the family purse was going to be in the year to come. Then Uncle Mitros performed his examination, and they both agreed: "Good news, good news." And now, *"kali orexi,"* toasts were exchanged in the more traditional way while some preferred the French *"bon apetit."*

"No problem about our appetite!" Aunt Anthoula said, and smiled. Then glasses clinked, and everyone began to eat. The lamb was delicious, and the drinks were plentiful. The merrymakers quickly got everyone in a happy mood for frivolity and lively discussion.

A little distance away, in a clearing under the trees, the phonograph played the hit tune *"Pipitsa, Pinelopitsa"* for the circle of dancers who twirled rhythmically around and around. My father cut a fine figure among them, swinging his nieces to and fro. We young kids played outside the main dance area, mimicking fox trot steps, and getting scolded for kicking up dust with our clumsy moves that scuffed the ground and irritated the grown-ups. We explored the cells in the monastery courtyard that smelled of incense, and the age-old columns that shone like antique, well-polished ivory. Then we played a game of hide-and-seek before we collapsed on the blankets spread out under the dense foliage.

In the mellowness of the late afternoon, the old timers took over singing melancholy cantos and serenades, and romantic songs of old.

"I loved thee, thou were my goddess, my soul fled to thine arms," lyric voices sang.

"Oh, what memories those old favorites bring back!" my mother mused.

"Gianko, sing us one of your heroic ones." she coaxed Uncle John who watched leaning against a walnut tree, and was resting a bit after all his efforts. He obliged for a while; then the stentorian voice of Uncle Mitros recalled songs of struggle and freedom from the national independence uprising of 1821 that brought tears to everyone's eyes.

Near sunset the valley echoed with the latest romantic hits while the sighs of a heartbroken lass were heard lamenting her lost love under the deep shadows of the trees.

After the Vespers service, we spent the night in the monks' cells, still smelling of incense and myrrh.

"Have you had your fill, eh?" The loud voices of two townspeople startle me back to the present, as they approach to water their animals.

I'd been standing, lost in reverie.

"How long have I been daydreaming?" I wonder out loud as I move over to let them get by.

"I wouldn't know," one of them answers me in earnest, "but you better hurry along. This is no place to stand alone, you never know what can happen."

I leave the fountain at once and head toward the monastery. A huge crowd of townspeople has filled up the small space outside the courtyard and is seated under the walnut trees that stand high above everyone, far from our concerns. I look around for familiar faces, but they are none to be seen. One terror-filled face almost looks like another.

"Mommy! Mommy!" I call, running frantically. "Tasio, Tasio-o-o." No answer.

My God, the Stukas airplanes got them! I tremble.

"Over here, over here," I hear a voice from a distance, but in the confusion I can't tell exactly where.

Are they calling me? I wonder, and head in that direction, stumbling over bodies lying on the ground.

"Stop! Stop! Where are you going?" I recognize my mother's voice at last and fall into her arms, exhausted.

By nighttime the valley is full of people trying to find a few inches of space.

All night long, it's impossible to catch a wink of sleep, what with the fear of not knowing when the Stukas will strike next, not to mention the cries and the fussing of the babies.

After daybreak, the sky is deserted. Not a sign of enemy attacks.

"What does this mean?" The fear of the unknown is as alarming as the presence of danger itself.

"Where have they gone?" whisper the townsfolk. "Will they return?"

"You'd think the gorge gulped them up. May they rot in hell!" A villager cries out in anger. Overcome by exhaustion, she rests for a while on her knapsack.

"How do we know when they'll come back? You think they'll give us an account?" yells an old man sitting crosslegged further away, and a commotion starts up.

"Let's leave," they shout on the left. "We should stay," they insist on the right.

Timidly, a few people venture toward the clearing to see what's happening. Not a sound is heard. Finally, famished and melting from the heat wave that hit us early this year, we set out to leave.

"I'm hungry," Tasio complains. He looks so piteous. His hands and legs are covered with old rags since we have no bandages. He's been suffering from psoriasis for some time now, and the oozing scabs won't heal. No matter how many salves my mother has tried, nothing works.

"This heat is awful! I can't stand it any more." My mother's brow is covered with heavy beads of sweat, and her cheeks are flushed. "I'm roasting," she complains. "Let's go, come what may," she says decisively, and we leave, following the others who started out ahead of us, keeping a constant watch on the sky.

The raids of the past few days stop just as unexpectedly as they started and leave us wondering what the enemy's next move will be. We live in a state of constant alert hoping for the best and always fearing the worst. When we hear the slightest unusual sound, we jump up and peer intently at the sky to check if a raid is coming our way, as though knowing would make a difference. We've become so nervous; we can't stand still for very long, frightened of the danger that constantly threatens our lives. We pass each day not knowing what to expect, and that only redoubles our anxiety.

Before long, the summer is upon us, and we realize we'll be spending it here in my mother's hometown, opposite the tall mountaintops of Mount Olympos—ancient dwelling place of the gods—with my mother's oldest sister, Aunt Evangelia, who has just arrived from Paliocastro.

I'm thrilled when I find out that we can all stay in the old ancestral home, a humble house I came to love when I first saw it. A narrow cobblestone street leads from the whitewashed, low-arched gateway to the yard, now overgrown with mossy grass and weeds. On one side stands the old-fashioned kitchen full of moldy earthenware vessels for pickled foods and next to it, the laundry room lined with huge tubs, big enough to hold the woolen *flokati* blankets and *kilim* rugs. On the opposite side of the yard is

113

the main low-frame building. The bedrooms are lined with tall closets that reach up to the ceiling on one side, and low-hung windows that face the side street on the other. This was our secret lookout on the young men who came courting our older cousins in years gone by. They stood at the corner to serenade their beloved around daybreak in those seemingly long ago days that come alive when I see the old house steeped in memories.

Above everything else in that house, I loved a low-hung door that didn't seem to go anywhere. But I had discovered that behind it, a secret passage led to Aunt Galatea's house—the land of fairy tales. The trip to magic wonderlands started at her doorstep. Her golden-tongued daughters, Eleni and Maro, both tall and shapely, with dark hair and beautiful brown eyes, fashioned ornate, delicate fantasies out of a spoolfull of words. You wandered into mighty ports, you saw the wonders of the world where danger lurked, traveling through exotic lands and haunted palaces, encountering princes and queens, Cinderellas and dragons that came to life, turning into flesh-and-blood creatures before your very eyes.

Then, in the scorching summer heat, I had a terrible thirst and leaned over the magic little door to hear about the *"Athanato,"* immortal water, to quench my thirst with nectar that bestowed life-eternal to those who drank that magic potion. Then, I wandered far away on the wings of fairy-land creatures that roamed about, scattering silver dust in the four winds. "Spindles five, wound round and round, scatter wind-blown, ne'er to be found."

At eventide, an Olympian moon shone on the profile of Zeus—imposing and awesome—his voice bellowing to the far corners of the earth. The gods quarreled like mere mortals and nobly made up again, then returned once more to Olympos to taste ambrosian delicacies, to drink life-giving nectar, to join with ordinary folk in orgiastic feasts. At night they left behind their mountainous peaks to embrace passionately winsome nymphs and lithe Nereids in flower-bedecked valleys covered with ever-fragrant gardenias and blooming lilacs. Demigod heroes cavorted in foam-crested waves with mermaids who came tantalizingly close, then just as quickly escaped again to the far reaches of the sea, commanded from time immemorial by Poseidon. A clan-destine witness to ecstasy, he offered a divine blessing to the eternity of love.

Standing still before the house, my eyes stay riveted on the humble door-frame and I sigh. Familiar voices are no longer heard through the bolted passageway. Time has si-lenced them. Perhaps they've joined the mythical silent water.

"What's the matter?" Artemis, Aunt Evangelia's daugh-ter, asks me when she sees me pensive.

"Oh, nothing," I answer. "I was thinking about summers gone by."

11 BARREN SUMMER

"Harvest, you said?" a shepherd blurts out as he approaches a group of men. He leans on his hand-carved staff, looking at them intently.

Seated around a table under the big shady plane tree in the middle of the village square by the Stournari fountain, they sip their morning coffee at Moshovitis' *kafenio* and talk about the hot topic of the day: harvesting. One of the men moves over to give the newcomer room to sit and, then goes on.

"Who can harvest this year? It's out of the question. You got to be crazy, most of those fields are right next to the Dead Zone," he says, lifting his hand to chase away a fly that has just landed on his long, graying handlebar mustache.

"Them Nazis kill on the spot," a younger, ruddy shepherd adds. "If the enemy sees you, you're a goner. The bastards!" He groans, raising his clenched fist, full of anger. The brusque motion flings open his black woolen cape, exposing an empty sleeve tucked inside, and momentarily his stump catches everyone's attention.

"Considerin', you was lucky, just getting away with that," the first man ventures after an awkward silence. "War's war."

"Why do you think they call it the Grim Reaper?" another man says, lowering his voice, as he turns his bald head to check if anyone is listening to him.

116

"It's a wasted year," the older shepherd joins in again, straightening his black wool cap. "Our labor, the cost of the grain, everything's going down the drain."

"We should be grateful," chimes in old man Karanikas, one of the village dignitaries, rubbing his wrinkled hand over his weather-scarred face. "Some poor souls didn't just leave their fields unharvested, they left this world for good." He tilts the black cap covering a tuft of shiny white hair over to the other side. "They'll never see the fruit of their labor or anything again. Dead 'n buried in them wild Albanian mountains. Food for the black crows...even they don't last up there."

"There's no knowin' what'll happen next," the young shepherd says. "I just heard Germany's fightin' Russia now."

"Ou-ou-ou, that's far, that Rou-oussia country, another world. I wonder what kinds of people live there. I can't even picture what it's like," the man with the long mustache answers.

"What will happen now that the big Russian bear got in on the act?" Karanikas wants to know, but I can't wait to hear his answer. My errands are still undone.

"How far is Russia?" I ask my mother when I get home.

"Why, what makes you ask?" She looks at me intently. Her piercing brown eyes fix me with her gaze, and I tell her what I've just heard.

"What do you think, Evangelia?" she anxiously asks her sister, who seems to be deep in thought while she straightens the black head scarf that covers her thinning black hair.

"I'm sure the war is going into a new decisive phase. The military started in on what will surely be another bloodbath, but they'll end up beating each other's brains out.

You wait and see," she says directly, in her manner, without missing a beat.

"It looks difficult, Vangelia. The Germans have a huge, well-equipped war machine, the latest model tanks, and airplanes, not to mention the mercenaries from all over Europe. I think we're in a horrible mess that's only bound to get worse." She collapses on the nearest chair and sinks her head into her cupped hands.

"What can I tell you? I'm scared! Who wouldn't be?" Aunt Evangelia sighs, assuming my mother's melancholy pose, and for a while they both sit quietly side-by-side.

As I watch them from the corner of the room, I'm amazed at the striking resemblance between them.

"Who knows how much more suffering we're in for by the time this is all over? If we ever make it out alive," my mother mumbles to herself and shakes her head on the way to the kitchen where the pot of beans is almost boiling over.

"War or no war, we're going to the Prophet Elias pilgrimage, no matter what. I don't want to miss this," Artemis enters the room in long strides and declares with certainty.

"What kind of an outing can we have with an empty picnic basket?" My cousin Katina raises her usual objections.

"If we make up our mind, we'll find something," I insist impatiently.

"What? You think we can eat enthusiasm?" she retorts.

"Now, girls, just wait a minute. Why don't you bring along some of our local potatoes," Aunt Vangelia, our resident problem-solver, suggests.

"Potatoes, that's all?" chants a chorus of girlish voices.

118

"You can eat half of them sprinkled with salt, and the other half plain, for dessert. They're delicious," she tells us in mock seriousness. We all burst out laughing, and Katina agrees to go ahead with our plans.

"I don't know how you do it. I marvel every time. You're a practical philosopher, that's what you are," my mother says, looking at her sister with affectionate admiration. "It's a rare woman who could take over a whole store and manage it all alone, the way you did since your husband died, God rest his soul."

"It's not easy, without a man in the house," Aunt Vangelia sighs, with her usual modesty.

"Besides, you're a mother and a father to your children. That's hard," my mother continues. "You should have been a lawyer with your brains..."

"Oh, stop it now, you always say that." Aunt Vangelia brushes aside the compliment, laughing. "Let my children do that. I have enough of a burden. Besides, I've already sacrificed so much," her voice tapers off to a whisper, and the two sisters go back to their household chores.

"We'll set off real early before it gets too hot," Artemis suggests.

The night before we boil the few potatoes from last year's crop that our neighbor's daughter, Loukia, gives us.

"Make sure you light a candle to the saint for us, too, in return for the potatoes," she bargains.

Aunt Vangelia makes us her famous garlic and salt sauce for the potatoes, and the next morning we set off bright and early. With the first rays of sunshine, the little whitewashed country chapel of Prophet Elias sparkles from a distance, and we step up our pace to get there faster. The roosters, crowing at the top of their lungs, herald the new day, and the dogs, uneasy at our passing, dash to the front gates barking loudly to defend their territory.

As we near the sun-drenched mountaintop, the chiming church bells call the faithful to observance of the holy day. Inside the spotlessly clean roadside church, a handful of women are already praying. We light our votive candles in front of the icon of the saint riding triumphant in his horse-drawn carriage amidst a blaze of golden-red flames. When the liturgy is over, we stroll outside to enjoy the spectacular view, clear across to Mt. Olympos and beyond, to the valley of Thessaly. Ravenously hungry from the fresh air, we sit on the rocks to eat our boiled potatoes prepared according to Aunt Vangelia's recipe: half with garlic sauce and the other half plain.

"M-m-m." We all dig in. "This is the best dessert in the world," Katina is the first to exclaim, and we all agree.

On the way back, I run into trouble. I trip and fall on a sharp rock that tears a deep gash in my threadbare shoe.

"How will I go home? What will mommy say?" I start crying.

Katina, seeing the mess I'm in, laughs. "Walking has done you in."

That's all I need. "So, you're making fun of me, huh?" I answer, sniveling.

"Come on, don't fuss over it," Artemis says, shaking the dust off my clothes. "So what, you'll get new ones."

"Yeah, it's easy for you to say that, but where will we find the money?" I wipe the tears with the back of my hands and give her an angry look.

"Well, you can't go around barefoot, for heaven's sake. Go to the new shoemaker and order a pair," she suggests calmly.

"Are you kidding? Shoes on order? They cost a fortune." I rub my foot that's starting to hurt.

"So, get some sandals. What do they need? Just a couple of straps." She looks at me, smiling.

"Maybe, it's an idea. Then I won't get in trouble with mommy." I pick up my torn shoe and limp home. Luckily, my mother takes pity on me when she sees the bedraggled state I'm in and I don't get into trouble. At least for now.

"It's lucky you didn't break a bone or something. Prophet Elias protected you," Aunt Vangelia adds sympathetically. "Why don't you go straightway to the shoemaker's to order a pair of sandals? And tell him to be quick about it."

That same afternoon Artemis and I hurry to order them.

"You expect me to work on a holiday?" Takis, the shoemaker, shouts from the window. He sounds annoyed.

"Just take her measurements today. She has nothing to wear," Artemis pleads, disarming him with her charm.

The shoemaker comes downstairs and starts chatting with her while she stands there bursting into peals of good-natured laughter. So, sandwiched in between their witty exchanges, he takes the measurement, tracing the right and left foot separately on an old piece of brown paper. Then he gets up to see us off.

"Bye now." He turns toward me. "Let me double check those measurements tomorrow before I start. Leather is expensive and hard to get, I want to be sure."

What a bother. Isn't once enough? I think.

"Well, O.K.," I agree hastily, and we go.

The next day I wear an old pair of Artemis' clogs that are way too big for me, practically the size of a bathtub, and drag my feet along to go to the shoemaker's. They

121

make so much noise when I walk on the cobblestone street, I wonder if everybody is looking at me. Finally, I get to the store and go inside. As soon as Takis sees me enter, he raises his head and gives me an impish smile. In my confusion, I trip over myself and almost lose one of my clogs. I mutter something to try to cover up my embarrassment, but end up fumbling completely.

"It's all right," he says, "I'll take your measurements," and he starts humming a tune. His voice gets me all flustered. I'm totally at a loss. "Stand there against the wall and don't move around."

Mesmerized, I follow his directions. A customer walks in and interrupts him, giving me a chance to recover slightly, but the moment he leaves he starts humming again.

"I'll serenade you in the moonlight..." he croons.

A second and third customer arrive while I stand glued to the floor, tongue-tied. All of a sudden, Artemis walks in.

"Hurry up now, what's the matter with you? Have you lost your senses or something? At home they're waiting for us to eat." I put on my clogs and waddle after her like a duck.

"Hey, your shoemaker Takis' blue eyes are mischievous," Artemis tells me on the way home.

"So?" I feel my face burning.

"He could hardly take his eyes off you."

I listen dumbfounded.

"Come on, don't pretend you don't know what I'm talking about. I saw you looking at him."

The longer she talks, the more my voice catches, without knowing why. I hear what she's saying, like sounds floating out of a dream. I couldn't latch on to anything. Nothing connects, words don't make any sense. Just remembering when he touched me for a moment makes my knees almost buckle under. Why did I feel so agitated? I couldn't even see straight. "When did I look at him?" I hear myself saying, "I have no idea." It's a relief to get home so we can stop this discussion.

From that day forward, I wake up and go to bed thinking about my new sandals. They're the center of my life. One day the leather for the soles hasn't arrived, another the wrong batch is delivered. Always delays. I go back and forth in those stupid clogs, hurrying along like a duck out of water, but after a while I sort of get used to them. I arrive at the shoemaker's tiny store, my heart pounding, and stand there for hours on end. Customers come and go and I stay there, as though I'm nailed to the floor, listening to his songs, trying on the half-finished sandals dozens of times to make sure they fit perfectly, chatting endlessly. I haven't the faintest idea where the time flies.

"Where are you going?" I'm asked.

"For my fitting," is my standard reply.

One day, I run home in my new white sandals. I'm floating on air. I can hardly believe I'm actually wearing them!

"Look how beautiful..." I say, breathless, to my mother, who is standing in the middle of the street by our front door.

A loud slap hard across the face, louder than the sound of the clogs that fall from my hands, sends me to the ground before I can share my joy with her. I feel so humiliated by this thrashing in broad daylight where everyone in town can hear the thunderclap sound of my insult. What hurts most of all is her words.

"You tramp, you good for nothing! You're shameless!" she shrieks on and on, as she heaps abuses on me, lying there on the ground, stung to the quick, caught unawares by her angry mood. Her fury has no bounds.

I feel confused and can't understand why she is saying all these terrible things to me. So what if I spent most of my time at the shoemaker's? I did no one any harm. Why is she whipping me so mercilessly with her stinging words? What did I do?

My devastation is total. I wish the ground could open and swallow me, but it's no use. Is even the earth underneath my feet so cruel and heartless that it refuses my pleas? I cover my face to hide from the curious who are in every window witnessing my public humiliation. Left alone in the street, I stumble to the half-open courtyard door and drag myself inside after my mother's unreasonable wrath subsides. I head straight for the washroom and sprinkle a few drops of water from an earthenware jug that shakes in my trembling hands. I feel crushed. I stand there alone, leaning against the cold wall, enclosed by a ceaseless buzzing of everyone who witnessed my shaming. I'm left there, having no one to show any feeling to me, to care about me even if, unknowingly, I did wrong.

Artemis comes back a little later and hears me sobbing. She sits down on the stone bench next to me for a while to keep me company. The concern on her lovely face eases my pain. "It will pass," she says gently. Her tenderness softens the blow. At least someone cares a little.

From then on we become inseparable. She helps me weather the 'storm of the sandals' that I never got to enjoy. I throw them in the closet where I don't have to look at them. I'd rather wear the clogs. I'm not in the mood to do anything; all enthusiasm has been crushed out of me. Most of the time I eat all alone, any old leftovers, crouched in a far corner of the room. I hardly want to talk, words

124

taste cold in my mouth every time I think of my mother's harshness that wounded me so.

"Listen, listen! You won't believe what I just heard! Oh, my God, what will become of us?" Katina blurts out, out of breath, as she approaches the courtyard.

"What's going on? What happened?" Artemis rushes to pull the creaking, wooden doors open.

"Sh-sh, be quiet for a minute, Artemis, so we can hear the rest of the news report about Leningrad," Katina says and cocks an ear to the neighbor's radio across the street.

"What do you mean?" Artemis interrupts her.

"Leningrad is surrounded, I tell you," Katina replies sharply.

"The war continues at a relentless pace under Hitler's dictatorship," the news reporter continues. "His troops march steadily in an eastward direction, spreading death and destruction in their path as they aim at the annihilation of Russia. There's nothing but scorched, gutted earth. Blackened skies cover the endless steppes."

"Can you imagine where they've reached! I can't believe it," my mother exclaims, in a state of shock.

"What are you worried about? Russia, the Big Bear, will devour all of them. The steppes will be their graveyard, just as they were for Napoleon," Dino, the old schoolteacher offers his prediction. No wonder he's called "Mr. Know-it-all."

"That man hasn't got a clue about politics, but he pokes his nose into everything." Yiorgo mutters to my mother.

"He can be so annoying. His so-called theories drive me crazy," she whispers in his ear.

"Quit it, brother. You're not making any sense," Dino's brother-in-law Vasilis cuts him off short. "You don't have a leg to stand on. Can't you see the ship is sinking and you're promising us the moon and the stars?" he says, getting all worked up and then stops, obviously embarrassed by what he said. Usually he just lets Dino carry on, but this time he had had a couple of drinks and he went too far.

"I didn't mean to be offensive. Anyway, who knows what the hell is going on over there," he tells Dino.

"That's O.K., Vasili." Dino blushes and starts coughing—a pompous dry cough that drives away the crowd gathered around.

"What do you suppose is happening? How long will this mess continue?" my mother asks Aunt Vangelia when they go inside.

"Things don't look good to me. The blockade is here to stay, as you can see. Who knows when the big shots will end their horrible war games? They're playing power politics at our expense." She says, shaking her head pensively.

"Being in such terrible financial straits is wearing me down." My mother heaves a deep sigh. "No matter how hard I try, I can't find a way out. All the doors are shut, not a single payment."

"What can I say? It's a terrible burden," her sister answers, trying to console her, and her brown eyes fill with tears.

"My last hope was my trip to Kokkinoplo two months ago when I went to see if I could find some of the debtors and collect something," my mother continues. "That was all useless. Luckily brother Mitro came along to help me out, otherwise I couldn't have made it on my own. Besides the disappointment, a hornet stung me, and my leg got so swollen, I couldn't walk. If it hadn't been for him, I'm afraid to think what I would have done." She glances at her swollen foot.

"What more can you do?" Aunt Vangelia queries.

"Well, I sold my few remaining pieces of jewelry to pay off some debts to relatives and to cover some of our everyday expenses..." Her voice trails off to a whisper.

"That's just a temporary solution. What good will that do? You need some security."

"You're right. Between the skyrocketing food prices and all the other expenses, the little I got went like that." She snaps her fingers. "Now I'm back to square one," she says dejected.

"Patience, child, patience," her older sister counsels.

"Patience? I can't take it any more. How could their father leave me alone with two little children? How am I supposed to feed them? Didn't he realize we were at the edge of a cliff? Even the consulate warned us to leave right away because of the danger of war," she retorts. "He should see us now." She bursts into tears. "I've reached my limit." Her lips tremble, and her body shakes with uncontrollable sobbing.

"Don't despair! Maybe something will turn up," Aunt Vangelia answers in her most soothing, sage tone.

It's amazing how fast my mother's expression changes as soon as she hears her sister's comforting words. She lifts her hand slowly and wipes the tears off her face, brushing aside a wisp of hair that is covering her brow. It makes her look less strained and gives her eyes a glow. A faint smile appears on her face as she takes out an old, well-thumbed deck of cards with a polka-dot design on the cover and starts to play her favorite solitaire game.

"Let me see what the cards show today, Vangelia," she says hopefully. "Oh, no luck. I'll try again." She shuffles the cards slowly and deals them with the same unsuccessful results. "You see? Even the cards show it." She pushes them away annoyed.

"Show what?" her sister asks.

"Don't you see? No matter how many times I try, nothing happens. There's no way out."

"Worrying does you no good. You've got to pull through this winter and come spring, the Lord is merciful. By then the big powers will get fed up and stop fighting. This situation has lasted long enough, don't you agree?"

"Oh, God, I wish it were so easy," my mother exclaims, heaving a deep sigh.

"You just have to make up your mind. Why don't you spend the winter with your in-laws in Paliocastro since they suggested it? At least we'll be together and you'll have someone to talk to. What do you think?" Aunt Vangelia asks her.

"M-m-m, I don't know. If their father was here, it would be easier. Being so far away he evades all responsibility. I just received a telegram from him through the Red Cross that said: 'I am well. I hope you are, too.' I wonder if he received the letters I sent him the same way. But, what's the use? I have to think about your idea. You realize that life with in-laws, especially under these trying conditions..." her words catch in her throat. "Without a penny to my name..." She stops short and they glance knowingly at each other. The somber expression on their faces is more telling than words can ever be.

"You also have to consider the children's schooling. They already missed classes for a year. That's a long time to go without learning at their tender age. Do you want them to be left unlettered? Listen, I'm leaving soon. Get ready to go in time for the beginning of the new school year."

I haven't seen the shoemaker, Takis, since that dreadful incident that upset me so much. I wonder if he, too, heard the thunder-clap noise when my mother smacked me in the face? I try not to think about him, but I can't help hearing his voice talking to me or singing, sometimes, when I wake up at night. Once, I stir out of my sleep rubbing my eyes.

"I'll serenade you by moonlight..." wafts softly through the window into my room.

Can it be? I bolt upright. *Am I dreaming?* I jump out of bed.

Yes, yes, it must be he! I dash to the window.

I want so much to tell Artemis about it. But how? I'll wake up the whole house! I can't decide what to do. I'm caught between the devil and the deep blue sea.

"You see," she tells me the next morning, "he's in love with you," and she smiles at me.

That same afternoon Artemis runs into Takis' cousin on the street, and he gives her a message that Takis wants to see me.

"What should I do?" I ask her, and my heart beats faster. It's so strange talking about it with somebody, even someone I trust. How can I explain how I feel?

"I'll talk to his cousin and let you know. We mustn't raise any suspicions," she says, winking at me mischievously, and her laughter is full of life. She can lift everyone's spirits and spread joy all around. My mother's admiration for her is unbelievable!

"See how Artemis makes the bed? Without a single wrinkle. She does everything to perfection." But she just ignores all the things I try to do right to please her.

"You can't do anything right," she belittles me whenever she gets a chance. "Watch how Artemis does it and try to learn. You only do well in school, but life is more than good grades. You must discipline yourself to become a good housewife," she advises me over and over once she gets going. So I watch and try, knowing full well I can never please her, so I might as well resign myself to getting good grades. I have nothing else.

As she promised, Artemis arranges my secret rendezvous with Takis that I want so much by sending a message through his cousin. Delighted and terrified at the same time, I agree to meet him in an abandoned house way down by the St. Anargyri church, far from our neighborhood. I tremble with fear, but I want to see him, I can't wait any longer.

I remember wearing my checkered light and dark green dress and my white topcoat. Yes, that's it. I can still feel the whiteness clinging to my body, shining bright as day in the moonlight, as I run in and out of narrow cobblestone streets. Why did I wear my white coat? Why didn't I take it off before leaving? White attracts attention. Now everyone is looking at me and probably knows where I'm going. They can tell. My heart is beating faster than my thumping footsteps, blasting the news of my arrival to the entire neighborhood.

Half-running, half-walking as quietly as possible, I reach the little yard of the old house and, to my great relief, notice no one in the street. Takis is waiting for me in front of the closed door and greets me with his usual debonair smile.

I forget everything. He takes me by the hand and pulls me close to him, stroking my hair.

"Give me a little kiss," he whispers in my ear.

I look at him surprised.

"Oh, don't refuse me, just one." I try to step back and he holds me closer. Shyly I let him touch my lips. He asks for another.

"We agreed on one." I resist. He chuckles and kisses me again on the mouth, this time without asking. I can taste the bitterness of cigarettes on his tongue. I wish I had been left with the first gentle touch of his lips.

Men are so strange, I think on the way home, *they make such a fuss about an agreement, and then they don't even keep their promise. How can you trust them?*

The summer is almost over, and Artemis leaves soon to get ready for high school. I haven't seen Takis for what seems like ages. It's too risky without anyone to help me. Then, quite by chance I see him at the Kioski park flirting with someone else, and something instantly freezes inside me. I don't even want to face him. I feel crushed! I move away with my head bent low, fighting back a flood of tears. I glance back and notice that she's pretty and coquettish. She's older and more clever than I, and she knows how to captivate men, not like me. No wonder he forgot all about me.

When I hear that we're going to live in Paliocastro, I'm excited. The thought that soon I'll be seeing Artemis is like a god-sent gift. Only that lifts my spirits and makes the sorrow and pain bearable. I can see Artemis every time she comes home for the holidays, maybe I'll even catch her before she starts school. What a thrill! We'll be talking for hours, I think, anticipating our chit-chats. I have so much to tell her.

Soon we'll be leaving the cool mountain air for the heat of the lowlands, exactly the same month we visited Paliocastro after our arrival from America. I was so excited about seeing my father's hometown nestled in the foothills by the edge of the serpentine Aliakmon river.

I can visualize what happened in graphic detail, as though they're right before my very eyes. I can remember that day that we rode from the Siapka forest through the Sarantaporo narrows as though it were yesterday.

Riding tall on my horse that galloped downhill, warm and sweaty under my thighs, I suddenly heard the animal neigh, and before I knew it, he was standing upright on his hind legs, just as I'd seen in the Hollywood westerns. For that one special moment I became a movie heroine, ready to take off in a gallop with my chosen cowboy who had come just in time, riding on a white stallion to save my life.

In Paliocastro, the whole town was there to greet us. Relatives and friends came down to the highway intersection to welcome us, to enclose us in a circle of love. At dusk swarms of kids of every age came to greet the little American girl with a permanent and a pretty garland of colored flowers in her blond hair, and we roamed all about town. The Amerikana was the envy of all the young girls. What an intoxicating evening: parties, dancing, enjoyment. Then for days to come, picnics, trips to the vineyards—the air full of the smell of crushed grapes and heady, fresh-brewed ouzo—merrymaking at bazaars, the *panygiria,* to the sound of gypsy music and lively songs. Like nothing I had ever seen before.

This time our arrival is burdened by the oppression of our country under a triple occupation: German, Italian, and Bulgarian. The proud white and blue national flag is hidden behind the heavy black clouds of foreign tyranny. As we near Paliocastro, I get so impatient, I jump off the mule ahead of the others to run to Aunt Vangelia's house, hoping to catch Artemis before she leaves for high school, only to be disappointed that she has already gone ahead of time to register early. They tell me not to fret.

"She'll come home for the holidays. Wait." So I wait.

Artemis comes back sooner than I expect. But not for the holidays. She has frightful headaches and a terrible fever. She has meningitis. The doctor visits her at least twice a day, but she continues to wilt from the high fever that refuses to go away. There is no cure. I sit next to her in the half-darkened room, stroking her golden hair, wiping her burning forehead, watching her mute, unavailing movements. The pain is unbearable. Every now and then she escapes momentarily from her coma to look around, to say something, to stare ahead, and, then just as quickly withdraws from us, sinking once more into incoherent, inarticulate rambling. Pursued by the dark angel of Hades, she fights for her life, but doesn't win. A double defeat...

TO ARTEMIS

Autumn. Infinite desolation.
Foliage, pale and wan.
Not a single bird flutters.
The swallow forever gone.

A dream, lost in the dark of dawn,
frozen midstream.
Drop by drop, stillness
floods the sunless earth.

Anguish, sleepless,
haunts the night, seeking,
The smile on your lips,
engraved on your face
for an eternity.
The tresses of your golden hair,
reminiscent of blue-green eyes,
and meets only denial.
The shimmer of your laughter.
The sureness of your movements.
The joy in your soul.

Implacable, you fail to respond.

Unrelenting silence surrounds
myriad fragrant flowers fraying in your arms.

12 BLEAK WINTER

The winter that follows is bitter. Artemis' loss tears apart my life.

I imagine that my turn is next. Only that could free me of my terrible pain. Whenever I get sick, I think it's a signal of approaching death. Any day now I expect to follow her, but it doesn't happen.

Why? I wonder every morning as I run to school, my hands tucked under my armpits to fight off the freezing cold. I squeeze my books against my body to stop the chill from running through me and the hunger from tearing at my insides. The shriveled olives and dry bread I gobbled up in the morning to stay yesterday's hunger don't last very long.

Every morning on my way to school I pass by Aunt Vangelia's house. She, widowed for five years, is now in double mourning after Artemis' death. Just opposite her front door, right in the middle of the road, stands a fountain. The closer I get to it, the more I quicken my pace. Not casually, aimlessly, but intentionally. *Suppose I'm stopped by the German SS?* I think, and shake all over. They go to the fountain every day and strip to the waist to wash themselves in the freezing water. My terror is obvious. I can't stop my teeth from chattering and my sweat, that smells of fear, from soaking my body. What I dread most is neither their brutal, barbaric voices nor their big shiny guns by their sides. It's an inhuman, frozen, satanic flame that shines in their eyes and spreads around an invisible, penetrating beam that destroys without even touching you. There isn't a shred of humanity in their venomous glance, not a spark of emotion. It has been extinguished along with every tendency toward compassion, understanding, empathy—even the simple feeling of closeness for warmth—died forever. Human instinct is deadened, cast away in a demonic abyss.

From the very moment I catch sight of them, I'm overcome by a terrible, uncontrollable fear. A feeling of panic grips me that my legs will bend like two thin candles and I'll collapse on the ground unprotected, crushed to pieces—worse than a worm—by their tall, black-as-a-snake boots. I will disappear forever.

I reach school out of breath, my hands a pair of icicles. I try to slide into the classroom cautiously before my teacher notices me, and tuck my numb fingers between my knees to thaw out enough to be able to grasp the pencil.

I'm famished and the growling in my stomach is so loud, it's hard for me to ignore it so I can pay attention to my lessons.

"What's your hurry?" my cousin Ted asks, tugging at my sleeve on the way back from school.

"I'm freezing, and if I get back ahead of the others maybe I'll have a chance to sit close to the stove and warm up before they elbow me out," I answer, shivering from the cold.

"What do you expect with eight of us in one room fighting to find a place near the stove? Remember the time you rushed to get close to the stove and you fell over and got your leg got stuck against the hot metal? I thought you'd burn your whole body when you fell off that little stool."

I shudder.

"How could I forget? My leg was all swollen—I could hardly walk for days, and the raw flesh wouldn't heal in the cold weather. Besides, going to class in the morning on an empty stomach didn't help. See, I still have the scar there."

He looks at me compassionately.

"Let's talk about something else. It makes me nauseous every time I think of that foul odor of burning flesh hanging in the air of that room for days on end, and we couldn't even open the window, it was so bitter cold. But, enough of that."

"You started it! It's too cold to talk, anyway," I mutter after a while, feeling gloomy.

We move on the uphill road without talking. In front of us the gray house we live in rises like a fortress.

"I don't feel like going on," Ted grunts in a hoarse voice.

"You're dragging your feet as though they're taking you off to the gallows. Don't worry about anything," I add, with my teeth clenched tight.

"I've had it. I can't stand it any more!"

"Me neither. The thought of going into that place, it's like a prison," I moan. "It scares me."

"It's not the same without my mother waiting inside for me, God bless her soul," his voice cracks.

"I know," I sigh, gently touching his arm.

Once inside we each get a piece of dry bread with a cup of tea. I huddle in a corner to do my homework. His older brother Petros walks in red as a beet from the cold. We all move aside to let him pass.

"What were you up to?" Aunt Pelagia shuffles to the door looking pale and sullen, as usual.

"Wouldn't ya like to know...ha, ha, ha," comes a dry, cackling laughter.

"Whatcha laughin' at? Ya got somethin' to be cheerful about?" she asks, with scorn.

"Have we got anything to worry about?" He struts toward the stove to warm his chapped hands. A savage smile contorts his good-looking face into a grimace, his dark brown eyes glint like well-sharpened steel blades.

"Petros is something else again," my mother gets in the talk, shaking her head, "no one can mess with him. He tells it like it is," she says and affectionately pats his bony shoulders.

"When it comes to eating he has no equal. Nothing gets past me," Aunt Pelagia grumbles as she shuffles about in her black slippers, the thick batch of keys she inherited from her mother securely tucked in the waist of her long, dark gray skirt.

Pelagia, widowed and childless for many years, has been keeping house for her brother Leonidas, a well-to-do local dentist. She also looks after her aged mother who gave up her command of the household only when she got arthritis, developed cataracts, and became senile. All she can manage now is to leave a telltale trickle each time she makes a trip to the bathroom. Petros doesn't miss a chance to needle her.

"I see you've got a river going again. Ha, ha, ha," his taunting laughter follows her. "You lost your way again?" He teases her.

"Shut up, you good for nothing," she tells him, furious, now, shaking a threatening hand toward the ceiling.

"I'm over here. Why are looking for me over there?" he sneers, laughing. "But you never get lost on your way to the kitchen. You wanna taste the food, to make sure it's O.K., huh? To make sure you get your bowlful, then you can pour in a pitcher of water to make it nice and tasteless for the rest of us." He piles it on without mincing his words.

"You big-mouth, you, have you no respect for your elders?" She shakes her walking stick in the air, but Petros deftly ducks out of her reach.

Petros is constantly a thorn in Pelagia's side, and she never fails to give him a tongue lashing for it. She follows in her mother's footsteps as the new keeper of the house, doling out the stale bread that she keeps safely under lock and key in a cupboard where no one can get hold of it, for about a week, until it's thoroughly hardened, like a stone.

"So-o-o-o it won't go fa-a-a-st," she drags out each word about as quickly as she moves. She maneuvers her short frame around, adjusts her thick glasses, and assumes full command of the storage room full of flour, rice, beans, olive oil, and other provisions.

Petros, diametrically the opposite, gets under her skin. Quick-witted, outspoken, even brazen at times, he's an annoyance and a frustration that she has great difficulty handling while Ted is gentler and more diplomatic in his dealings with her, all of which work to his advantage. She favors him and openly makes allowances, excusing her weakness for him by saying: "He's a young 'un. Can't you see he's frail, he can't take too much, poor thing, born too early and then, all the trouble he had with his eyes..." She coddles him, secretly dishing out bits and pieces of food whenever she finds a chance, "to keep him going." And whispers, "Run along before the big guy grabs it from you."

139

Petros grows taller by the day, and so does his hunger. The meager scraps he eats aren't enough to keep him going. So, he never misses a chance to get food—by hook or by crook. This keeps his aunt always on the alert.

"I know him. He has no equal! He can't fool me, though." This doesn't sit well with Petro, who quickly gets wise to her ways and often snaps back at her whether she intended malice with her remark or not.

"Where have I been? To visit the devil and back," he retorts.

"Why, you heathen, have you no fear of God at least?" she warns, crossing herself thrice to ward off the evil spirits she believes he might have brought along with him.

But that's not enough to scare him. His hunger is a far more powerful force than her threats. Try as she does to keep watch on him, he usually outsmarts her— by speed of action, if not by guile. His ingenuity has no bounds. Sometimes he hides right under her nose while she stands with her daughter at the storage room door taking stock of its contents, as she did in the past when she held the reins.

Crouching low, he hides in the folds of his grandmother's multi-layered, ample skirts and snatches bits of cheese or dried fruit or whatever is within the grasp of his long arms. By the time she gets wind of something being amiss, he's slithering away, smirking at her complaints that "the house is full of rats running around loose."

Eagle eyes Petros is our leader in the unending battle against hunger. Not only because he's clever, but also, he inspires fear around him.

"Tomorrow morning we'll attack," he tells Ted, Tasio, and me in a hushed, conspiratorial tone. "Uncle Leonidas is leaving early for his clinic, and I want you to be ready, O.K.?" His words leave no room for dispute.

"And Aunt Pelagia?" Ted asks meekly.

"She has to go downstairs to get his things ready. Got it?" He flashes a confident smile.

"So, we're all set," I say and huddle over the stove to get warmed up.

Bright and early the next morning, Ted, Tasio, and I, with Petro as our leader, lay an ambush for our uncle's breakfast leftovers. We all pounce on the half-teaspoon of marmalade and the small piece of fresh bread, gobbling up the delicious morsels before Aunt Pelagia has a chance to lock them in the cupboard.

"I thought he was in a hurry, but he finished the whole lot," she mumbles to herself.

Sometimes Aunt Pelagia catches him in the act.

"You ambush me, you wily dumb-wit, but you'd never make it out in the open," he hisses, his teeth clenched tight, waving his arms in the air.

"What d'ya-a-a say?" She fumes. " A-a-a curse on your black soul. Have you forgotten all the things I've done for you? You ungrateful rascal." Whatever she says, though, Aunt Pelagia knows she's met her match, and she's afraid of him.

It's quite another story if Uncle Leonidas happens to come back from his clinic to fetch something. At the mere sound of his footsteps, Petros instantly vanishes through the back door. His uncle is the only person he is afraid of. And if he's caught, all hell breaks loose. As soon as Uncle lays eyes on him, he is beside himself with anger, foaming at the mouth, his piercing eyes narrowed to a slit, his body shaking like one possessed. Poor Petros freezes. Uncle pulls and pulls and pulls his ears, first one, then the other, with such force, he practically lifts him up to the ceiling. Then the tirade starts.

"You shameless ass, that's what you are. If you raise the donkey's tail and spit at it, it has no shame. Once an ass, always an ass. Will you ever get any sense into your thick skull?" He continues with each sadistic yank of Petro's blood-red ears. "You're a mess," he goes on, ranting and raving like a maniac, his swarthy face turning darker and darker. "You'll become a person when I see my own ears. Get lost, out of my sight."

Petros, deathly pale, slinks away like a wet cat. He sneaks outside to kick around a stone or something until things simmer down.

The quarrel throws the whole household in turmoil. All the younger kids go into hiding, to make sure we don't get caught in the crossfire. Then we sneak out of the house for a couple of hours to avoid Uncle's wrath. When we return, frightened to death, we whisper, "Holy Mary, protect us! Don't let Uncle cross our path." We run to take cover until we can find out how things are going. Is Uncle still angry? That's always the big question.

My mother doesn't have a choice. Bent over a wet rag, she's stuck in a corner of the kitchen, scrubbing the floor. She doesn't dare show her face! Being in a servile position, she's the one who has to stay and bear the brunt of Uncle's anger. She works nonstop, wiping her chapped hands with her patched apron to obey all the orders:

"Did you make the bread, did you do the wash, did you cook for the guests? Have you set the table? Is this, that, and the other taken care of?" Uncle issues his tyrannical demands.

She has to get everything done. Slavishly she follows her sister-in-law, Pelagia, the commander-in-chief, with her bunch of keys dangling from her waistband, to get all the food supplies from the storage rooms. My mother watches her as she locks and unlocks doors and then is left to carry the boxes upstairs. By the time they fetch one item, they have to go down to the double-locked cellar again because she "f-f-forgot the lard and the sugar."

"It takes the two of you twice as long to go back and forth," Aunt Chrysie remarks when she stops by for a while one day.

"I know what I'm doing. You mind your own business," her sister shuts her up fast and after that, nothing changes.

"It's enough to turn your hair gray," laments my mother. "We spend most of the day getting the ingredients because she's forgetful and I'm not trusted to do it alone." She wipes her brow. "What could I possibly do with the stuff? Squirrel away bits of lard and flour?" she confides in Aunt Chrysie.

"It's the same old story!" She sighs and leaves with her head bent down.

On days like this when there has been a row, Uncle comes back from work tired and still upset over the earlier incident. He picks a fight with everyone, but mostly with those who are in the front-line, so to speak, giving vent to his anger for no reason.

"Women, women, they need a good beating. Me! Me! You won't catch me getting married, I'll never be enslaved by a woman," he hisses, glowering at my mother.

He blasts off sarcastic rockets at women, pauses for a bit, and then gets going again.

"All of you vampires, you suck my blood, and I work my head off so you can sit around and eat up my food. Get lost. I'm fed up with the whole lot of you!" His venomous words that sting like burning coals are heaped on all of us, but it's even worse for my mother.

143

"Your husband didn't have enough sense to take you with him. He left me holding the bag."

She just stands there being belittled in front of everyone, afraid to utter a word, lest that redoubles his wrath. She knows that, as an in-law, she's an outsider, and she's always the scapegoat; so she bends down to do her chores.

Only Aunt Chrysie, his older sister, sometimes dares to stand up for her.

"It's a pity, the poor thing. She's struggling all by herself to raise her children, without the support of her husband. Do you suppose she wanted it this way? Leave her alone. Don't add to her worries."

He listens without saying a word. She can bring him to his senses with her calm manner.

"Can't you take a little pity on her? She is shaking like a dry leaf. She works like a slave. Who else can you find like her to run this household and make you presentable to your guests?"

When company arrives in the evening, Uncle Leonidas is another person altogether. He charms everyone with his sharp wit, his dark good looks and charisma, a model of hospitality.

He sits contented in the armchair, entertaining his guests with his conversation; his sense of humor and only an occasional ironic laugh momentarily betray his tempestuous nature. He artfully shows his sparkling white teeth that his dentist colleague, Dr. Krystalos, cares for with devotion.

"You are fantastic," he collects raves from the ladies and beams back at them, obviously adored by one and all. Uncle reaps the compliments, never once acknowledging all the things my mother does. Only her fixed smile belies her anguish. She deftly skirts around the table serving the seated guests, making sure everything is in order, knowing

144

that she'll have to pay dearly the next day for the slightest flaw.

After dinner the sliding glass doors open and the ladies withdraw to the adjoining room to let the men continue their heated political discussion. The women don't appear to show any interest in it and become involved in their own chatter.

"Oh, such a host," the ladies coo with delight. "And what a superb dinner," they exclaim.

Dutifully my mother stands by the door while the merriment goes on at a distance. Only her deep-set, melancholy dark brown eyes give a fleeting hint of the pain she endures.

Mrs. Krystalou, the other dentist's wife, turns her chair toward Mrs. Angelidou sitting near her.

"Isn't Leonidas the most charming man? I find his manners so enchanting." She casts flirtatious glances in his direction.

"I can see why," Miss Pappa, her niece, giggles coquettishly, "he'll do anything for his friends. For their sake he'll even 'fetch milk from a bird's nest,' as the saying goes." She tosses her head back with well-practiced abandon, casting a seductive glance at him, but he's too absorbed in conversation to notice her.

"You know, he's the same with his clients," her aunt picks up where she left off, "so devoted. He's worse than my husband, if the truth be told." She smiles demurely at her niece. "Imagine, he's so generous he won't charge the needy peasants a single penny. If they can't pay cash, he'll let them pay him in kind whenever they can." She sips her demitasse coffee, keeping her pinkie extended, according to the latest etiquette. "That's the kind of man you should marry," Mrs. Krystalou lowers her voice, leaning toward her niece for *tête a tête.*

"Such a man," her niece sighs. "And so cheerful."

"If you win him over, you'll be a very lucky girl, my dear." She winks at her, conveying a world of intimacies, as only women can do.

"His brother Stelios takes more after his father, Judge Kriton," Mrs. Angelidou enters the discussion. "You know, in the years of the Turkish occupation, his fame was widespread as a fair-minded member of the bench. He commanded the respect of all the people, Greeks and Turks alike." She stares momentarily into her half-finished coffee cup.

"Yes? And how do you know that?" Miss Pappa asks, playfully.

"Of course I know. I remember my father often talked about the judge's remarkable qualities. It's quite rare, you know, to be truly just. He made landmark decisions that have stood the test of time, my father, God rest his soul, used to say." She carefully dabs the corner of her mouth before continuing. "His word was as good as gold, better than a contract." She pauses to catch her breath.

"You don't find many judges like him nowadays," Miss Pappa interjects.

"Oh, yes, that's so true, but he didn't live to enjoy the fruits of his labor." Mrs. Angelidis rests her cup on the table. "You, of course, have only been here in your teaching post a short while and evidently have not heard about some of these old timers," she adds, suddenly cocking an ear toward the other room.

The dinner guests have interrupted their affable chatter to welcome Uncle Leonida's brother Stelios, who arrives late, as usual, sweaty and tired after his long trip on horseback from the nearby village of Miliohori.

"Hey, there, miller," he's greeted jovially, as he takes the comfortable seat by the fire and fishes out his old pipe.

The two brothers are practically look-alikes, although Uncle Stelios' appearance is more on the rough-hewn side, in line with his trade. Both have striking dark features, a swarthy complexion, a lively smile, but in other ways they're brothers only in name. In temperament they come from opposite poles. Both quick witted, they often vie with each other for attention. The sharp edge between them is palpable, especially when there is talk of marriage.

"Why don't you get yourself a wife?" Uncle Stelios asks his brother from time to time. "How long will you remain a bachelor?"

"That life is not for me. What good has it done you?" comes the sharp retort.

Uncle Stelios is quick to react to any suggestion that his brother is the smarter of the two.

"You know, you ought to have become a lawyer, such a clever mind," Mr. Angelidis strikes up a conversation with the miller.

"Actually they do the same thing I do. The only difference is they grind out words. At least I make an honest living with the sweat of my brow. No double talk, no deals under the table. You know what you're getting," he says, puffing on his pipe.

"Excuse me for just a moment, please," Miss Pappa remarks. "I overheard something about the U.S. Let's find out what's going on." She turns her attention to the dining area where the men seated together are talking.

"Japan..." Mr. Angelidis is saying.

"What's happening?" his wife asks, interrupting him.

147

"Well, I heard that the Japanese navy and air force made a surprise attack on December 6 on American bases in Pearl Harbor..."

"What does this mean?" Miss Pappa asks.

"War, certainly." Her uncle's voice softens. "The U.S. had remained neutral until now, but this attack will definitely expand the war operations," he explains.

"A second front is opening, it's a land campaign against Germany." Uncle Leonidas clarifies the point. "The war is entering a new phase."

"So, we can expect new developments in the Far East," Uncle Stelios suggests. "Maybe the war will end a little sooner."

Mrs. Angelidis turns her head in his direction. "Let's hope so," she sighs.

"Where is that port—that place the Japanese attacked?" Mrs. Krystalou asks her husband.

"Oh, you wouldn't know it," he tells her impatiently.

"Why, did you know it before?" she checks him, and he grimaces, swiveling uncomfortably in his seat.

"Pearl Harbor," comes his curt answer, "but we must be going." He gestures toward the door.

The other guests have picked up the cue and are getting their coats. They're all leaving earlier than usual, their mood apparently dampened by the latest turn of events.

The next day Uncle Stelios is looking gloomy and starts picking a fight with his brother.

"I heard you were in one of your nasty moods again yesterday. You certainly switched pretty fast from dictator to prince charming, bowing to the ladies, kissing their hands, complimenting the young miss. But you left out your sister-in-law who made the fabulous dinner." He nee-

148

dles him. "She doesn't count, huh? You're good at that, aren't you? Whatever serves you best."

"Leave me alone," Uncle Leonidas snaps back, his eyes a thin blade of steel, glistening in the raw morning light.

"You're lucky our brothers went to America and worked their asses off to give you an education, otherwise I'd see how cocksure you'd be right now," Uncle Stelios says in a rage and his eyes flash.

"O.K., O.K., I've heard all that a hundred times. I can't be bothered with the same old stuff. Stop it, Stelio, I'm warning you," he shouts grabbing his coat, as soon as he hears his friends outside...

"Wait a minute, what's your big hurry? I'm talking to you. But, of course, your friends are waiting for you. Don't I have the right to talk to you? Just because things are rosy for you and..." Uncle Stelios gasps.

"I'm fed up with you grinding out the same old stale nonsense time and again," Uncle Leonidas retorts. "Leave me alone, my friends are waiting for me."

"Let them wait," Stelios snaps back.

"I can't expect people to hang around for your sake," he answers, flashing a sarcastic grin, his glinting green eyes a shaft of mercurial light.

"You hide your evil schemes behind that hypocritical smile of yours, but I know you too well, you can't fool me. You and that ego of yours," Stelios hisses, "that's all you give a damn about, you arrogant—" his voice struggles to get through his choked throat.

"You can go to hell." Uncle Leonidas runs down the stairs, taking two steps at a time, whistling a tune by the time he reaches the front door.

149

His brother stands alone rooted to the floor like a wooden post. The sound of laughter drifts in from outside. Slowly he turns his head and smashes his raised fist into the wall.

13 DAYS OF WOE

Spring and Resurrection—a sunlit, youthful, well-matched coupling; a festive pairing of nature and the church. One responds to winter's long agony with triumphant hymns of joy; the other replies to the wails of the holy passion with a doxology of victory over the powers of darkness.

Holy Week! Every night I join the other choirgirls from the neighborhood, and we run to church to chant the Passions of Christ. First, we go to the church of St. Nicholas because the services start earlier, then to St. Catherine's, our parish church.

Today is Holy Thursday and the service lasts a long time because it's devoted to the recitation of all the Stations of the Cross from the Scriptures, the Evangelion.

The bells at St. Catherine's are chiming, and we haven't left yet. The choir members are getting restless. A steady murmuring reveals how anxious we are about the delay, and the priest scowls and keeps giving us dirty looks.

"Oh, no! We'll be late if he doesn't finish soon," Sophia grumbles in a hoarse whisper, spitting into her red-stained handkerchief.

Before the priest even finishes reciting "Our Father," we make a mad dash for the door, taking a shortcut through a side street to save time. We run as fast as we can when a bright light startles us.

"They did it on purpose, to scare us. I'm so annoyed," says Irene.

"Do you think it's the choir boys?" I ask.

"Who else would do such a stupid thing? They know we're running late," she fumes.

"For heaven's sake! We'll break our necks," Sophia's angry outcry makes her start coughing again. That's the worst thing for her consumption.

"*ALT, ALT, ACHTUNG,*" a voice bellows in German. Down the street I hear guns clicking.

They all start running at top speed, and I follow them without a second thought. Just as I race with all my might to reach them, I go around the corner too fast, and suddenly I fall down, and the centrifugal force propels me forward, dragging my hands and knees. The sound of girls' hurried footsteps fades in the darkness. I'm in terrible pain. It's unbearable. *I must catch up with the others,* I keep telling myself. *I've got to...,* I say, trying hard not to swallow a handful of thick dust that fills my mouth. Half blinded, I feel the dreadful light fast approaching. It will swallow me up. I must do something.

I want to run and catch up with the others. Loud voices are coming closer. The earth echoes with heavy footsteps. My vision is blurred. Whenever I try to get up, my body feels like a flaming log and my legs bend like clay. I slither forward and stop, wetting my parched lips. I try again, biting my lip, and limping along bent over, I begin to run. Just as I make the turn around the bend, the spotlight flashes behind me. I run like the wind without losing time to glance back. I've stopped feeling any pain.

I reach the churchyard panting and rush inside, gasping to catch my breath. The serene, tranquil candlelight, the haze of incense, and the harmonious choral voices startle

152

me. Nothing bears witness to my anguish. I want to be inconspicuous and hide behind the choir where no one can notice that I'm covered with dust and blood. I'm shaking all over. My eyes are glued to the door. At the slightest sound I expect the Germans to come and arrest me.

ACCUSATION: leaving the scene of the crime.

PENALTY: death.

I try, in vain, to cover up the bloody evidence of my escape. The choirgirls catch sight of me and look confused. Some smile, obviously relieved to see me, but I motion silence because I'm afraid that their glances will betray my presence.

I decide to leave the church before someone starts asking me questions and silently edge my way through the unsuspecting crowd as soon as the service ends. Once outside, I take the deserted road toward home. Absolute stillness reigns in the starlit night. No one has returned from church yet. I quickly rinse my wounds, change my clothes, and quietly allow myself to merge with the soft, protective stillness of the night. It is Good Friday eve. Tomorrow I must chant the Passion of the crucifixion of Christ. I shudder to think of the close call I had—the choir might have been lamenting my death.

In these days, many young people from the choir and around town are dying of tuberculosis. We often get together and chat before they die. They know they're dying. We talk about that, too.

"I'll go before you," petite, moon-faced Irene says with unnatural calm and firm conviction in her sweet, lilting voice.

Sophia, her neighbor and friend from the choir, listens without interrupting. Her wavy dark hair frames her pale, uncommonly beautiful face, and a melancholy, dreamy smile gives her an air of otherworldliness.

"You'll weave a garland for my hair," Irene insists, as though she has definitely made her decision, and all that is left is to settle a few minor details.

But Sophia's health takes an unexpected turn for the worse, and within a few days she succumbs to her phthisis. At her funeral, Irene sheds bitter tears as she lays down the garland of flowers she was sure had been destined for her. In her melodious voice she sings the verses of a mournful dirge: "Where have you gone, my little one? Why have you left me alone? You will never wear your bridal wreath, my sweet. Never will your lovely voice fill the emptiness of silence."

Her loneliness is short-lived, and before long we go to Irene's funeral, as we have gone to all of them—to weep for the friends who have departed from our midst and to eat some *kolyva,* the wheat porridge that is served on such occasions. Funerals have become the gathering place of young people. Weddings have ceased. Rarely is there a baptism, so the village youths find a new meeting place at funerals where they can get some food.

Most of all, I think, we mourn the sudden death of a seventeen-year-old boy attacked by consumption, who departs for his final resting place in no time at all. As though that grief isn't enough for his hapless mother, within a month her only daughter, Kiki, becomes deathly ill. The mother trembles with fear of losing the only child she has left. Her slender, petite body darts back and forth like a ferret from the kitchen to her sick child's bedside. Pain is written all over her sensitive face, and she can hardly hold back the tears glistening in her blue eyes.

Then comes news of a divine oracle from her husband who, it is said, is on a kind of holy pilgrimage. "The girl must go to the mountains. She needs a change of climate," he pronounces from afar. "That's where she'll find her cure."

Her mother, Hermione, immediately takes Kiki to a wild forest in the mountains for "a cure of her fever." The guide leaves them in an abandoned hut. The mother looks at the barren mountain facing her. There's nothing but bleakness, except for another shack on the other mountainside. No one dares approach them. Even the shepherds are apprehensive.

"What, take a chance on bringing the scourge to our homestead? That girl has the bad sickness." They spit three times on the ground to ward off the evil spirit, afraid that even mentioning the dread word might bring on the disease.

Hermione stands alone, bewildered and mystified. Nightfall surrounds them with madness. The wails of the lawless mountain beasts mingle with the hissing of the wind-blown trees and the delirious incoherence of the girl burning in fever, her eyes now jagged shafts of lightning in the half darkness, now reflections of the long shadows crossing the barren hut. The mother circles about in a frenzy, her perplexed stare hooked onto the edge of despair.

By dawn the blowing of the wind subsides, leaving in its wake the sound of Kiki's delirium and hallucinations. There is no other sign of life on the triple-peaked mountain. The mother remains frozen, still. The day passes in a void. The sunset, a flaming sky.

Unexpectedly, the footsteps of a lone passerby echo in the canyon. A rather short man, walking briskly, passes in front of the hut and pauses before the girl's mother.

"Woman, if you don't take your daughter away, you'll lose her forever," he calls out in a commanding voice, and then vanishes over the horizon. The impact of his words momentarily shakes the forlorn woman, and she lets out a desperate cry. "Send some he-e-elp!" Her voice echoes from afar.

Around nightfall the fierce wind begins to blow again from the sky-high Pieria mountains, swiftly tearing the clouds into thousands of pieces. The girl awakens in the middle of the night drenched in her own sweat. "Mother, take me away, I'm dying," she screams, and then falls down again, unconscious.

The next morning a man approaches the shack, but the sleepless woman wanders aimlessly without sensing his presence.

"What do you want?" she asks, noticing him at last. *Is this the same stranger who passed by before? Did I ask him to come back to save my one and only child?* She wonders. *How can I remember now what I said to him?* She stands there shaking her head, dazed.

"Come, we're going home." Her brother, Thomas, comes inside the hut, lifting Kiki's limp body in his arms. The mother mounts the sturdy mule standing by, and he puts the girl into her lap. From a distance, a lone shepherd watches in awe.

After Kiki's return from the "country," her bronchitis turns into double bronchopneumonia. The doctor says she must stay in bed for a long time. The loss of her brother, her health, her schooling, and her friends leave her lonely and discouraged. Mother and daughter are thin as rails.

I visit her often to keep her company and enjoy the times when her mother, obviously well-read but never boastful or proud, joins in and talks with us about history, French, and many other topics that interest me. These discussions become a small oasis in the monotony of provincial life, quickening my desire to explore foreign lands, unknown customs, and different people.

One day, I return home and an ominous silence tells me that something is wrong.

No sooner do I open the door than I'm attacked. *What can be amiss?* I wonder.

"Where were you? What were you doing? Why are you late?" My uncle fires one clipped question after another.

I listen patiently, wondering what has set him off. I have nothing to hide.

"Don't you realize you can catch T.B. in that infected place?" His withering tone of voice makes me shrivel.

"But—but the room where the boy died is locked up, I—I don't go in there."

"Shut up!" he bellows, "but, BUT, I tell you in no uncertain terms you are not to set foot again in that house. Nowhere, in any room. Otherwise you'll have to deal with me!" He yells and his spittle covers my face, stinging like venom.

"Understand?" he barks.

I leave, feeling shattered. *How can I bear such humiliation? Everything has gone wrong,* I think, as tears well up in my eyes. *Who ratted on me?* I ask myself, wiping my face with my fists.

Kiki pines away in her loneliness. Every now and then I can see her leaning on the window that frames her lovely, pale face. She gazes longingly at the passersby, never so much as a faint smile gracing her lips.

I walk past her house one day pretending I don't see her. I don't even dare to greet her. Inwardly I can hear myself screaming, but I'm afraid to do anything because I dread the consequences. One day I can't take it any longer and wait for nightfall.

Then, after carefully surveying the neighborhood, I wait for the right moment to push open Kiki's front door a crack, just enough to slide in sideways and dash up the stairs two at a time, holding my breath. At the top landing I turn my back on the door with the deathbed inside.

"You've come to visit me!" Kiki shouts when she sees me, her deep blue eyes—the same color as her mother's—shining bright.

"If they catch me, they'll beat me to death, and I'll never hear the end of it!" I blurt out. "Just thinking about it makes me shiver all over," I say, still scared.

"You'd think you had killed someone, for heaven's sake. Anyhow, let's talk. I'm starving for news. What's happening? I feel like a prisoner...except for my sweet mother, of course," she says with a smile.

"Yes, I understand," I tell her, as her mother comes in with a welcome cup of hot tea, and then it feels like always, warm and comfortable.

"What's been keeping you away?" Kiki's mother asks me, and I tell her the incident with my uncle.

"Child, there are souls that are black and evil, and that's how they see everything. Someone who envies your friendship with Kiki probably squealed on you to your uncle," she says, "to put a wedge between you and keep you apart," she adds, sticking the needle in her pin cushion before taking out another garment.

Before long springtime arrives and, through her mother's untiring efforts, Kiki improves enough to return to school and go outdoors, so I'm no longer anxious about getting in trouble for visiting her. On Sunday we take up our strolls down the main highway, the town's weekly outing and matchmaking scene. That's where lads and lassies eye each other, flirt, pick, and choose. Kiki and I watch the goings-on from our perch on a rock near the fountain of spring water, breathing in the cool breeze that blows across the fields washed clean by snow and rain, twirling our chains between our fingers, like worry beads. We love to twist and turn them to pass the time while we chat on and on. As luck would have it, one day the school principal, Mr. Hazlenut, sees us. He is a big man with a massive chin and steel blue eyes. His stocky frame moves past our little perch, and I can see him casting sidelong glances at us.

"I'm ashamed of you both, school girls playing with chains, parading in front of the boys and showing off," he says, glowering at us Monday morning during roll call in front of the school assembly.

We just keep quiet.

"You will both be punished for this," he says, shaking a tobacco-stained finger in our faces. "Go in my office," he bellows in a gruff tone. "You sit here and you there. Now write one hundred times: 'I am ashamed of my be-havior. I will never do it again.' And not a sound out of you," he shouts. "Hear me? I know what a couple of gossips you are."

He's full of ideas.

"Your misconduct is ruining my day." Mr. Hazelnut storms in and out of the room. His frizzy, graying hair is a tangled mess, his beady eyes peer closely at our writing.

He pokes in his head, looking first over Kiki's and then over my shoulder. He sits at his old worn desk, twirls around, gets up again, and comes over to examine my writing.

I try to write the boring sentences in my best calligraphy style, when suddenly I feel a hand rest on my shoulder, then slowly it reaches lower and lower down my back. I squirm in my seat. He goes back to his desk, nervously taps his pencil two or three times, and returns, now going from one desk to the other to "check our work." I can feel his breath on my neck. Who knows how far he would have gone, if Kiki didn't have the courage to confront him.

"Professor, this is too much! If you don't leave us alone, we'll report you."

She yanks me out of my chair and slams the door in Mr. Hazlenut's beet-red, overstuffed face. Since then we are never again bothered by the professor for going on our Sunday walks or for swinging our chains. Now, whenever we see him coming toward us from a distance we chant, "Hazlenut, nut, nut, nut, don't rock the boat."

Mayday is drawing near, and for days now Kiki and I are planning to climb to the top of the mountain to welcome the new month by gathering Mayflowers, a celebration of the rite of spring that symbolizes the spirit of oneness of light and beauty with nature. As is our custom in these parts, on the first of May we set out at dawn, taking the path toward the remote wayside chapels perched one above the other on the high cliffs overlooking the town below—like three white birds with heads uplifted in a sacred offering to the crystal-clear spring sky. We scamper on the rocks with the wild goats, breathing in the fragrance of myrtle and fern.

By daylight we reach the top and spread a white cloth on the dew-damp ground to have some bread and feta cheese, fresh grown garlic, and sparkling, ice cold water from the fountain. Soon Avyoula, the "little devil," as I'm fond of calling her, one of our new friends from Velvendo, a nearby village, comes along with a crowd of young fellows and girls. We scatter, gathering wild flowers to weave May time garlands. By noontime the joyous sounds of young voices fill the ravine below, as some of us sit on the rocks, others on the soft grass. Meteoritis lies down next to me, shading his dark eyes from the sun, and we soon become involved in a serious discussion, as is his wont. Whenever a rare smile crosses his lips, he locks his jaw, exposing a set of tightly packed, grinning white teeth that dominate his face, holding you there spellbound, creating the impression that he's about to reveal a deep secret. He looks mysterious. And attractive. You are drawn to the unknown.

"May time now, cool winds blow, May time now, summer begins," lilting voices sing. Meteoritis rests his head on one of the rocks and falls asleep while murmuring the song. A yellow wildflower standing all alone leans toward his swarthy face without touching him. I watch it sway with every gentle gust of wind. Each time the wind blows, it comes closer and almost touches him. I feel like picking the little flower and gently awakening him, to look into his eyes, and then let him return to sleep.

"What are you waiting for? Why don't you wake him up? What are you afraid of?" Thanassis, Avyoula's brother, urges me.

What is he saying to me? Did he read my mind? I wonder without making a sound. *What can I say?* I pick the flower, and the wind blows again. It falls from my hand, insignificant now. Meteoritis, unaware, wakes up.

I rack my brain to figure out what does all this mean? It is a marvel that nature joined the thorn with the most beautiful flowers. I have never before met anyone like him. A distinguished intellectual, as everyone agrees, he circulates around the town square like the rest of the young men, yet he has a private self. Not that he doesn't keep company with the other fellows, but something sets him apart. A little more mature in years, in his actions, in his reserve. His words are measured, and everything about him is strong and dynamic. He has a soft spot for Aunt Vangelia, maybe because, unlike many others, she can follow his intellectual turn of thought, maybe because they're neighbors and she's known him since he was a child, perhaps because he frequents her dry goods store, mostly tended by her oldest daughter Eleni on whom he might have a crush. How can you tell what profound secrets his heart holds?

Every now and then we chat, standing in a corner of the village square whenever he visits from Thessaloniki where he's studying law. We talk for a while, that is, he talks and I listen.

"You know, you'll never be truly happy," he says. His remark stuns me. "Because you'll always probe into everything, you'll scratch the surface to discover the truth. You'll seek the deeper reasons of human suffering, and what will you find?"

I look at him, completely absorbed by his words, his movements, his expression. He continues talking as though I've given him all my answers, yet I haven't uttered a single word. *What must he think of me?*

"You'll try to get at the root of human misery and suffering," he goes on, indifferent to my silence. "You'll always realize how difficult it is to change the world for the better. That will be painful to you."

Then, he abruptly raises the collar of his blue trench coat, digs his hands deep in his pockets, mumbles some words, and disappears around the bend of the dirt road.

I stand there dumbfounded. His words, still fresh in my mind, pelt my brain like a sudden rainstorm that soaks you to the marrow of your bones, but only later, after it stops, do you realize what has happened. It takes me a while to come to myself, to find my own center of gravity. *Something has changed. Something doesn't let me penetrate into a mystery that troubles me, that I can't fathom. How can I be certain now about his forecast of the future? And how did he know all that without my saying anything?* And yet his words come back over and over, as though I'm listening to a familiar, half-forgotten tune he mysteriously heard ages ago and now he reminds me of it. Without quite understanding how, I find a sense of myself emerging, coming to life with a growing longing to explore who I really am. I rack my brain to figure out *what does all this mean?* It *is* a marvel that nature joined the thorn with the most beautiful flowers.

The mystery of Meteoritis confounds everyone, including his mother. Even she doesn't understand him that well.

"He seems good, sensible, he cares for me and for others, but I don't know. What do you think, Soula, you're sensible," she asks her neighbor.

"What can I tell you, Marigo, he's always well mannered with me. He's a good fellow…talks well…may he live a long life," she answers, fumbling a bit over her words.

"Then why do they say he's a leftist when he's actually right handed, always was, from first grade. Is it anything bad?" Marigo sighs.

"The young educated folk today are full of ideas. Whatever he hears at the university, that's what he says, too, just to be like the others," she answers.

"I don't find fault with him, to tell you the truth. Not because I'm his mother, but it's just how I see things with my own eyes." Marigo pushes back the black kerchief she's worn since she was widowed.

"Go about your business and don't worry. He's your son, and he's fine. Come on now, let's have some coffee," Soula urges.

"Right away." Marigo breezes into the kitchen and prepares it with rapid, deft movements, apparently relieved by her friend's counseling.

Afterwards Soula says, "Now you must tell me my fortune, Marigo." She turns over the coffee cup, pouring the dark, thick coffee grounds that had settled at the bottom into the little saucer decorated with pink flowers and a fading, gold rim.

Meteorite's mother carefully studies the patterned contents left in the cup, peering from one side to another, tilting it to look better at the signs that will foretell the future.

"I see something happening…it could be in three hours, or three days, or three months, Soula." She starts.

"What, what, some good news?" Soula is eager to know.

"Ma-a-a, Ma, Ma," Soula's son screams from the back yard door, calling her away. "Come home, quick."

She rushes out and halfway across the yard trips on her slippers that she put on in a hurry.

A boy's heavy whisper, then a chilling silence.

"Oh, oh, what happened to me?" Soula's voice shakes the neighborhood.

Everybody runs over to see if something happened to her child.

"They killed my husband," she wails. "The Germans hanged him, may they hang in eternal perdition. What a calamity has befallen me," she moans, pulling at her hair. "What will I do alone with four orphans?" She beats upon herself. "My home is ruined, my heart burned, turned into black coal." Soula collapses on the road when she sees the villagers carrying her dead husband.

It takes a long time to revive her. "I can't face this nightmare. Tell me it's not true," she sobs, embracing her husband's dead body. "My soul is numb. What did he do to them? An innocent man minding his own business." Her lament can be heard all over the neighborhood. "A woeful hour." She laments, shedding bitter tears.

No one ever finds out why Soula's husband was hanged. The woeful hour.

Day after day the enemy kills, burns, maims, destroys.
The woeful hour.
Mass executions, torture, cruelties fill the valley.
The woeful hour.
Women in black mourn their dead.
The woeful hour.
Children are orphaned.
The woeful hour.
The land is destroyed.
The woeful hour.
The river runs blood-red.
The woeful hour.

14   BAREFOOT BRIGADE

A pale, melancholy afternoon. Thick storm clouds gather on the horizon.

"I'm thinking of going to Vangelia's." My mother sighs, scanning the deserted, dimly lit street from the closed window. "I need something to break up this terrible monotony. Come along before the cloudburst hits."

"Sure, I'm coming," I eagerly agree.

"Hurry, now, I don't want to get saddled with another chore," she whispers emphatically. I grab my coat on the run to catch up with her.

"Let's ask Eleni over for a cup of coffee," Aunt Vangelia suggests as soon as we arrive. "She is just back from Athens, and I'm anxious to hear her news," she adds and sends me with her youngest daughter Elpitha to call Eleni.

"Welcome, welcome," the two sisters chant in unison, as soon as they see Eleni climbing the steep flight of stairs. "How was your trip?" they ask before she even crosses the threshold. "Is your brother-in-law back yet?"

"What can I tell you?" Eleni takes a deep breath at the top of the landing and lifts her full skirt to enter. She seats her plump body on the faded dark blue easy chair and dabs the sweat beads from her high forehead with a dainty pink handkerchief. "Mihalis just returned. His mother passed away, and he looks dreadful," she answers, leaning back.

"May God rest her soul," Aunt Vangelia says, nodding her head.

"What I saw in Athens? Don't ask, it's terrible. The black marketeers are skinning people alive. The rich carry money around in sacks. They need trucks to transport it. Have you ever heard? Trucks full of drachmas!" Eleni casts a sidelong glance at the picture hanging on the wall, framed with a black ribbon, of Aunt Vangelia's husband, Thomas, who died many years ago.

"What about all the talk of scarcity?" Aunt Vangelia asks.

"Not a bit, if you have plenty of this." Eleni rubs her thumb against her two middle fingers.

"Money talks," my mother cuts in, "as the old timers always said."

"The world is going crazy, and it's always the poor who pay for the damages," Aunt Vangelia remarks, and goes to the kitchen to bring the coffee and some dry rusks on a scratched metal tray. She makes room for it by pushing aside Elpitha's and her brother Anestis' schoolbooks and rests it on the low table, the *"sofra"* where they are doing their homework. Then she picks up where she left off.

"We're lucky here. At least in the countryside if things get really bad, you can dig the ground for wild roots or something, but in the cities? What can they do? Scratch the cement pavement?"

Eleni picks up a rusk, dips it in the thick brown coffee, takes a small bite, then shifts the weight of her massive frame and raises her head.

"Pity those," she murmurs in a rumbling tone, "who don't have enough to buy a piece of bread to feed their starving children." Her jet black eyes dart back and forth, then stare out the window. "You can't imagine what it's like in Athens." She halts. "Awful, awful." Mihalis was horrified. "I've been sick ever since he told me what he saw when he went there to be with his dying mother."

167

All eyes are riveted on her, following the slow motion of her hand as she rests her coffee cup on the table. Then she bends down to pick up a nonexistent crumb from the floor and furtively wipes a tear from her eyes, never one to let others witness her deepest feelings.

"Is it really as bad as we hear?" my mother asks after a long silence.

"Worse. You can't imagine the horror." Eleni snaps back, flashing a dark glance at her. "If Mihalis hadn't seen it with his own eyes, he wouldn't have believed it. People die in the streets like dogs," she says, in despair as her limp hands drop to the floor. "The poor things! And the children, oh, it just breaks your heart! You see them shuffle their bloated bellies around and scrounge in empty garbage cans for scraps. Anything they can find, they put it in their mouth. Anything. Whether you can chew it or not. Worse than animals."

We all listen, spellbound. All you can hear is the rhythmic sound of breathing. Then she continues.

"In the end, they collapse in the middle of the street and the dull look in their eyes fades away with their last feeble breath. That's it. One of God's creatures, gone forever! Finally, a swarm of black flies shrouds the emaciated bodies scattered here and there."

"Doesn't anybody pay any attention, even to the children?" Aunt Vangelia asks.

"No one. Everybody looks after his own skin. What can I tell you? It's sheer torture. Every night I wake up with nightmares. The sight of those helpless children hounds me. I can't rest in my sleep or in my waking hours." A long sigh escapes from her dry lips. Then she digs in her apron pocket and produces a dog-eared piece of newspaper. "Look at this picture. This child's mother had just died when Mihalis happened to cross the street. The poor baby was trying to suckle at his dead mother's breast, crying pitifully, 'Mama, mama.' The cries got louder and louder, following him down the street. Oh, how frightful. They collect the dead from the streets like garbage."

My mother muffles a cry. "Hunger is killing the flower of our youth."

"Can't we do something about those orphans, at least?" Aunt Vangelia asks.

Eleni swiftly dismisses the idea. "What can we send? Potatoes? First of all, this year's crop is meager, but even if we stole from the mouths of our children to save a few lives from starvation, how do we know the horrid black marketeers won't steal them for their own profit? Our efforts will be wasted."

"There must be a way," my mother insists.

"Then why don't we bring some children here? They can eat whatever we do. If every family in town adopts a child," Aunt Vangelia suggests, "we can save so many lives."

Eleni bolts upright from her seat. "What a good idea," she answers, her voice animated for the first time. "But how will you bring them over here?" They all look pensive again.

"Do you think your brother-in-law can help?" my mother asks.

"Maybe. He knows a government functionary in the so-called health department. I'll ask if he can get in touch with him." Eleni says, shaking her pleated skirt as she gets up to leave.

"The sooner the better," Aunt Vangelia urges. "A good deed for the salvation of his mother's soul, may she rest in peace."

Eleni takes a shortcut through the back door and soon we, too, say goodnight and leave.

The winter in all its fury is fast upon us, but the plan to save the starving orphans is at a standstill.

"What's happening with the plan to save the children?" Aunt Vangelia stops Eleni one day when they happen to meet on the street.

"I've managed to get in touch with a lot of nearby villages and enlisted their support," she puffs, out of breath.

"Bravo, Eleni, they are praiseworthy for wanting to take part in this good work, but unless this transportation problem is solved soon, it will be too late. How long can the poor children last? They'll freeze in the streets. No one will be left alive."

Eleni wipes the perspiration from her forehead and tightens her headscarf.

"Vangelia, if what I heard is true, we're saved. They tracked down some discarded prewar buses that the authorities promised Mihalis we could use to transport the kids. For nothing." She says, smiling with satisfaction.

"Really! That's wonderful! And when did he say they can give them to us?" Aunt Vangelia asks impatiently.

"I don't know. I'll know for sure tomorrow, and I'll tell you." Eleni sees her daughter coming toward her and signals her to wait.

"*Adio.*" She waves, taking the child by the hand and heading toward the marketplace.

Within a month a dilapidated bus arrives packed with children, all about twelve years old, though you can't tell for sure by their looks. The rickety old bus struggles to make it up the hill, groaning and belching black smoke, but it's no use, so the kids are unloaded on the highway by the police station. They climb down the bus steps one at a time, carrying tiny bundles in their scrawny hands, just like old people. They stare straight ahead in a daze. Not a trace of liveliness. Nothing childlike either in their expression or their movements.

"Where's the bread?" a pale girl pleads, like a beggar.

"Will you feed us?" another waif chimes in.

"Timoleon!" the village clerk calls out from his list.

"Yes, present," answers a boy who looks around ten years old, wearing short, threadbare pants. He has bright black eyes and makes rapid-fire movements from the minute he arrives, darting from one end of the bus to the other, directing some of the other newcomers. He stops short as soon as his name is mentioned.

"Come here, kid," the clerk motions.

Timoleon stands up straight, stretching himself to his full height.

"No, I'll wait here to see where my little brothers will go, and then you'll assign me," He answers loud and clear.

"A gutsy guttersnipe," Uncle Leonidas says, as he watches the little Athenian take care of his brothers. "He looks after them like a father."

As soon as Timoleon gets wind of the special attention he's getting, he grabs Uncle by the sleeve.

"I want to go with you. My name is Timoleon," he says, trying to sound manly.

"You can't do whatever comes into your head; they gave me someone else's name."

The kid looks him straight in the eye.

"Change it. We don't know anybody here, so what's the difference? It's all the same to you," he argues, leaving no room for dispute.

Uncle smiles. He isn't used to being contradicted, and now this pipsqueak comes along and is giving him orders.

"O.K., let's go. I'll straighten out the paperwork later," he says.

"Wait a minute, I've got to check my kid brothers," Timoleon asserts boldly.

Uncle waits for him without any objection.

By the time Timoleon is finished making sure his brothers are taken care of, almost the whole town is gathered around to welcome the "barefoot brigade," as Eleni's brother-in-law Mihalis nicknamed them. The other waifs, meek as lambs, have already started leaving to join their "families," except for Timoleon. He carries on with lively, amusing stories all the way home.

"What does your father do?" We're curious to know.

"Oh, he's a fixer. He fixes oil, machines, anything you want."

"So, he's a busy guy," Uncle says.

"What's all this fixing business?" Aunt Chrysie asks and, instead of answering, Timoleon starts telling stories about the trams in Athens. He can rattle off all the routes, one by one, but you can't pin him down about anything in his life; he weasels out of every question he's asked. The next day his kid brothers, Niko and Yiorgo, tell us the same stories. Identical, word for word. Obviously they were well tutored.

Timoleon knows all his schoolwork without ever studying. He learns everything on the run. He does his home-

172

work standing up, leaning against the wall. He whistles and writes, sings and copies. He knows every popular song.

"You're nothin' but a clown," Aunt Pelagia chides him. "What'll stick in your head with all them songs you sing?"

"Yeah, yeah," he says and grabs her to dance, she in her slippers and he barefoot.

He just loves to cavort around, turning somersaults, jumping from one end of the room to the other like a circus monkey. Sometimes he runs into the snow without any shoes on and never listens when he's told that he'll catch a cold. Everyone likes Timoleon, and his tall tales have become the talk of the town. Then one day we hear him jabbering nonsense and think that maybe he's gone berserk.

"Hey, what're ya rantin' and ravin' about?" my grandmother asks him. "I can't make any sense of it. Have you gone bananas at that farm where you're workin' or did they give ya some silly water to drink?" She grins, exposing her toothless gums.

We all rush over to listen to his gibberish. He talks nonstop. His tongue outruns his speech, but we can't understand a word he's saying. Then Petro struts in, grinning from ear to ear. We look at him, waiting for an answer to this riddle.

"He's talking Pontic fluently." He laughs heartily.

Uncle watches Timoleon with genuine admiration.

"Imagine, he talks like a native from Pontos. The farmer is from the Hellespont area, so he learned it right away from the other workers since he started working at the farm. He's so smart!"

Timoleon is doubled up in laughter.

Above all, Timoleon enjoys the weekly market day. That's when he's in his element. He's on the run from dawn till dusk, going from the mill to the village square, back to the house, downstairs to the clinic, to the town square again with a new sack of corn, and once again over the whole route. The peasants come to town bright and early from near and far to barter and bargain. To sell their produce—wheat, rye, corn, butter, cheese—in return for other food supplies, like salt and sugar, for merchandise—fabric, boots, nails—and to pay their debts.

"There's no butter left over for us," they complain bitterly.

"And we have no money to send our kids to school, just what they learn in the first couple of grades," protests a villager from Kastania where they grow lots of chestnuts. "We're always in debt. We even have to borrow money for seed." "Those slick city lawyers have been milking us dry for years now," another villager adds.

A centuries-old burden. An endless pain.

The peasant villagers put off for market day not only all the chores that have been accumulating for weeks on end, but illnesses, too. They wait for Monday to come along so that they can go and seek a cure. Only as a last resort, if somebody is half dead and there's no time left, will they go to the doctor's clinic midweek. An ox-driven cart, bent with age, labors uphill on the bumpy cobblestone street, carrying a motionless body covered with a coarse, goat-hair shepherd's cape. The heavy guttural breathing halts and starts, the inert body shakes with each jerk of the cart. By the time they reach the doctor's office, the death rattle in the throat can be heard clearly. Before they even get a chance to uncover the patient it stops altogether. He's gone.

"Oh, what happened to us! We lost him!" the women shriek and cover him all the way up to the top of his head.

The cart is slowly turned around to take the downhill road and bring the dead body back to the village, amidst the weeping and wailing of the women.

The sick who come to the clinic on Monday have to wait for hours on end for their turn in front of the doorsteps. They cough, spit blood, vomit, scratch their infected sores until the pus oozes out and then wipe it away with filthy rags. Others, deathly pale, sit bent over their knees. Some have waited and waited for some home remedy to cure them, hoping to save their money for more urgent needs, and now, you can tell by the look on their face that they're too far-gone to benefit from the clinic.

Those who need to buy medicine go across the street to the druggist, Andronikos, a short man of small build, thin as a rail. Two beady green eyes peer from behind his gold-rimmed glasses at the prescription that the patient hands him through a small, square window, then he pushes his spectacles above his bushy eyebrows to read it. Resting the prescription on his wooden bench, he takes out small rectangular pieces of paper from one of the drawers, lays them down flat, and fills each one with a white powder from a variety of glass jars labeled "quinine" or "aspirin" or other medicinal names that are sitting side by side on his shelf. He weighs the contents of the papers on his tiny brass scale, and then folds each one without dropping so much as a speck of dust. His mouth moves incessantly, methodically, slowly chewing his cud like a masticating cow. When his job is finished, he lowers his glasses to the bridge of his nose. With two yellowed, bony fingers he takes a cigarette out of a flat tin box, lights it, inhales deeply two or three times, and with his left hand writes something on the carefully folded paper, which he gives to the patient who is waiting outside the window. Then the next patient hands him a prescription, and he starts his slow chewing movements again.

From time to time he gets some help from his wife, Ayape, a slow moving, buxom woman with flabby flesh that hangs loosely from her enormous body. She is his direct opposite. While he waits for her to finish filling a prescription, he smokes at least three cigarettes. Finally, restlessness gets the better of him, and he sends her to minister to their son, the spitting image of himself. She goes upstairs to their small (like him) house situated directly above the drugstore. Every Monday the candle burns late to get all the orders filled.

Mondays—busy with the marketing that lasts past sunset—always end later than other days. One way and another, people always have some last minute shopping to do. Just as the notions store starts to close, a round-bottomed, red-cheeked peasant girl runs over to buy some colored ribbons, or thread, or a length of velvet cloth for her trousseau. "I want *'katife,'* the best velvet, for my wedding vest," she insists.

I watch as the village square empties, enjoying the last hurried movements of people trying to get another chore done. Before I know it, it's dark. I start running and suddenly hear fast footsteps behind me. I hasten my pace, not daring to look. Someone taps my shoulder, and I jump.

"Timoleon, it's you!" I cry out, relieved. "What's the matter, you look upset? Was there a fight?" I ask him, panting.

"No, no. Come with me, I want to show you something."

We hurry down the road and sneak through a side door into the medical clinic. All the lights are out, and everyone's gone. It's pitch dark.

"What are you doing?"

"Sh-sh-sh," he whispers in my ear. I keep quiet, but I'm anxious to find out what this is all about.

Noiselessly Timoleon opens the door to the treatment room, which reeks of iodine and alcohol, and we go through a hall lit by a faint stairway light to the clinic, lined with two rows of iron frame beds. Just as I'm about to go in, I almost trip on a sack heaped on the floor.

"No." Timoleon quickly draws me back. "Look," he motions.

In the dim light I see a frightful sight.

"Oh-oh-oh-oh!" A long-drawn howl screeches past me from the open wounds of the mangled mass of torn flesh steeped in blood. His distorted face has no mouth, his body hasn't any arms. A bloodied shepherd's boot is all that's left on the remains of his shattered leg.

I go closer and when I kneel beside the body sprawled on the floor I recognize the features of a youthful boy. I want to moisten his nonexistent lips, to whisper comforting words to his ravaged ears, to ease his pain. I just stay there motionless. He moans pitifully and a cry bellows, as though it's coming from the bowels of the earth.

Timoleon tries to pull me away by the hand.

"Wait a minute, does anyone know he's here?" I whisper. "How can they leave him alone like that?"

He shrugs his shoulders and looks at me with a pained expression. Just then the sound of hurried footsteps sends us tiptoeing out in a rush before we get caught.

The dark, deserted street shelters our trembling bodies. Before we go home we need an excuse for being tardy or else we're in big trouble.

"Let's carry a load of wood inside," Timoleon suggests, "maybe then they won't notice we're late."

We each grab an armful of logs from the back yard and dump them in a box near the stove.

Afterward, the thought of suffering won't leave me alone. The anguished cries of the mutilated body echo in my ears. I sneak out and head straight for the clinic to find out what happened to the injured shepherd. Not a sound is heard. Absolute stillness. I enter as before. The moaning has stopped.

He must've been given an injection, a painkiller, I think, trembling.

The clinic, steeped in darkness, is empty, deserted, cold, and the mutilated body of a human being is sprawled on the floor. I stand watching him in his awful loneliness, riveted in place. I can neither stay nor go away. The shadow of death flutters in the dark.

The next day the whole town is buzzing. The fifteen-year-old boy from Kastania, unawares, stepped on a land mine and lost his life.

15 REVOLUTION

The Bishop is just finishing a top secret dinner meeting with the partisan chiefs of staff, and as is his habit, he wipes his long black beard, folds his napkin lengthwise without regard for the creases, folds it again into a square, and puts it down on the table next to his water glass.

It's the first time he's stopped talking for so long. His restless, penetrating glance studies the intense, ascetic faces seated around the wooden dining room table in his brother-in-law, my Uncle Leonidas' house.

This meeting in the spring of 1942 with the valiant Bishop Seraphim captures the full attention of the partisans, who lean their elbows on the table waiting for him to continue. His zeal and enthusiasm for the revolutionary movement stirs them deeply. In the dreary darkness of the occupation, the dawning resistance against the oppressors radiates like a ray of hope.

"Ready?" the Bishop booms and continues. "We have charted our course. Our aim is forthright and correct. We are following the path dictated by our national conscience as descendants of the revolution of 1821. May God be with us and guide us in our sacred endeavor. May you go well, my children. You have my blessing."

The spiritual leader of the liberation movement of northern Greece gets up, deeply moved. I notice a slight quiver in his lips that he tries to hide in his thick black beard. He waves goodnight to his comrades, opens the double glass doors, and leaves the smoke-filled room to head for the terraced roof.

179

I remember scampering after him with my cousins Petro and Ted and my brother Tasio. We climb up the narrow staircase, careful to keep a safe distance to avoid stepping on his long cleric's tunic. He doesn't mind the little ones as long as we don't bother him.

The Bishop reaches the top, takes a few deep breaths, raises himself to his full height, and directs his fiery gaze toward the infinite.

"Those stars," he pivots around, locking us in his gaze, "those distant luminous sparks of light you see have traveled for millions of years."

The other kids wander off one by one. Only I stay listening to him intone the names of the stellar constellations. Each one stands out among the others, becomes organized into a special configuration. I'm thrilled with my new acquaintance of the stars (those phosphorescent garlands of light) and for a moment feel a mystical union with the universe.

Bishop Seraphim devotes his full attention again to the heavens above. I abandon myself to the soft as velvet parapet of the night.

"Revolution, my child, revolution," he says with his thundering voice and rests his strong hand on my shoulder, like a father. "But you are a gentle little lamb, what do you understand about such things?"

"Yes, but the revolutionary flame sparks in us, too, in spite of our apparent meekness," I answer without hesitation.

I'm surprised at hearing myself sound so bold, perhaps inspired by one of the earth's luminaries. The Bishop rests his hand more steadily on my shoulder, looks up at the sky, and continues, more animated now. "That is the Great Bear, those are the Pleiades, and over there you see Orion."

The partisans' meeting with the Bishop that historic night was the starting point of the liberation movement in northern Greece. For months now, Bishop Seraphim has been traveling back and forth between my uncle's house and the seat of the Holy See in Kozani to meet secretly with the partisans and organize the loosely joined independent groups of scattered freedom fighters into a united anti-fascist front.

Whenever they gather for a meeting, I join the bunch of other kids to eavesdrop on their long discussions about one or another problem.

"The traitors among us are doing serious damage to our movement and undermining our sacred mission," asserts Bishop Seraphim.

"A few opportunists are distorting the meaning of our struggle and are taking advantage of the movement to settle personal scores," Kapetan Argyris says, in an angry voice.

"Such issues must be settled at once," protests another partisan, "the people must understand that our common struggle needs everyone's participation. A few profiteers who are in this for self-serving purposes can't be allowed to jeopardize our goal: the freedom of our country."

They stop for a while, ask the womenfolk for some coffee, and continue.

"We have no time to lose. We must make every sacrifice to fight the enemy who has at his disposal a colossal machine-driven force. That is our goal. The people must gain our trust," continues the voice of Kapetan Aetos, the Eagle, who was a noted university professor in Athens before he joined the liberation movement.

Bishop Seraphim has the final say. "Our country is cringing under the blows of the occupation, hunger, mass executions, and other cruelties. Alas, traitors are in our midst. All of these forces will mobilize our people against the fascist invaders, the powers of death and annihilation of the whole world. If we don't resist now, if we don't fight decisively to win our freedom, we will never be able to raise our heads with pride as honorable human beings who fulfilled their trust and did not yield in the face of subjugation and tyranny. My brothers, let there be light, spread the message of freedom and human salvation to our tormented land. Answer the clarion call of the holy struggle for a free land, for human dignity and world peace."

One by one the freedom fighters get up to leave through the back door, braving the strictly enforced German curfew and the frequent enemy patrols before they head back to the mountains.

Suddenly, a loud knock on the door stops them in their tracks. They exchange hasty glances from one to the other, to size up the danger.

How will they face it? I wonder. *Should they leave by the secret vaulted passage, a relic from the days of the Turkish occupation? Or maybe it's better if they hide somewhere.* What's certain is that any further delay might arouse the Germans' suspicions. Just then, Uncle Leonidas hurries in from the other room. His dark, unshaven face looks more forbidding than usual. He lights a cigarette to cover the dense cloud of smoke in the room that stubbornly refuses to leave, knowing full well that his gesture couldn't fool anyone, let alone the Germans. His brow is covered with beads of sweat and I hear him mutter: "if they catch us, we're done for."

Bishop Seraphim remains impassive, as he glances around him.

"Who will open the door?" he whispers gently.

"Let Pelagia go," my uncle suggests, casting a swift glance at Bishop Seraphim. "Go," he orders his sister, whose laggard, clumsy movements are least likely to alarm the Germans. She meekly agrees and slowly goes downstairs in her floppy slippers.

"Y-y-yes?" we hear her stammer tremulously, as she opens the door. Gruff voices, then footsteps are heard.

Are they coming up the stairs? I ask myself, frightened. The hands on the clock seem to be glued to the same spot.

Only the sound of our breathing can be heard.

In a short while, I hear her footsteps.

"I f-f-f-forgot one of the lamps on downstairs," she says, as she slowly climbs the stairs. "That's why the Germans got mad," she mumbles an excuse. After that terrible scare, everyone is too exhausted to complain about her foolish mistake.

The escape resumes under even greater pressure. It's way past the nine o'clock curfew. Silence and time are critical. The partisans exchange signals and lower their heads to follow the Bishop one-by-one down the steep steps behind the kitchen door.

These secret meetings of the freedom fighters, under the leadership of Bishop Seraphim, become a regular part of our life all through the winter and spring of 1942. They occur less often in the summer and then resume again more frequently during the fall. We soon find out that from the beginning days of the occupation, people in cities and towns have become actively organized into a united front that spreads the message of freedom. "In the land where fear and oppression dwell, we will plant the fertile seeds of liberation and peace," the freedom fighters cry out, as people by the thousands join the fight for our liberation, marching along the difficult road against tyranny.

The popular outburst reaches into every corner of life. Even our school. If someone were to see us seated at our desks with our hands folded and our attention riveted on Mr. Terzides, our history teacher, they would suspect nothing. After all, he is teaching us about the past glories of Greece—the revolution of 1821 against the Turkish occupation, the heroism of men like Diakos and Kolokotronis and women like Bouboulina and the Souliotises who threw their babies one after the other into the dark ravine below, then danced to their death one by one rather than be taken hostage and dishonored. As he recalls that heroic past full of sacrifice and struggle for the freedom of our motherland, his hoarse voice vibrates and his thin mustache trembles while he recites: "How much longer, brave lads, will we live in bondage?" This is the poem he assigned to us to learn by heart. "Write it not only one hundred times in your composition book but, most important, in your heart in flaming letters," he says, as his sharp eyes fix on us one by one. He spares no one, but neither is he unjust.

The higher grades, inspired by his words, follow in his footsteps and become involved in helping the freedom fighters smuggle guns from one part of town to another or finding hard-to-get replacement parts for military weapons. If they're caught, the penalty is harsh—even death. The younger grades at night write slogans as big as life on the walls: "we shall not perish, we fight for freedom, our cause is just," they carry secret messages from one house to another and can't wait to be old enough to be entrusted with bigger jobs. Everyone does something to help, but we have to be very careful and vigilant because if the school principal, old Hazlenut, catches us, we're in big trouble. He is a die-hard reactionary, and his vengeance would be our undoing.

It is a time when "intimidation casts a pall" throughout the land and no one speaks openly of resistance.

September 14, 1942, the day of the Holy Cross, is a day that the faithful of Paliocastro will always remember. When the liturgy is finished, Bishop Seraphim rests the holy chalice on the gold-embroidered cover of the altar with the hand-carved ivory cross, slowly goes up the steps of the pulpit of St. Catherine's Church holding his staff covered with precious stones, and publicly defies the Germans. On that momentous occasion when terror reigns, the Bishop declares:

"My good people, today again, like true patriots, we are confronted by the sacred duty to raise our voices against the powers of darkness that were unleashed by the Axis to achieve their aim of world supremacy. There is, however, a greater power. It is the force of life that will lead us to decisive victory. Our church teaches us love for one another—that will prevail.

"Our enemies are trying to defeat us, to enslave us. They have told us that, if they could, they would even take away from us the very air we breathe. Inhuman thought. Abominable act. We reply with the confidence given to us by our true love for the salvation of humankind. We declare that no one—absolutely no one—can or has the right to take away our precious freedom. This instinct springs from the depth of our existence: the preservation of life, the most valuable virtue in the world. With our very breath, with our soul, with our arms uplifted, with the cry of the just we chant 'FREEDOM.' Let the bonds of oppression be broken. Let peace and liberty reign on earth."

There is a sacrosanct silence. A mute applause of the faithful. Hope is revived. Evil is cast out. Darkness is metamorphosed into a brilliant flame that fills the air with diaphanous light. The sun is not forever lost.

At such liturgies his faithful ecclesiastical counselor and brother in the liberation movement, Archimandrite Seraphim Poulias, accompanies the Bishop. "A man of uncommon charisma," Uncle Stelios had said, and truly, from the minute he entered a room he attracted admiring glances from everyone. Women couldn't keep their eyes off him; let alone what they chatted about amongst themselves in the kitchen.

"It's a pity he can't marry, such a good looking man. We have so many fine girls who would make a lovely bride for him. Right?" Aunt Chrysie asks while beating the eggs and lemon for the *avyolemono* soup.

"He deserves the best, he has everything. Tall, handsome, flashing dark eyes and what a beautiful voice, he mesmerizes you when he talks. I think he ought to leave the priesthood and we'll find him a pretty girl with a nice dowry." Aunt Chrysie pokes my mother in the ribs.

"Sh-sh-sh, don't let anyone hear you, we'll become the laughingstock of the town. God forgive us. The Bishop is my brother-in-law. Of all people, I shouldn't be talking like this. What would my husband think if he heard me?" Her green eyes, a bit too large for her face, flash as she walks toward the door to see if anyone is listening.

The talk ends as soon as I enter the kitchen to fetch the tray they're preparing with little cups full of thick brown coffee, glasses of water and quince preserves that are served in small, colored glass dishes.

Priests and deacons from the surrounding villages who have come to visit the Bishop after the liturgy are waiting in the reception room to receive his blessing and get advice about problems in their parish. The minute Bishop Seraphim is ushered in and offered the seat of honor in the house—a large, overstuffed maroon chair—he is bombarded with questions.

I listen to the Bishop addressing every issue with amazing speed as I pass around the large copper tray, too shy even to look up. He can take in several conversations at once, answering each person individually with dazzling swiftness and mental agility. His black eyes sparkle, darting back and forth, and the whole room reverberates at the sound of his voice. He can inspire awe and put the fear of God in his listeners, all at once.

He even terrified the Nazis. Time and again they went to his official residence at the Archdiocese to capture him. After all, they couldn't just slaughter him and throw him in a ditch the way they did with ordinary folk. Despite their hatred, he commanded their respect. A Bishop with a reputation far beyond the boundaries of his own country, a top member of the church hierarchy who had distinguished himself in theological studies at the most advanced institutions of Constantinople, who could speak fluently in ancient Greek and Latin, could not be trifled with.

The message of defiance that he proclaimed openly from the pulpit and the fearless way he spoke out against the fascists was a constant thorn in their side. The Nazis dreaded his influence on the people and could not allow such an outstanding personality to remain free.

The Nazis tried to arrest him three times, and he got away from their bloody clutches every single time!

The last time they arrived late at night. He greeted them dressed in the full ecclesiastical gold-embroidered regalia. On his head he wore the holy miter decorated with precious stones and in his right hand he held the exquisitely crafted silver staff covered with rubies, diamonds, and sapphires. They were mesmerized!

He began talking about the glories of ancient Greece: art, drama, sculpture, the marvels of our antiquities, then he recited Homer, Euripides, and Sophocles, and extolled the virtues of the philosophy of Plato, Aristotle, and Socrates. He had conquered the conqueror. He had disarmed them of their most powerful weapons: fear and intimidation. They left spellbound.

Once outside, they realized their gaffe and no sooner had they left than they returned to carry out what they came to do.

The Bishop lost no time and rushed out the back door. We listen to him describe his exploits openmouthed. "My escape was a miracle," he heaves a deep sigh.

This is his last visit. In early 1943 he came to bid us farewell before heading for "free Greece."

Suddenly, the back door swings wide open and Meteoritis rushes in out of breath. He's been working in a top-secret part of the underground resistance and his appearance signals trouble. The color is drained from his swarthy face; his eyes are pools of fire as he stands there like a condemned man. His puts his hands in the pockets of his dark gabardine coat, looking intently at Seraphim.

"Your Holiness," he says, taking a deep breath, "the German Gestapo captured Archimandrite Poulias."

His face twists out of shape with each word, and his deep sorrow is visible in his expression. The beads of sweat on his broad forehead glisten in the dim lamplight, as he clenches his jaws so tight the muscles make little jumps every time the blood vessels throb in his neck.

The motionless faces have turned an ashen yellow.

"What happened?" the Bishop asks at last, in a hoarse whisper.

"They grabbed him while he was praying alone in church. He was arrested before he knew what happened and immediately sent to the dungeon at the *Yedi Koulé* jail, the medieval fortress on the hill overlooking the port of Thessaloniki." Meteoritis bows his head.

"Who...?" Kapetan Argyris asks after a long silence.

"One of the local traitors. He nabbed him. It happened right after Archimandrite Poulias called on the people with revolutionary fervor to rise against their oppressors. It was the clarion call to arms from the pulpit: 'a nightingale on every sprig, a freedom fighter on every twig.' Your Grace, that gave a clear message to the people of the full blossoming of our resistance movement in the mountains." He agonizes over each word, knowing that not only were the two men ecclesiastical brothers since they had the same name, Seraphim, but they had also formed a strong bond in the liberation struggle.

"I know he would do it all over again. Such is his faith in our cause," Kapetan Argyris adds in a low voice.

"We must save Brother Poulias," Bishop Seraphim cries out in anguish, "Mobilize every resource," he orders, facing Meteoritis.

"I'll do my utmost," he assures the Bishop before hastily disappearing into the thick night. His footsteps leave a raw thud that echoes in the dead silence.

"Brother Poulias is bearing the brunt of the enemy's fury over my escape, I know," the Bishop whispers. The creases in his face grow deeper.

It was months later that we heard news about Archimandrite Poulias. Little did we know what would be the aftermath of his brutal arrest on the liberation struggle and on my own life.

"Now I must go, the risks of staying are too great. From now on, I will govern my flock from the mountains in 'free Greece' and I will redouble my efforts to free our country of this miasma," he vows.

"Bye, little lamb."

I can't bear to see him leave. The house will seem empty.

"Can I go, too?" I ask, unmindful of Uncle Leonidas's wrath.

"Soon, child, perhaps you can. Our cause needs everyone, including little lambs." He smiles, patting me lightly on the head.

Then he turns to the others and adds, "Be courageous in the difficult struggle ahead. You will always be in my thoughts and in my heart."

He tosses a rough-hewn shepherd's cape over his black cleric's tunic and hurries down the stairs in his heavy mountain boots as he carefully lifts his long black cassock, trying to conceal a small pistol. Kapetan Argyri and his men follow his lead. I envy them.

I cast one last glance in his direction. A sinking empty feeling drags me down. I slump on the stoop. I'm losing him, just like I lost my father before there was a war. It all rushes back, with an outpouring of sadness and anger, every single moment of what happened that day in May 1940, such a long time ago, it seems. When I was still a little girl...

16 THE FLAG

I try to bury my frozen ears in my hunched up shoulders to avoid another smack of the frenzied, shrill, wind driving icy needles deeper and deeper into my brain.

I bend my head low and push with all my might against the raging wind that spins me around with all its fury. I can feel every breath turning into icicles inside my nostrils. I'm afraid to take my hands out of my pockets to stop the tears streaming down my face.

Hunger delivers a sharp pain in my belly that's constantly growling, as I try to keep going. I put every ounce of strength in each step to keep moving till I reach the front door.

I'm almost there. My ordeal is coming to an end. Finally! I think, and dare to lift my head, just as the wind dies down all of a sudden.

I take heart, thinking that I can only be a few steps away from the wide stairs leading to my uncle's house where we're living now.

The blood in my veins turns to ice. I can't move.

Directly in front of me I see a detachment of German soldiers. All eyes are riveted on me. I look left and right for a way out, but there is no escape. I feel them move in closer, tightening their grip around me, suffocating me. I stand stone still, surrendering myself to the inevitable.

"Your father inside?" one of them asks in English.

"No." I answer without a second thought.

What business do they have with my father? I wonder. *Why is he talking to me in English? Why not Greek or German?*

Their questions come pouring out, one after the other.

"Are you British? How come you know English? When did you come here? Why?"

Obviously they latched on to my "no" and surely I'm headed for trouble, I think terrified.

I swallow hard, realizing the trap I've fallen into, but it's no use. There's no room to maneuver. I admit I am an American citizen. One of them moves in closer, clasping his gun tighter. I see his knuckles blanching and I can feel the blood draining from me, as though not a single drop is left inside me.

Oh, my God, maybe they know about the secret meetings with the resistance fighters in our house? I ponder with fear. *Maybe they suspect I know something about the Bishop? Maybe they figure a kid would spill the beans right away, before anybody could tell me not to talk. What will they do to me if I don't talk?* I wonder, out of breath, and a violent coughing spell roots me to the ground.

With a revolver thrust in my back, they push me to go ahead. I can feel my mother's torment searing me as I move away. *Surely she's seeing me alive for the last time.*

The soldiers march me to the German headquarters, housed in the police station near the highway. They shove me inside a cavernous empty room with a high ceiling like the ones in old houses from the days of the Turkish occupation. I feel that the heavy iron grating and my unbearable loneliness jail even my thoughts. My body is numbed by fear. I wish I were a bird that could fly out the window through one of the narrow openings; my mind soars, free and unafraid. I lean on the crumbling, faded wall left un-painted for years, with my eyes glued to the window.

Heavy footsteps cut short my fantasy of escape. A German soldier comes inside, and I notice a guard outside the massive wooden door. The two soldiers mutter something in German and lead me to a narrow, disgusting room where I face a tall, scrawny officer with rheumy, ashen-gray eyes and thick glasses. He leans over an old desk and opens a large book (their registry, I suppose) turns over many pages, and motions me to sign without looking at me. As I bend down and my shaking hand scrawls my name on the long, lined page, I hear him grunt something and without even knowing how, I find myself alone again in another empty room.

"Achtung!" the guard yells, and I follow him to the stone-lined yard. *That's it! My end is near,* my sentence howls like a siren in my head. No flashbacks, no sudden insights, no thought. I can only feel a cold numbness. *When will this torture end? I can't stand this...this nothingness.* I feel beaten down to the ground, unable to do anything about it. It's as though I don't even exist.

A sudden shuffling of feet catches my attention. I turn my head and notice that others are waiting to be shot, just like me. *Must I stand on line for this, too?* I refuse to cast even a momentary glance at the guard who stands there like Cerberus. My anger is mounting now and so is my hatred. *They can shoot me, but they can't kill the me that's inside. I am I. They can command a death squad, but I can keep alive to the very end what I believe and what I feel. That's mine. No one can possess that, ever.*

The guard's rifle shoves me in another direction that leads to a closed door. It opens to a room that looks as though it belongs to an officer. He doesn't even look up. *What now?* I wonder, startled by a harsh voice behind me.

"You must tell me everything you know. Absolutely everything. You and your family will be punished by death if you don't obey. Understand?" I nod, shaking my head left to right. "Do you understand?" he yells, covering me with his foul smelling spit, cracking his whip against his boot. Mercifully, a crackling noise interrupts him, and he turns his head in that direction. The radio transmitter makes a rattling sound and disgorges a piece of paper that his subordinate immediately hands over to him. The officer's attention is engrossed in the message he just got. Every now and then he wets his dry lips with his thick tongue covered with foaming spit. More communiqués follow one right after the other. The officer shouts at the guard who shoves me out the door. I follow him into another room, dragging my feet, feeling diminished and defeated. Just as Meteoritis had said, the enemy demands absolute obedience. They inflict complete subjugation. His words ring true, more than ever, "The tyrants methodically repress their victims to the point of extinction to assure their own survival." Now I begin to understand their real meaning.

Only if I could be a bird, I think, *I could escape. Only the birds are free.*

"This ruthless occupation," I can almost hear Meteoritis' voice, as though he's right in front of me, *"bears down on our lives with unprecedented fury."* I let my mind wander, imagining the time when he was telling me about the tyranny of the occupation, reliving those moments when we were huddled together near a storefront where we wouldn't attract anyone's attention. I was so scared. *Suppose we got caught? What would I say?* My mother would have been furious. That notion, though, instantly went out of my head. It had no connection to this reality. His words

had captivated me so much that nothing else could affect me. All that mattered at that instant was the riveting emotion that had possessed me.

I strain to remember every word, the way he said it, serious, his brow knitted, his dark brown eyes smoldering with anger. I could feel the suffering of his soul pouring out through his words. In them I try to find the comfort and courage his presence would have given me. "This terrible oppression depletes us drop by drop, drains our resources, scattering them to the wind like so much waste. Our heads bent far down, bowed low before our captors, makes it hard for us to fathom the depth of our misery." *Surely, he was right. That's how it is. Now I can feel it in my bones.*

"Most of the time we can't see beyond the narrow confines of our prison bars." I look up and see the lattice of heavy black iron jailing me in. "The Nazis try in every way to instill fear in us. How wrong they are," he paused to light a cigarette, cupping his hands around the match to keep it from blowing out. I could feel the soft tufts of white smoke circling over my cheeks. The pungent smell of tobacco, mingled with my excitement, made me sort of dizzy.

Then he continued, "Terror may be intimidating, but in the final analysis there is another power which is greater and stronger: FREEDOM," he smiled, lifting his head to glance around swiftly. "They'll never know this. It's alien to them. Other forces—terrorism and bludgeoning—drive them. That's how they think they'll win their game, but they can't understand that deep down inside, we're not afraid of them," his resonant voice echoes in my ears. "We're even willing to die to defend our freedom," he said, thrusting his hands deeper in the pockets of his blue gabardine coat, as I watched him walk briskly down the narrow cobblestone road.

Abruptly, quick footsteps draw my attention. I think they're coming from the courtyard and glance out the window of the empty room where I had been left. Loud rapid-fire commands rush past me, echoing in the huge empty space. By the time I realize what's going on around me, the courtyard's enormous double wooden doors swing wide open, and what looks like the entire German unit stationed at Paliocastro marches out, one by one, and heads for the trucks revving up outside, ready to go. *What can this mean?* I wonder, terrified. I stand sideways by the window, and listen to the roar of engines getting louder and the wheels screeching on the dirt road as they hurry away, leaving in their wake a dead silence.

Soon, a buzz of the other prisoners' voices fills the empty courtyard. Timidly and still frightened, I sneak out the big door and watch some prisoners working their way downstairs. "Where can the Germans be going?" they ask each other in whispers, almost afraid of being overheard by the walls still echoing of the Nazis. No one notices me. I tiptoe outside and huddle close to the building, shuddering in the fierce March wind. I strain to listen for the sound of engines that might be coming back, before I make a mad dash through the half-open gate, to escape from this torture.

Word quickly got around that the unexpected had happened. For no apparent reason, the German command post left town on March first of '43 for an unknown destination to the north, as rumor had it.

News like this, in such times, spreads more swiftly than a blazing midsummer fire.

By the time I reach the public square, the whole town is buzzing. "What does this mean? Are the Germans leaving for good? Maybe it means the end of the war?" For sure, nobody can tell.

I walk through the streets, tingling with excitement, bursting with curiosity. *Why go home when there's so much going on here?* It's more fun listening to the people who've poured into the streets. At first, everyone seems to be in a daze. Then, gradually they start asking questions.

"The patrol unit hasn't returned yet. Isn't that a sign?" the baker calls out as he wipes his flour-covered hands, to greet a neighbor passing by.

"Who knows what to expect next?" my mother says, frowning, as I enter the house unnoticed. "The devil you don't know is worse," she mutters to herself, and then glances briefly in my direction, relieved to see me. "Thank God, you're safe and sound. You'll tell me about it later. Now I have some chores to do," she says and rushes away.

For the first time since the occupation, mingled with the anxiety, the "liberation," brings forth a burst of exhilaration. Swarms of people gather in the streets in an outpouring of enthusiasm, disregarding their fear that if the enemy returned, the consequences would be disastrous.

"This is a sacred moment," the mayor, Mr. Papanikos, declares in the center square, and everybody nods in agreement. He is dressed in the dark blue suit and white shirt he wears on Sundays to go to church. His thinning black hair is carefully combed back, showing off to best advantage the bushy long mustache that accentuates his profile. "We must celebrate and pay homage," he solemnly reads from the handwritten page and then gives the public announcement to one of the young men standing near him to post prominently on the bark of the old plane tree for everyone to see. This official declaration of "freedom" thrusts the town of Paliocastro into a frenzy of activity, as though

197

awakened from a long winter's deep freeze to greet the coming of spring. People suddenly burst into loud laughter, gesticulating and exchanging remarks without their usual caution.

The next morning, the national flag is raised in the middle of the square for the first time in two years of occupation. The azure-blue flag billows proudly in the free air. Exuberant children's voices from the school choir fill the air and I feel a deep shiver run up and down my spine. Our singing adds a special stirring lilt to the verses of our national poet, Dionisios Solomos, who spoke of another time of oppression in his "Ode to Freedom:"

> *The burden of bondage*
> *Was crushing us all.*

I, too, stand tall, but timid in the front row, dressed in a faded blue skirt and a yellowed blouse over a thin gray sweater to ward off the chill of the March wind.

"Chaere, oh, chaere, eleutheria," voices chant.

I find myself uttering sounds that until now were mere words printed on a dry piece of lifeless paper. Now those very same words springing forth out of this new oppression have acquired a new meaning that transforms them into a living emotion. I tremble.

"Rejoice, oh, Rejoice, Freedom," chant steady children's voices.

Rejoice, whispers the flag gently touching my face. Rejoice, murmurs the blood flowing through my veins. Rejoice, chants each breath escaping through my lips. Rejoice, the rejoicing of Freedom.

The next day the Germans return just as suddenly as they had disappeared, stunning the unsuspecting townspeople, who had assumed they were gone for good. Now, more than ever, nobody has the faintest idea what is going on or why. Everything is shrouded in mystery.

"Will they come after me again?" I say shuddering every time I hear a sound outside. I think they're coming to get me and run down to the cellar to hide.

Again, the winds of fear and terror are blowing strong. No one can stop them. No one knows what is coming next. Doors remain shut, and the streets turn into a deserted no-man's-land.

In a few days, the German patrol is gone again. The explosive situation is plunged even deeper in darkness. There is no way of finding a beginning or an end.

"Run! Run!!" my cousin Petro calls out to me from the bottom of the front stairs.

"What? What?" I cry out, expecting to hear the worst.

"The bridge is on fire," he yells even louder. His short, loose-fitting pants make him look thin and tall, as though he's grown inches since he left for school that morning.

"What are you talking about?" I shout back.

"Will you listen, the partisans set fire to the Aliakmon river bridge, and the Germans are cut off," he says, grinning. His steel gray eyes glint in the half shadow of the windowless hall.

"So what will happen now? Tell me! I can't stand it any longer."

"The partisans took over the police station, and they occupied the German headquarters," he says, lowering his voice to a conspiratorial whisper.

This simply can't be true. Either I'm dreaming or he's hallucinating.

"If you don't trust me, come and see for yourself." He waves me on, sensing my doubt.

I dash downstairs two steps at a time, bursting with curiosity.

"Unbelievable!" I cry out. Real live partisans in town. Right under the nose of the Germans and the Italians and the Bulgarians, the whole vicious mob of Nazi fascists hell-bent on strangling us to death.

Seeing the freedom-fighters live in front of me, standing there before my very eyes, I'm overcome with elation. These are not humans. They are demigods. Brave heroes carrying rusty old shotguns in their bare hands confront the whole Nazi war machinery that's terrorizing the entire earth.

What an achievement! I think. *I can't get over it.*

I watch the black-bearded, serious partisans dart back and forth, checking, planning, moving, conferring amongst themselves, directing others to action, holding this war-ravaged, small world in their hands. "We raise the torch of freedom high," one of the partisans proclaims, as he hoists the blue and white flag in the courtyard of the police headquarters where it billows in the air. "It heralds the dawning of a new day that will pave the way to a life of long-lasting peace."

I spring to life watching them. I want to follow them in the mountains, to run away from the suffocation I feel, to breathe again free and alive. I'm tired of always doing someone's bidding, a slave to others' wishes and whims.

Either it's being forced to learn seamstressing so I can be a good housewife some day—which I have no interest in—or to do meaningless chores, or to obey—always that. Obey others. *What about me? Nobody asks me what I want.* My uncle has his own ideas. If he hears a boy whistle in the other end of town, he shrieks. " Who's that whistling at you?" I cower in sheer terror. How should I know? I shake and look at the tips of my beaten-up shoes, too scared to breathe. He's liable to lash into me, just the way he did that night when my mother called him to take a look at me because I had a high fever and he said. "Get out of bed, let me see." So I crawled out, making sure my nightgown covered my legs, and he let out a yell. "There's nothing wrong with you, you're a hysterical female, just like your mother!" he hissed, storming out of the room, leaving me there, drenched in sweat and shaking all over—just like my mother.

I know the partisans are fighting for freedom and I know that's what I want to do most of all.

No sooner do I begin to fathom the depth of my excitement, to know this is real and not a fantasy, than Petro says. "Come on, we have to go."

"What are you talking about? Have your senses left you?" I protest. "I haven't even had a chance to talk to the partisans, you can't ask me to leave now." I insist, all shaken up.

"I'll explain," he says putting on his most convincing tone of voice, but I'll not hear of it.

"I don't want to go. How can you even think of taking me away from the very people who will save us? I want to follow them to the mountains, to fight for our freedom." Petro just looks at me. "Don't just stand there, say something. Agree with me. You know I'm right. You feel the same way, don't you? You're my mentor. At least that's what you've been saying. Or have you changed your mind so quickly?"

He takes me firmly by the hand. "Your mother..." He drags me away. "She said to hurry." I refuse to listen and try wrestling away, but it's no use, his grip is tight.

"Enemy troops are coming back!"

I turn to face him in complete shock, yet, somehow, sensing it must be so. I'm unwilling to accept defeat so soon after that tiny moment of triumph that's evaporating before my very eyes. The hope it inspired is vanishing into thin air.

"That can't be true. How can they? The bridge is burned down."

He gives me a stern look. "They're coming from the other side. They have Italian reinforcements from the south and rumor has it they're hopping mad because the burning of the bridge stopped those Italian fascists from advancing to the north." He hastens his pace and I follow.

"Who told you, the partisans? Who?" I press him for an answer.

"The town must be evacuated as soon as possible to avoid a bloodbath. Your mother is waiting. You know she won't leave without you," he casts a hurried glance in my direction, without answering my question.

"Would they be so mad if there was no resistance movement?" I venture, confused.

"Of course." Petro stops short. "They're hell bent on cutting our throats." He says as his bare hand makes a slitting motion that frightens me.

"Is, is it safe to, to leave?" I ask panting uphill.

"The partisans will guard us until we get past the highway. That's a Dead Zone now. Then we're on our own."

"We have to cross the Dead Zone? And risk getting killed on the spot?" I ask, knowing the answer full well.

"There's no other choice. Not unless we risk staying here, and that could be even worse than getting shot. Who knows what the enemy would do to us."

I move faster, shaken by this new turn of events.

"Where will everybody go? So many people leaving all at once..." I begin considering the aftermath.

"Wherever they can. Wherever the wind blows..."

"Wherever the wind blows," I echo.

And so begins the diaspora.

17 TO THE FIVE WINDS

March 5, 1943.

"Enemy attack! Enemy attack!" The rumor spreads like wildfire.

The partisans notify us that everybody, without exception, must leave town immediately.

"You see?" a villager says. "The enemy lost no time and is sending a heavy contingent that's heading our way."

"How do you know?" Mihalis asks him.

"That's what Kapetan Argyris told me. They're furious, we heard, because the partisans burned down the Aliakmon bridge, probably to block their access from the south to the seaport of Thessaloniki, along with other parts of northern Macedonia. Heaven only knows what suffering they'll inflict on us," he answers.

"I'm afraid we'll pay a heavy price for our short-lived freedom, when the Greek flag was raised in the town square to celebrate our liberation. We thought we were rid of the enemy once and for all! Now we are the main target in their destructive path," he says and leaves.

When our *Koumparo* Balsanidis hears about the advancing enemy troops, he harnesses his old cart early in the morning. His gray-haired ox turns a pair of velvety brown eyes toward him, following its master's every move. *Koumparo* takes the reins in his weather-beaten hands and comes to help us move some of our belongings before the town goes up in smoke. *Koumparo* is a man who doesn't

204

impress at first sight: plain, short in height and a little stooped, with a windblown, ageless face. But his kindness and humanity are without equal. Not just to keep on good terms with my uncles, or because his daughter, Niki—named to bring victory to our land—was baptized by my mother. That is his nature; he never changes his ways just to satisfy others.

"What I'm doing," he says in his native Pontiac style of speech, "is for my *Koumpara* who christened my daughter and doesn't have her husband here to look after her." He gives my mother a look full of compassion and adds, "I feel sorry for you, *Koumpara,* and whatever I do for you and your children is not enough." Tears well up in his dark brown eyes as he bends down to pick up a bundle.

My mother's face softens, as though she's just been caressed. "No one else thought of saying that to me," she replies, deeply moved by his sensitive feelings.

Koumparo Balsanidis offers each of us a handful of almonds and pomegranates from his recent crop, then signals me to follow him. I pocket them and go with him to the chicken coop where he had put three eggs in the nest for each of us. He gently places them in my hands. "To have strength on your journey."

The precious offering warms my wind-chilled hands, spreading that good feeling throughout my whole body. I thank him, and we hurry to meet my mother, who is waiting at the road. "You must be ready to face whatever comes your way," he counsels as we walk back. "There will be much trouble. I know. My people suffered, oh, so much. A refugee is a stranger wherever you go, a nobody. Always at someone else's mercy." He mops his brow. I listen, not completely sure of the full meaning of his words, except for a sense of alarm.

My mother is waiting with a bundle in her hand. She rests it on the ground, and we each take an egg and eat it, with almost holy reverence. Then we make the sign of the cross, ready to take off for the unknown.

The small oxcart is packed to the gills. Seated in front with our *Koumparo* is my brother Tasio. My mother and I walk alongside with a bundle in each hand and a backpack. The rest of the townsfolk follow behind us, wordless, like a litany with a mute church bell. By the time we file past the old Turkish neighborhood, the highway is full of people. Everyone is carrying something: suitcases of all colors— some tied with rope, others with straps—fish net bags, woven baskets big and small, straw bundles. Some of the lucky ones who ride on donkeys march faster, and a very few, even luckier ones, ride ahead of us on mules.

The cacophony of chickens clucking, sheep ba-a-a-ing, and babies screeching is reminiscent of *panigyria,* village fairs of old. Only the Gypsies with their shanties and drums are missing. As we trek along, that almost festive sound begins to disappear in the din of confusion and pushing. So many pairs of feet kick up a cloud of dirt that clogs the very air we breathe. Soon people's faces are covered with the same ashen veil of dust, creating an impression of tragic sadness in the mass of slow-moving humanity.

In the afternoon, tired out and thirsty, we reach Rimio, one of the nearest villages tucked out of the way in the Aliakmon valley. The narrow streets are quickly flooded with the sounds of noisy folk who move around in bunches and stir the natives from their naps. The minute the towns-people come out in their yards to see what's going on, the throng of refugees attacks like swarming bees.

"Do you have a room where we can spend the night? The kids can't take it anymore, they're little and they're exhausted." People run from house to house out of breath, trying to find a friend or even a stranger who will help them. "Please let us in."

"What do you think, will the Rimiotes take pity on us, or will they tell us to go back where we came from?" Aunt Chrysie asks Mihali, Eleni's brother-in-law, who is standing near us, in the same plight as everyone else.

"Oh, I don't think they will do something like that. The village folk know what it's like to be a refugee. After all, they had to leave their own country near the Caucasus back around 1919, when the Pontiac Greeks came to their homeland in exchange for the return of the Turks during the First World War."

"I hope you're right," she says, glancing about anxiously.

"And they've done an amazing job here since they arrived. They're hard-working people with a lot of know-how about farming and cattle. They've converted this to a blessed land."

The people standing around nod in agreement.

In the meantime, one of the villagers who knows us joins the conversation.

"In these hard times that you're going through, I open up my door to welcome you as our brethren. As refugees years ago we, too, had to drink that bitter potion and understand."

These simple, kind people shelter us in our hour of need. As soon as the landlady sees us, she comes to greet us and sets us up in a corner of their sitting room. At night she offers us a bowl of hot soup, hearty country bread, and a cupful of cow's milk, a rare treat.

Night falls before long. The din gives way to the customary serenity of the small, narrow streets. Only the donkeys can be heard in the yards, accompanied by the musical chiming of the mooing cows from the distant meadow. One way and another, most of the people settle in, spread out here and there.

In the haste and confusion we lost track of Aunt Evangelia and of many other relatives and friends who disappeared in the whirlwind that sucked all of us into its fury. Only later do we discover that Timoleon has sneaked off to town with *Koumparo,* who is to return shortly with the last load.

Just as we get ready to lie down, an unexpected streak of light glares from the east, and the sky is transformed into a sickly, yellowish-gray canvas. All eyes turn in the direction of Paliocastro, and the room fills with muffled cries. Then, we move *en masse* toward the window like sleepwalkers. Silently we watch the bizarre sight, mute witnesses to this menacing glow.

I press my forehead on the cold windowpane and watch in total disbelief. The crimson-red flames soar, reach the peak of the sky, brighten momentarily, and transform the darkness into a phantasmagoria of yellow, orange, and red pyrotechnics, before dying out in the vastness of infinity. No one utters a single word, yet we all know that Paliocastro is burning. I stay up all night leaning against the windowsill, hypnotized by the monotony of the rising and falling flames.

"I can't believe…" my mother lets out a whisper, "that this frightful sight is unfolding before us."

Vyenoula's baby stirs in her sleep and lets out a sorrowful wail. Vyenoula nurses the child without even so much as a look at her. Lost somewhere in the distance, she casts a cross-eyed glance that shifts from the window to the bare wall. A split image, like two visions that never merge. A world that will never again exist for her. The newborn babe fusses again, and Vyenoula rocks her rhythmically back and forth until mother and child close their eyes and slowly drift into sleep.

By the light of dawn, unable to watch any longer, I can feel my eyelids grow heavy, and I fall into a deep slumber. Before long, an unnatural reflection of light surrounds me, and an awful stench permeates the air, something like a rotten egg. I awaken startled. The sight brings me back to the terrible truth hovering in our midst. All around me heads turn, eyes stare, and faces remain immobile, uncomprehending, as though somebody has cut off everyone's tongue.

In a moment—or is it centuries later?—Aunt Chrysoula, tall and imposing as always, stirs and nods to us to grab our stuff. We follow her from the room. The landlady, wearing a shawl over her thin shoulders, briskly steps out and offers us a loaf of bread.

"Don't worry about your things, they can stay until someone comes to fetch them. May you go well."

At the edge of town we pass a group of neighbors from Paliocastro standing in a yard, secretly talking among themselves.

"Why are you leaving?" Niko, the owner of the notions store, calls out. "We have to go back home, as soon as the Germans put everything back in order."

Aunt Chrysie looks back at him, steadfast, saying: "Can't you see what's happening? The Germans got a terrible beating in Stalingrad, and then the freezing winter and hunger wiped them out for good. They're stuck there. What kind of order do you expect?"

"Wait and see," chimes in Phillip, the butcher, middle-aged with strong arms, and red hair just like his mother. "We got work to do. We got to build our houses again." He grins.

"Oh, we'll see about that," says Aunt Chrysie. "I hope God gives us strength to do that one day." She quickly distances herself, taking long strides toward the narrow road that leads toward the monastery. "Hurry," she calls out to us, "we can't dawdle any longer. We've wasted enough time in idle talk."

I run to catch up with her. "What will we be doing at the monastery?" I ask impatiently.

"Child, we'll seek refuge there, as the travelers and hermits of old did in the middle ages. Perhaps they'll take pity on us when they see we have nowhere to lean our head," she answers in an anguished voice and abruptly ends the conversation, hastening her step.

At first, the road is level and straight. The farther uphill we go, the more our pace is slackened by the heavy snow and mud. Thick, red mud. Bottomless mud. Awful mud. It clings, drawing you down to its inner depth, pulling you into its siena-colored abyss. It offers no resistance. Only when you try to pull out your leg that's stuck knee-deep in the brick-red glue, only then do you realize it has captured you for good. Then the worst torture begins. Your leg, heavy beyond belief, slides and collapses in the snow-covered ditch. You try once, twice, three times, until you lift this unbearable weight to advance half a step. Not even that. Only to start all over again. The same, and worse.

"Mother, dear, what a road this is," I mutter. Such an interminable ordeal I could never have imagined. Marching for hours on end.

"Myth… Sisyphus…" I catch some words. *Who said that? Or is the wind playing tricks on me?* I don't recognize a familiar voice.

"What does it mean? Is this a time for philosophizing? Racked by hunger and thirst," I mumble, half to myself.

I don't even turn my head. Whoever said it, it doesn't matter. Truth and lies have merged into one. Who can tell them apart?

All around, the snow has dressed the bushes in bridal white. The holly, covered with feathery tufts of snow, sparkles with jewel-bright red berries. The tree branches, like candy-coated goodies, beckon invitingly.

At last we climb to a high spot. The cold penetrates to the bone. The withering north wind forces us to hasten our pace. The mud-covered shoes are frozen solid. They must weigh a ton. Where can you find the strength to hurry?

"The road must be crossed. It's the only salvation." A voice brings a message from the north. But who can look back to face it, eye to eye?

We march on... The north wind blows...

18 AT THE MONASTERY

A stark, white vision that surely must be a mirage appears in the distance. It stands tall and imposing amidst the evergreen trees.

"There…there's the…Zdani…monastery!" A tired voice is heard struggling to utter the words against the gusting wind that instantly swallows the sound.

With a last surge of energy we trudge up one more steep hill and behold the impressive, whitewashed monastery.

The loud barking of sheepdogs announces our presence, and a resonant voice sends them scurrying.

"Come in, come in, you poor souls, you must be frozen." The abbot, *Iyoumenos* David, greets us with warmth from the courtyard.

The strong wind blows his long, brown working cassock in my face as he steps forward to help my mother. When he bends down, I notice his deep furrowed brow and the look of concern and compassion in his brown eyes.

"Give us a hand," he calls out to two lightly bearded monks in their dark cowls, who waste no time in relieving us of our heavy bundles. We hasten to take cover under the welcome roof. Inside, the lit fireplace and the simple room offer us the warmth we need. A frugal monastic table is set and, ravenously hungry, we partake.

The location of the monastery—nestled between mountain and valley—is ideal for the secret meetings of the partisans, the *"andartes."* Located at the crossroads of "free

212

Greece" and the Nazi-occupied region, it can be reached from the main highway along the Aliakmon river and serves as a connecting link between the *andartes* and other freedom fighters doing undercover resistance work on the opposite side of the river. The Bishop Seraphim, the spiritual leader of the resistance movement in northern Greece, has chosen it as an outpost of his main headquarters, situated in the remote mountains. During his frequent visits he directs the partisan staff operations and coordinates the combined military expeditions that are carried out with the allied American and British troops who frequently come and are briefly stationed there. Occasionally, a few Russian officers join the other allied troops and plan joint expeditions with the freedom fighters. Before long, our own pace, spurred by the general frenzy, gets revved up to a feverish pitch. New faces constantly appear and disappear, waking us in the middle of the night. The flurry of unusual activity and the huddled meetings in low voices are unmistakable signs that important plans are afoot, although we have no idea what they are. Usually, the next day we find out that a bridge was blown up on the highway or an enemy truck convoy full of ammunition was ambushed in the straits of Sarantaporo. Then we know for sure what had been planned the night before.

Evenings, we sit in the common room in front of the crackling fireplace in the company of long-bearded monks and partisans.

The partisans carefully place some of their precious tobacco into tiny pieces of newsprint and roll them into cigarettes while others oil their muskets, polishing and shining them until they glisten in the flickering light. The guns are a source of wonder to us kids, and we watch what's going on to find out how they work. Petros first and foremost has a passion for them and offers to help the *andartes* in the hope they'll take him with them, but his folks won't dream of it. Only Timoleon is missing from our midst.

After the fire that razed Paliocastro to the ground, a friend managed to salvage two sacks of grain from the cellar, and every night we sort through the half-burned grain. We place round, shallow trays on our laps and pick out the charred kernels, leaving the rest that will be saved to make bread. We pore over the large shiny metal trays until our eyeballs are ready to drop. In the end that bread was so bitter, just like poison, that it could not be eaten.

Barba Lambros is seated a little farther over, on a low bench by the fire, and sings old partisan songs from the revolution of 1821. From the innermost recesses of his heart, his sonorous voice quivers, full of pain and anguish. *Barba* Lambros, the *Iyoumeno's* faithful servant and con- fidant, knows many half-forgotten songs, but the one he loves most is "Kitso's *Mana.*" When he sings his bright eyes glow, his proud, strong body straightens and his creased, weather-beaten face, rejuvenated, is given with abandon to the past.

We follow the death march of star-crossed Kitsos, a free- dom fighter of old, as "1000 men lead the procession, and 2000-strong bring up the rear." We lament his grief- stricken mother's mournful chant: "I sit at the river's edge, stoning it, imploring it, run slow, river, turn back. Let me cross over to the other side, over there where the *kleftes* fighters are." Countless times we weep for Kitsos' "hapless youth." His last words to his *mana* can tear your heart into pieces: "Loony mother, daft mother, mindless mother, you cry not for my forlorn youth and wasted vigor, but cry over my hapless arms, my hapless *'tsaprazia.'*"

"Who knows what grief her pitiful soul felt when she saw him facing the end of his life robbed of the arms that had decorated his proud chest," Aunt Chrysie whispers.

The monastery staff is having a hard time under the heavy load of so many visitors, passersby, and refugees who come and go to take care of various partisan operations. We all decide to pitch in and give a helping hand with the preparations in the kitchen: peeling potatoes and onions, gathering wild roots for salad greens, baking bread. My mother offers to help cook, and she makes herself instantly popular with the kitchen crew.

"Oh, my, that's quite a dish, you're a real good cook. Pretty soon you can join our staff, you can become an *Iyoumenissa*," says Kira Frosini, the buxom, kind-hearted woman who loves raw garlic. Her breath announces her presence a mile away and when she comes up close there's no doubt she can ward off germs from near or far.

I've been asked to help take care of Vyenoula's baby, to give her some free time. She's playful and lots of fun now, and I enjoy dandling her on my knee. Just as I run over to feed her one day, one of the British officers, about twenty-five years old, with a brown mustache and laughing eyes, brushes past and stops short in front of me. The minute I see him, I feel the blood rush to my face.

"Why are you as red as a poppy?" my cousin Ted asks, sidling up to me, and I mumble something to hide my embarrassment. "He keeps saying, 'Inglis, Inglis'—maybe you can help him." He grins.

"I no speak English very good," I whisper to the Englishman awkwardly.

Then within seconds, out of the blue, I feel inspired and find myself chattering in English a mile a minute. Ted takes off. There's so much I want to say, but first I try to find out what the Englishman wants me to translate for him. He's so cute, I think to myself, and become uneasy again, blushing to the roots of my hair once more.

The Englishman is polite and doesn't interrupt, but listens attentively, apparently impressed with my language facility.

The exchange doesn't last long because he's called away, and I stand alone in the long corridor holding the baby whose smiling face is lifted to mine. She lets out a loud chirping, as though she's proclaiming her own new beginning.

Before long, a bout of the flu starts making the rounds, and most of us are laid low with sickness. In addition, my grandmother's condition has been worsening ever since she had to be carried for hours to get her to the monastery after the fire. Now she needs someone constantly at her bedside, but prefers my mother's ministrations even above those of her daughters, Pelagia and Chrysie, so she's always calling out to her to come over and rub her aching bones or to wash her bedsores. The pain gets worse. She senses that her days are numbered and calls us one after the other by name to kiss her hand and receive her blessing.

"For forgiveness when I die." She gives us all something, and to me, as her only granddaughter by a son, she offers a monogrammed ring she wears that was a gift from her father when she was wed. Then, exhausted by her effort, she says, "I'm leaving this world contented to have you near me. I've had my fill of life, I'm almost ninety. May you reach my years," she adds in a thin, breathless voice.

When she dies, she's buried in the monastery graveyard that is covered with simple wooden crosses. We weep for her, and for all the slain refugees. After spending almost ninety years in her hometown where she raised ten children,

216

she's dispossessed at her age, in her state of infirmity, cast out of her bed, and made to suffer hardships in a strange land.

Most deeply we lament the deaths of *Koumparos* and Timoleon, who got caught in the crossfire of burning Paliocastro. They were shot in cold blood right on the highway, before they had a chance to escape. We shed bitter tears for them, and for so much else in our troubled hearts that remains unspoken in a frozen silence.

At the monastery I take refuge in my cell and enjoy the sweet loneliness of monastic life. Walking down the long corridor that separates the monks' quarters from the main courtyard, I reach my tiny, ascetic room and gently push open the old wooden door held together with big hand-wrought hinges. Noiselessly, to avoid disturbing the sacred silence, I sit cross-legged on my narrow, iron bed. For hours on end I read the few schoolbooks I managed to salvage when we left Paliocastro. I do my homework all alone; I copy lessons and memorize passages in geography, history, and Modern Greek. Combining all the information I can collect, I put it together again in my own way, letting my imagination wander to unknown parts of the world, to different ages. Without recess, without interruption, until my legs are numb.

Then I seek Boris's company. We've become inseparable. We both love to run carefree along the mountainside, whirling round and round the bushes and trees, jumping over big boulders or low-lying evergreen hedges, twisting and turning, creating countless sketches in motion. Endless games.

I also have to do chores, like gathering dandelions or wild roots to make them into a sauce with water and flour for our evening meal. Boris then loses his rhythm and stops. His dark eyes dart back and forth, perplexed, and he goes around in circles two or three times before deciding it's time for a pause. Looking rather pensive, he casts restless glances at me but always agrees to stay nearby without complaint. Once in a while I stroke his pitch black, shiny coat, and then when I'm finished with my chores he sits next to me, contented.

On our way back, Boris's littermate, Pitela, greets us. She's exactly her mother's look-alike: slow-moving, chubby, brown-haired, with guarded friendliness; in fact, she's rather indifferent.

Boris is a breed apart: lean, slim, he runs as fast as the wind in March, and above all, he's expressive. A whiz at everything. Yet the two of them love each other in their own way.

Toward the end of March, Boris is in a dilemma. The monastery's sheepdog has just given birth to a litter of five pups, two all white, two brown, and one spotted. At first, he takes the matter very seriously. Fussing, bouts of depression, and jealous outbursts whenever he sees me approach the pups. Gradually he simmers down and, reassured, returns to his former self.

For a few weeks, before they get gigantic, the pups are delightful. They amuse us for hours on end with their bearlike games: mock barking, biting, pushing, scampering about in a frenzy of activity, before getting all tangled up in a woolly ball. Meanwhile, a short distance away, lying down on the new grass, their mother watches their escapades, seemingly unaware. Provided no one makes the mistake of even thinking about getting near them. At the slightest whiff of trouble, she springs up ready to pounce, flashing her bared and well-sharpened teeth, poised for action. She stands watchful guard until all risk of danger subsides, and only then withdraws and lazily stretches out her limbs while the young suckle and paw at her upturned belly, and she falls asleep. Who knows what dreams she revels in?

During these early spring mornings, I taste the secret mystery of seclusion. Dawn sets the day's rhythmic beat with the monotonous call of the cuckoo-bird, which steals into the vivid dreams of early morning sleep and awakens me. The sun's still-gentle rays wish me good morning. First, they touch my legs discreetly, and then gradually embrace my whole body until I can taste them in my mouth, warm, receptive.

Barefoot, I run to the wooden balcony to savor the rich awakening of the woodland, as birdsong heralds the coming of a new day. The early morning light filters through the newly blossoming foliage and blends with the grass-covered rich tapestry of colors, transforming the twinkling dewdrops that gathered all night long into shimmering jewels that slowly begin to disappear as the cuckoo's song ends its morning rounds. Timidly, the wildflowers begin to make their appearance in the fresh grass, dewy from the night's cool air. A cackling pack of turkeys, nesting under my tiny balcony, break up the silence and gobble "gula, gula, gula" over and over again. Why don't I greet them, too? The idea strikes me, and I respond, "gula, gula, gula." To my surprise, they reply with a horrendous cacophony. We play that game—which I'm sure they enjoy as much as I do—whenever I poke my head over the railing, until either my voice gets hoarse or my patience is exhausted.

Never before have I experienced such an intense, such a harmonious awakening of the earth as this springtime at the monastery. Each new daybreak proclaims another expression of spring, a new discovery of an unexpected bird's chirping, a burgeoning multicolored flowering of the earth, as though an invisible compass sets the daily course for

219

the birdsong, for the wild cuckoo-flower that blooms when the cuckoo is heard, for the exuberant flowering of each tree branch covered with myriad blossoms. I skip down to the creek to fill the earthenware jugs with water and listen to the orchestration of the early morning music. I watch the red-breasted robin flitting along the stream that meanders under the shadow of the trees in the valley, I marvel at its timely appearance to announce the new season. I run beside the stream, chasing the rivulets that are freed now from the frozen trap of winter, and the wet pebbles slide under my bare feet as I splash along in the powerful swell of the water.

The towering almond tree opposite the entrance to the monastery is in full bloom, dressed in her most triumphant costume. On light-bedecked Easter Sunday, the gentle wind sprinkles the pale, ivory-rose petals over the two blue-and-white flags that proudly crown with freedom the freshly white-washed archway to the monastery's courtyard. Under the tree, the seasonal lamb, being barbecued on a huge spit, is full of aroma. Instantly the pups get wind of it and circle around impatiently, cavorting around like little bears, now that they've grown almost to full size. But who has time to pay attention to them? Everyone is busy doing chores: monks, women, children, partisans, we all go back and forth, preparing for the traditional Easter dinner.

The hour of the feast arrives, and everyone is seated on the grass around the white tablecloth. The *Iyoumenos* blesses the daily bread in the center of the gathering and leads us all in prayer, chanting three times "Christ is Risen, *Christos Anesti.*" He wishes peace to everyone and offers a toast to freedom for our country. The festivity begins with the ceremonial red Easter egg cracking, and, in its turn, the roast lamb ready for carving is placed on large branches of freshly cut fern to give it a rich, woodsy fragrance.

Kapetan Argyris deftly draws his shiny sword and cuts the meat into portions. He gives the shoulder bone to *Barba* Lambro, and then lets the other partisans distribute the rest. *Barba* Lambros looks at the lamb bone, and there's a hush. He studies it carefully, holds it up to the light, turns it over a couple of times, frowns without raising his head, and says in a dry voice,

"Victory and peace, that's what I see," he says and stops abruptly.

"What else do you see? Tell us." The voices of the older monks join in the merriment. "We want to know too."

"It's good, it's good, what else can I say?" *Barba* Lambro insists, but a dark shadow clouds his eyes.

The meat portions are distributed, and the ravenously hungry crowd digs in.

"We haven't eaten like this in ages," we all say and chew every bit of meat off the bones before tossing them to the barking dogs that finish them off in a minute. We sing and dance and by nightfall songs of heroic struggles for freedom echo well into the night from the meadow to the mountaintop. Only the two rows of the partisans' machine guns that guard the national flag by the pillars at the monastery's arched gate are constant reminders of the foreign oppression mercilessly hounding our country.

To everyone's surprise, Bishop Seraphim arrives a few days later to conduct the liturgy with the refugees in the small but beautiful church of *Zoodohos Piyi,* the Life-giving Fountain, decorated with exquisite hand-carvings. His imposing stature graces the tightly packed, candle-lit interior, his stentorian voice resounds through the rafters. Tears of sadness mixed with joy well up in the eyes of the faithful. He offers a message of support and encouragement in this hour of darkness.

"Have faith, my brethren. You have been expatriated, but once again, in good time, you will find yourselves in the bosom of your native land. A joyous Anastasis to all of you, may it be a true Resurrection. As Christ was risen from the dead, so will our country rise like a phoenix from the ashes of the destruction wrought by the enemies of our beloved land. The will of our people shall prevail. We Shall Be Victorious."

Bishop Seraphim pauses to kneel by the flag, kissing it reverently before saying farewell.

"Be brave in the difficult struggle ahead of us. You will always be in my thoughts, and in my heart," he calls out. Just as he's about to head for the road, he notices me standing in a small ravine, fighting the surge of tears in my eyes, and turns aside to say, "I expect great accomplishments from you in the struggle for our freedom. We need everyone, including little lambs."

I'm amazed that he remembers calling me a little lamb that starlit night on my uncle's roof terrace, after one of his planning meetings with the partisans, seemingly so long ago.

Just then, a messenger from German-occupied Greece arrives in great haste and hands the bishop an envelope marked "URGENT. He opens it, and scans it swiftly. We watch his expression change, becoming more and more gloomy until his head bows down low, covering the letter with unconcealed tears.

June 5, 1943
Concentration Camp Pavlos Melas
Thessaloniki
To The Bishop of Kozani Seraphim
Your Grace,

It seems that my hour of departure to our Lord has arrived. Today or tomorrow the barbarian invaders will lead us to our execution ground. I am proud, my Bishop, to be dying for the freedom of our country and moreover because in the sacrifice for our nation I represent the Greek clergy and the glorious heritage bequeathed to us by Papaflessas, Samouil, Isaias from Salona and you yourself are continuing that struggle today for the Freedom of our Nation.

I kiss your hand

In Christ and in the struggle a brother,

Seraphim

On June 6, 1943, the beaten body of Seraphim Poulias was dragged in chains to the prison yard where other prisoners also facing execution by the death squad were standing.

"You are about to die," a German officer told Seraphim. "Do you have anything to say?"

In the short time left to him before dying, Seraphim delivered his last speech. His fiery restlessness was reawakened, the impatient movements of his hands returned to their former vigor to weave vivid images, circling the air with passionate gestures. His once vibrant voice, recharged with uncommon vitality, captivated the mesmerized prisoners waiting execution nearby, stirring them, firing a new spark of life in their eyes, moving even inanimate objects in the courtyard where they were waiting to be killed.

"You are powerful only because you carry guns. The true strength is in our hands. Our struggle is noble and just. You have lost the war. WE WILL W...." The prolonged sound of machine gun fire cut short Seraphim's voice. His bullet-riddled body collapsed on the ground, but his words still echo in the air.

The revolutionary leader of northern Greece leads a solemn memorial prayer for the slain Archimandrite Seraphim Poulias, and then prepares to leave. Kapetan Argyri and a small retinue of trusted *andartes,* each carrying a small machine gun slung over the shoulder, go with him.

As one, we follow them to the path leading east and wait to see them disappear in the forest before turning back.

At that moment I vow that I will do everything I can to vindicate the brutal murder of Archimandrite Seraphim Poulias and devote myself wholeheartedly to the struggle for our freedom.

Soon we, too, have to leave Zdani. An urgent message arrives in the middle of the night that a German attack is imminent.

19 COOL WATER

Tranovalto, a big pit surrounded by swamps and low-lying mountains, chokes in the still air and the monotonous drone of mosquitoes. The dark, fertile land, that never failed to produce a rich harvest, lies fallow. Acres and acres of crops are either destroyed by fire or neglected because enemy attacks kept the villagers from getting close to their fields. The village square, if you can call it that—a palm's length of beaten down earth near the church—gathers the handful or so of natives and refugees from Paliocastro who listen to the evening news broadcast in Greek either from London or Moscow. Always dreading, of course, the sudden appearance of one of the known traitors who are forever snooping around when people are unaware. "We can't trust 'em," the villagers say, as they recall with horror the stories of many countrymen who were betrayed by their own brothers—blind followers of the foe—and suffered a horrible death at the enemy's hands. Traitors are loathed even more than the enemy.

The latest news bulletin always sparks a lively chatter and the usual give and take. "When in the world will they open the third front?" someone is bound to ask.

"Why are the Allies hesitating? Can't they see there's no other solution?" Mihalis, the tax collector, says, with rage.

"Not again," Niko, the red-haired butcher, cuts him off short. "That's enough! We heard that before. Anyway, what do they need another front for? All they have to do is strengthen the eastern flank, that's what I think."

"If they only knew at the Allied headquarters how much we're suffering…they would have already made the decision to open the front." My mother can be overheard chatting with the womenfolk in the backyard.

The days go by without anything changing. Our condition gets worse day by day from the relentless enemy attacks and the constant sicknesses that plague us.

My mother is skin and bones from the repeated bouts of malaria. Tasio suffers either from stomach problems or psoriasis, a terrible skin condition that covers most of his frail limbs and refuses to leave him alone. Hunger adds to our misery. No sooner does one hardship ease up a little, than another attacks us. In two and half months that we've been here, the Germans have made three massive raids, cutting down to practically nothing the meager scraps of food and clothing we have left.

"Run! Attack! Run!" The message of rapidly approaching German troops takes us by surprise. Totally unprepared as we are, there's hardly enough time to grab a loaf of bread and a handful of clothes before we rush into hiding. The enemy is already in the outskirts of town before we even have a chance to get to the nearest valley.

"What's the use of running?" Aunt Chrysie puffs. "They can probably see us with their spyglasses," she adds, stopping short. "We're just fooling ourselves. If they want to get rid of us they can do it in a jiffy."

"You're right." My mother heaves a sigh. "So what should we do?" she asks, and goes on without waiting for an answer. "I guess we might as well stay here, come what may."

And we wait. Five days and nights in the heat, the malaria-infested swamps, the hunger, the thirst. The enemy never shot a single bullet. They paid about as much attention to the rocks and the soil as they paid to us. Their minds must have been somewhere else.

We return to find the village ransacked. In their violent rampage through the countryside, they confiscated cattle, chickens, produce, whatever they could get their hands on. In Tranovalto a few houses were also burned down, but at least there are no victims, as there are elsewhere.

Round about sunset, most of the townsfolk go straight to the hillside to listen to the radio that, luckily, Mihalis quickly put into a hiding place before we left. Listening to Allied radio broadcasts is forbidden with the penalty of death, so strict secrecy has to be observed to make sure none of the traitors is lurking around. He shovels the dirt and, drenched in perspiration, he yanks it out, mumbling.

"Those Nazi bastards! Let's see what's going on. Maybe the Allies finally stopped their delays and opened up the third front."

Kostis, the village schoolteacher, shakes his head and says, pensively, "It's perfectly clear that only a profound change in the international situation can save us."

"Sh, sh, sh, quiet," Stelios the watchmaker yells out, annoyed.

What with the grunting pigs and the static from the old radio, the announcer's words can hardly be heard.

"No good news. All the battle fronts are at a standstill." Mihalis snaps the radio shut. The rest drag their feet as they leave, knowing that again nothing has changed. There's no relief in sight. Only the pigs keep on wallowing joyfully in the thick mud.

After living in the swampland through the whole enemy offensive, malaria attacks pound us. Some are hit worse than others, but none worse than my mother. All night long she burns in fever one minute and quakes with chills the next. In the morning she wakes up dying of thirst. Her throat is parched, but she finds no relief in drinking the tepid, brackish water from the village fountain.

"Run along, child, may you live a long life and bring me some cool water from the spring. My tongue is glued to the roof of my mouth. I can't take it any more," she pleads, and I run to fetch the jugs.

"I'm going," I call out to her and set off.

"How can you go alone?" I hear her tremulous voice through the door. "It's an hour's walk, don't get lost."

"It's nothing, I'll find the road all right," I say, flying down the steps. I quickly reach the spring, fill the earthenware jugs, take a drink of the refreshing water, and head back just as fast.

In the vast expanse of the deserted valley, the village church bell can be heard from afar, slow, soulful, ringing like a cracked silver urn. Instantly my mind rushes to my sick mother's side where she lies flat on the floor. The bell continues its mournful chime. Uneasy thoughts run through my head. *Did her condition take such a swift turn for the worse? Was she deathly sick and I didn't know? Without the advice of a doctor, how can you tell? Maybe her life was in danger and no one knew it,* I think, and begin to tremble. My knees bend. My hands, that only moments ago held the earthenware jugs steadfast, give way, loosening their grip.

Swiftly I take stock of myself, trying to put my thoughts in some semblance of order, to hold in check the anguish that's tearing me apart, but it's no use. My racing heartbeat refuses to slow down. I can see my mother right here before me, lying down limp on the plain straw mattress, just as I had left her, one minute trembling like a bird, the next burning like a flaming log. Her face all wrinkled, her lips dry, her eyes deep-set, gazing vacantly in the distance. Only her hair has not changed. Black, silky smooth, as always. I stroked it this morning to comfort her, to ease her pain, to believe even for a moment that I can bring back her former looks, to find a little rest from the present torment.

I start running faster, yet the quicker I run, the slower I feel I'm going, as though my footsteps are measured by the rhythm of the mournful church bell. Fear doing battle with hope on the common ground of my aching heart. I don't know what to do. Pour out the water to rush like a bird to be by her side? I can't even catch her last breath. *Was anyone with her when her soul departed? Maybe the bell is ringing for an enemy alert?* I ponder. I have never heard it sound like a dirge before. Still undecided, I start running at full speed. Then I stop to listen again. *Can it be just an illusion? Oh, maybe I'll find her alive, and she'll be so happy to drink the cool refreshing spring water*—I timidly dare a tiny ray of brightness to surface.

Buoyed by that glimmer of hope, I speed up my steps, and what comes to my side but the beloved shadow of my mother's face. I feel encouraged and start racing faster. The sun at the top of the sky shines with a raw, midday light. The scorching heat bears down on me. Mingled sweat and tears run down my face, half-blinding me. Now and then I cool off when the jugs bump against my bare, sweaty legs.

As soon as I reach the houses at the outskirts of town, I rush over to ask the first woman I see on the road for whom the bell tolls. She looks up at me dumbfounded—her eyes clouded—mumbles something, turns her back on me, and leaves. Farther over, it's the same thing. For a moment I have forgotten that out on the street the peasant women neither talk nor greet anyone for any reason. I try to move and stop short. The last drop of endurance has left me. I feel exhausted by this effort to prove false the terrible truth that is tormenting me. I drag myself to our house, shuffling my bare feet along the rugged, dusty road.

I go inside the darkened room and notice the straw mattress on the floor, where my mother's ashen face with her closed eyes is frozen still. The earth splits in two and swallows me up. The lump choking my throat must have stirred her, and slowly her eyes open. I approach in reverence, bend down in silence, and hold her head to give her a sip of cool water from the metal cup lying next to her. A faint smile appears on her pale lips; she closes her eyes again and rests her head on the pillow.

Kneeling next to her, speechless, I shed warm, salt tears for the unknown dead villager.

20 THE SECOND SPRING

It is the summer of 1943, the summer of the second spring. Caught up in the excitement of the revolutionary fervor, nature herself is blooming twice. Once at springtime, as usual, and once at midsummer.

"Unheard of," many say.

"It will bring plenty for the hungry," declare others.

The enemy has been pillaging the village food supplies, and our meager provisions are exhausted. I start working in our landlord's fields to get my ailing mother something to eat.

Every day at the crack of dawn, I go to the swampland with my two cousins, Petro and Ted, to gather corn and beans. The hot, humid bogs soon turn into a steaming cauldron. By noontime we're melting in the heat. I try hard to gather the tall corn that stands at twice my height, reaching high up on tiptoe to break the ripe husks from the long cane. The beans are just the opposite. To collect them you have to bend down, crouching low—almost kneeling—for hours on end, soaking wet. We work hard all day for a mouthful of food.

Around sundown, after I get back from the fields, I do some digging in our neighbor's vegetable garden at the bottom of the hillside. By the end of the day I'm exhausted, but when we eat the delicious fresh food, we all agree it's worth the effort.

"Some luck. I came here from America, the land of plenty, to end up a refugee and suffer such hardship!" My mother swallows the roasted corn with a deep sigh.

"How true," Aunt Chrysie agrees, shaking her head. "What a life! We're homeless and miserable."

After the fire, the other refugees from Paliocastro were scattered to the five winds. Penniless, ailing, without a roof over their heads, they run from one poor village to the next begging for a helping hand to save their children from starvation. The peasants willingly open their doors to let us in, knowing full well that the townsfolk would not have treated them as kindly.

"You wouldn't even have shoved us in with your dogs," the villagers say. "We know, don't take us for a bunch of fools."

But they don't bear us a grudge. "Don't worry, we won't let you loose to get eaten alive by the wolves and the bears."

The peasants' homes strain under the heavy load of hundreds of strangers trying to survive. A whole family of refugees jammed in a cramped space next to the all-purpose room, usually located above the stable for warmth.

Everyday needs are cut down to the bone: food and shelter. No shopping at the grocer's or butcher's, no visits to the seamstress or tailor, no time spent at the local *kafenio* for coffee and a friendly game of backgammon. Only a dogged drive to keep going. But even now, people sometimes need a shoemaker, a barber, a doctor or a midwife in an emergency. They find them scattered in the rugged mountain villages, the doctor in a tiny shack here, and farther away, the once prosperous living right next to the poor and downtrodden.

Three weeks after the last attack, a messenger from a nearby village, Microvalto, calls out, panting. "Enemy troops are heading our way!" He kicks up a storm of dust as he zooms through the dirt roads.

"Not again. They just left, why don't they leave us alone?" my mother cries out. Her patience is worn. "As though all our other troubles aren't enough," she whispers in a broken voice.

"Do you suppose for a minute they care about us? They're out for a killing. Let's go into hiding before they find us here, or we'll really be in trouble," Aunt Chrysie snaps back.

My mother kneels to bury the keepsake photographs she managed to salvage, pausing momentarily to look at the one of Bishop Seraphim in his full ecclesiastical regalia. They slide from her hands as she looks away for a fleeting moment and a sigh escapes her lips. Then she carefully wraps them in some old rags and places them in the dug-up ground between some other clothing for extra safety.

"Hurry up and load the donkey with our bedclothes," she calls out to me. "*Barba* Yiorgos loaned it to us to bring our things to the shelter, and he needs it right back." I lose no time loading the donkey and set off on foot with my pet goat Goldie tagging along. She's a lively kid with a shiny silvery coat, despite her name, and she always follows me wherever I go, baying pitifully when I leave her side. I rush to unload the stuff in a sheltered clearing near the marsh and on the way back climb the donkey and tie Goldie to the saddle. She trots along the dusty road swaying and gently shaking her hindquarters.

All at once a distant sound buzzes overhead. I look up and see nothing. It can't be thunder. There isn't a cloud in sight. The far away noise gets louder and louder, piercing the still, humid air. *An air attack!* I tremble, frightened to death.

I glance up again to get a better look while the sun is momentarily hidden behind a wispy cloud. Squinting hard, I make out the bright, pewter-colored microscopic planes sparkling like shiny Christmas tinsel against the deep blue sky. Fluffy white tails grow in their wake, shedding streams of thread-like ribbons that slowly break up into a thousand and one pieces. They gently float down, fluttering like silvery-white seagulls until they reach the ground, covering the scorched earth with a wide expanse of shimmering whiteness as far as my eye can see. I catch one of the wispy feathers floating in the air. They're leaflets! Printed on pure white paper. I've never seen such beautiful paper. Who ever sees any?

I hop off the donkey and grab a whole bunch of leaflets. The Americans are sending a message to the Greek people! I can't get over it. It's coming all the way from my country, the USA. I read without stopping:

MESSAGE TO THE GREEK PEOPLE:

SUPPORT THE ALLIED WAR!

EVERY BRIDGE YOU DEMOLISH,
ENEMY YOU DESTROY,
EVERY TRUCKLOAD YOU DELAY,
PROVIDES VALUABLE SUPPORT FOR OUR JOINT
STRUGGLE AGAINST OUR COMMON ENEMY:
THE NAZI-FASCIST AXIS.

EACH OF YOUR EFFORTS BRINGS US A STEP
CLOSER TO VICTORY.

FRANKLIN DELANO ROOSEVELT,
PRESIDENT OF
THE UNITED STATES OF AMERICA

Traveling at a donkey's pace, I watch the planes disappearing at the speed of lightning, godlike birds sounding lively, joyous, hope-inspiring. How very different from the deathly groan of the Stukas which constantly threaten our lives. Hugging the leaflets in my arms, I feel I'm holding our liberation from this bloody, burdensome war in my very own hands.

I quickly scoop up as many leaflets as I can to bring back so the others can share in my enthusiasm. I show them to everybody with a glowing feeling of triumph. No one turns a head to look.

"Is this a time for leaflets?" One onlooker scoffs.

"Can't you see how much work we still have?" Aunt Pelagia scolds me, slowly dragging out each scornful word like so many drops of poison, and marches off.

"You're not in your right mind, girl, the enemy is after us, and you promise us manna from an American heaven," complains someone else who's standing farther back.

"Leave us alone before we get caught with American leaflets in our hands. The Germans will slaughter us all." Mihalis, the tax man provides the final put-down.

Numbed, I put them down and someone throws a match, turning the paper to ashes. This joy, too, flies away.

The digging and burying of our things is all done. Just as we're getting ready to leave, I catch sight of one of my schoolbooks that in the rush was left out. Now it's too late. What can I do with it? Bring it with me? That's out of the question. Either I'll be laughed at or scolded for my thoughtlessness. Can I hide it somewhere? That's impossible. Just as I bend down to drop it near the fence, I see a flat rock. I lift it and slide the book under it.

I hear my mother's angry call. "What are you doing there tarrying? You're holding us up."

"Nothing, I'm coming." I run to catch up with the others.

We leave for our retreat. The shelter is sheer torture. Millions of buzzing mosquitoes bite us all night long. They won't let us get a moment's rest, not to mention the babies' nonstop screaming, the unbearable damp heat, the hunger and the brackish water that's not even good for a footbath. This misery goes on till daybreak.

In the early afternoon on the opposite bank, we can clearly make out masses of enemy troops, antiaircraft guns and so many tanks you'd surely think they're heading for the battle of Stalingrad.

"Maybe they didn't read the map right and came over here by mistake." It's so absurd; all we can do is burst out laughing.

"We must really rate. They need heavy armor for protection. That shows you how scared they are of the partisan surprise attacks," Petros calls out.

We watch the German armored troops start heading south, but don't have a clue what's going on. Not knowing what's happening is so unbearable. How long will this ordeal last? Are we condemned to remain here for days, months, years? No one knows. That's probably the worst torture.

Bogged down in our misery, shut out from everywhere, we go through one monotonous day after another without any sign of relief. Our plight deepens. We face hunger, sickness, and constant bickering. We can't find salvation anywhere.

"Why did you do that?" yells Maria at her hungry and weary children sniveling on the soggy ground.

"Who said I said so?" shrieks Voula. "Is there a curse on me? Why me all the time?" She moves away to get some peace and quiet, but there's nowhere to hide.

"Do you know, if the enemy strikes, we don't have a single gun to defend ourselves," Petro cries out, furious.

"I know what you mean, we're so helpless, totally at their mercy," I say.

"I feel awful. I wish I could go off and fight in the mountains with the partisans. At least I'd feel I'm doing something. Not just waiting to be massacred." His dark eyes flash.

"Take me with you," I plead.

"You're too little, your mother won't let you."

"Maybe you'll convince her; she listens to you."

"Yeah, sure," he adds with a faint smile.

In a week, we return to the village. We find it in a pitiful state. Some houses are burned to the ground, others pillaged, and those who were found inside were shot down right in front of their homes. The roads are scattered with dead bodies. The stench of burned flesh is unbearable. The lament of the living reaches into the sky.

What pained us most of all was the cruel destruction and the bloodbath at the Zdani monastery.

"It was ravaged!" A passerby tells us, in a voice racked with pain. "What can I tell you? I barely escaped from the claws of the enemy." We listen in a state of shock.

"What happened is more than words can say!" He heaves a deep sigh. "The monastery is gone. Burned to the ground. They didn't even spare the church, the brutes!"

"What?" Mihalis cries out. "That sacred relic of the middle ages. No respect... Unbelievable!"

"What can I say? It's too much."

For a moment I picture the monastery as I knew it, and realize how much we missed the incomparable singing and genial company of *Barba* Lambros.

"And *Barba* Lambros? What happened to him?" I venture a question.

"Oh, my child," he says and looks at me with compassion, sensing my anguish. "He's gone. They shot him in the back," he adds, choking down tears and speechlessly follows the downhill road out of town.

Barba Lambros was killed, just like Kitsos, the hero of his favorite song. Alone, like him, he lost his life without the comfort of mother or friends or even his bandoliers, abandoned along a roadside ditch where he lay covered with blood-red earth. *Barba* Lambros is gone forever from our midst, but his song, echoing in the deep ravines, shall live forever in our hearts.

The fury of the enemy reached a peak as they moved farther inland. They defiled the holy and the human. The innocent were not spared.

Listening to the recounting of their abominable acts, I begin to feel faint and walk in a daze without stopping for a long time. The nightmarish visions refuse to leave me. The moans follow me everywhere. By chance, I pass by the ruins of the house where we lived. It was completely destroyed. All the buried goods were dug up and lay there, turned into a heap of ashes. I hesitate going any closer. Since everything has been burned down, what do I expect? My book is also lost, along with everything else. Another victim among all the others.

Without knowing why, I start moving toward the charred fence standing alone in the barren yard like a black skeleton. I bend down and lift the heavy rock. I see my book. Just as I left it! Only the edge is singed. Nothing else. I pick it up with trembling hands and clutch it in my arms. It's saved! My book is saved! That very same geography book without an outside cover, and the picture of Stockholm, the capital of Sweden, on the first page. Such a distant land, almost nonexistent, as if something out of a dream. But the picture shows the royal castle, regal, enormous, imposing, exactly as I would come to know it many years later.

I turn to leave, carrying the book in my hand, when a plum tree standing by the burnt fence catches my attention. It is in full bloom, its second flowering. The blossoming tree stands next to the gray rock—the very color of the book's first page—near the clearing in the earth that had sheltered my book.

21 WHO SHALL MOURN THE DEAD?

Hunger is a chronic affliction.

"Hunger and the Lord's prayer," as the saying goes, only for us it's a daily worry.

"Click, click," the worry beads in my mother's hand snap, sliding down the twisted cord one by one, mimicking the hollow sound of one more hunger pang added to the constant ache going round and round. Each click a symbol of one less morsel of food, one click after another, endlessly filling my empty stomach with nothingness, to pass the time, to keep from screaming out loud.

"Give us our daily bread..." No longer a rote chant.

I'm constantly on the lookout for any leftover scraps that happen my way, but my mother and my brother Tasio can't take it.

"Look, mommy, they touched the food with snotty fingers," he cries out, clutching his stomach. She turns her head away in disgust.

"Never mind," I tell my mother, "don't let it bother you." But, even when they're starving, it's impossible for them to look the other way, as I've learned to do.

"It makes me nauseous," she complains. "I can't force myself, besides what good would it do?" She looks at me, wan and drained. I get a terrible sinking feeling of hopelessness knowing there's no way of finding a scrap of food for them. Tasio always suffers from bellyaches, and drinks

240

tea until it comes out of his ears. There's nothing else unless one of the goats happens to give birth.

So I go to our neighbor to beg for a smidgen of milk to save him from complete starvation.

"Nikolena," I yell from outside and push open the door, famished to the gills.

"What d'ya want? she calls from the fireplace where she's cooking.

As soon as I enter, the pungent odor of fried leeks draws me there straight as a magnet.

"A drop of milk for my brother, he's sick again." My lips move while my eyes stay riveted on the golden brown pancakes sizzling in the pan.

"Don't be bashful. Come inside and wait a minute, I'm almost finished." She motions with her head toward the frying pan.

I take a small step and stop short, trapped. I can neither stay nor leave to escape from this torture that has set my whole body aflame. Sure I can wait, but how can I endure this agony tormenting my insides?

Nikolena, as the wife of Niko is called in these parts, as though she's not entitled to a name of her own, makes more pancakes—flours them, then pats each one and puts them in the frying pan side by side—totally unmindful of my suffering. They grow big right before my very eyes. The longer I look at the small, perfectly round pancakes the bigger they get, until everything is fused into one gigantic cyclopean eye. All my sensations become merged into one: vision. I've lost all sense of time and place. Just then a hallucinatory hand appears before me. I try to grasp it and feel a warmth in the palm of my hand. Instantly, it hops into my mouth in one swift motion. It's Nikolena's pancake! In one sublime moment I'm transformed from a crea-

241

ture of flesh and bones into a delirium of taste and smell. Tripping lightly into the rosy sunset, I return home carrying a cup of warm milk for my brother Tasio.

"Ruff, ruff, ruff, ruff," the dog's insistent barking arouses me from my deep reverie. That bark is heard all of a sudden, unsettling me. I know not for sure whether I'm fully awake or dreaming. The howling often finds me at the hour when the vision of the Zdani monastery pursues me. I see my dog Boris accompanying me, jumping around the prickly bushes like a coltish deer flashing its shock of white tail. The *Iyoumeno's* smiling face steals in and out of the clouds, and my mother scolds me for looking so insistently. What's holding my attention so? A piercing glance is profoundly disturbing. I don't understand what it's trying to say. I can't find the words to talk. Each time it's the same. No matter how much I try, the letters, correct and in sequence, refuse to form into words. Just as I'm about to articulate them, they get mixed up in my tongue and vanish. Like trying to catch the wind that just disappears through your fingers. She says beautiful words, but they're not the ones I have in mind. How can they change so? When will my words emerge whole and complete, to be rid of her anger? The *Iyoumenos,* always smiling, looks at her with admiration. He pushes aside his cassock to sit on the bench, and then disappears. When I glance in his direction a deep furrow creases my mother's brow, and I'm severely reprimanded. I must go. No one is left. All is silence. Only the barking refuses to stop. It's deafening me.

At the house, Frosini, our landlady's youngest daughter, is waiting to ask me if I want to join her and a group of friends to gather cranberries in the woods.

"Would I ever!"

Sunday morning we set off very early, aprons tied to our waists, to harvest the cranberry bogs. Walking along, we chat amiably, far from the chores and the pressures of so many refugee families squeezed together in one house. A narrow footpath at the edge of the gorge—hardly enough room for the full width of a foot—lies ahead. The talk halts, and one after the other the girls scamper to the opposite side of the slope. My turn is next, but I freeze in my tracks. There's nothing to hold on to, and the steep chasm gapes down below. It makes me dizzy, and I break out in a cold sweat. Terrified, I hear the girls taunting me. I feel so scared and ashamed, my foot slips, and I almost lose my balance. Standing at the rim of the ledge, there's no space to turn. Not unless I can become a tightrope walker and spin around, without paying attention to the danger of falling.

"Come on, come on," the girls screech, impatiently.

"Hurry, hurry," they yell, and start moving away.

What's to become of me, caught here between Scylla and Charybdis? What possessed me to go on this outing? I can do without the stupid cranberries.

"Hey, come on," Frosini turns her head and yells, and finally she turns to join the others. A couple of more steps are left. I take heart and edge a little farther along, and then make a mad dash to put an end to the teasing. She can't stop laughing, but I don't care any more. I go straight into the forest where they're all scattered about, some uphill and others farther down below, to harvest the berry-laden bushes.

Quickly our aprons fill with the red, luscious fruit. All at once, Lenko's thin, strident voice surprises me." Hey, we're leaving."

"O.K., I'm coming." My words echo through the canyon.

I bolt ahead and run straight into a tree branch that snaps off and gets wedged in my eye. The sharp pain roots me to the ground.

Oh, no, I'm blinded! the thought races through my mind. *Now what do I do?* There's no way I can walk through this dense thicket of woods. *Stay here? It's out of the question. Who will ever find me?*

"H-e-e-e-lp!" I shriek. "Wait for me!"

"Come here." I hear from the opposite hilltop.

I can't communicate with them. The pain is getting worse. I cry out again. "HELP! HELP!" Not a sound. Only one thing is left to do. It can't be helped. I grit my teeth and swiftly yank the dry twig sticking out of my eye and at once darkness engulfs me and my eye burns with hot tears. Half-blind, I start walking, covering my eye with one hand and clutching my apronful of cranberries with the other. The treacherous terrain slows me down. Finally, on the small hillock, I run into Stavroula who's still gathering berries for her large family.

"What harm came your way?" she asks, and I tell her.

"You went right into the tree, like a blind fool." She snickers.

"Well, now I'm blinded for good." Bitterness creeps into my voice. "What else could I do?" I never mention my desperate cries for help.

"M-m, how should I know? You figure it out. Anyhow, hurry up. I lost track of the time, and I'm late." I follow, stumbling behind her the rest of the way without us exchanging a single word. We approach the narrow path. I don't even care about the dizzying drop below.

When I get back and my mother notices the shape I'm in, she seems upset, but doesn't show it. "Why is your eye swollen?" She asks in a calm manner. As I unload the berries from my apron, I tell her what happened.

She rushes to the neighbor to ask for an egg to make a poultice that she puts on my bloody eye and covers it with some old rags. For two days I go about one-eyed, trying to ignore the pain. When it doesn't seem to be healing, my mother insists I go to Mokro to see the doctor.

"You can't take a chance on losing your precious eyesight. It's not like fingers where you have nine others," she says. Actually, Petros has to go there also to take care of a bad toothache, so we can go together. It is a chance to kill two birds with one stone, so to speak.

He and I set off before daybreak to avoid the unbearable August midday heat that scorches the valley. My mother just had a bout of malaria, and she's still asleep. I kiss her good-bye, and we leave. Soon the road becomes steep, and we climb steadily toward the forest, chatting along and constantly watching out for snakes. We make it to Mokro, a village that's located near the main highway, in about three and a half hours. At the edge of town I ask someone where the doctor lives and find him without any trouble.

"After that hemorrhaging, you could have lost your eye. You got away with it lightly," the doctor tells me as he examines my eye closely. "You don't need a bandage now. In time your eye will heal completely, don't worry. You almost lost your eye. You were lucky."

Greatly relieved, I go into the market square that is buzzing with people. Petros is already involved in a heated political debate with the locals.

"We must act now, there's no other solution. We can't sit on our haunches and wait for the allies to liberate us."

"If we keep quiet and sit still, the Germans won't hurt us," his opponent objects.

"That's nonsense. The invaders' aim is to crush us to smithereens. You know what the Germans said?" He fixes them with his sharp glance.

"What?" the peasants ask in unison.

"They would deprive you of the very air you breathe, if they could." He makes a cutthroat motion.

They all listen, spellbound.

When Petros sees me in the crowd, he interrupts his discussion and tells me, "Let's go and get something to eat."

Just then a villager runs panting toward the crowd.

"What? What d'ya say?" I overhear someone asking in alarm. "Germans? They're here?"

Petros and I just look at each other and start running like rabbits.

"Boom, boom, boom." Cannons roar across the road. *"Bang, bang."* Shots burst in the air overhead. We quickly abandon the main road to head for the fields.

Lambent light, spasmodic explosions of machine guns, shimmering yellow-green fields, and flower-bedecked meadows with the intoxicating aroma of gold-studded white crocuses, everything in that fleeting moment acts in concert. All parts of me unified into one single-minded purpose, the need for escape. Each nerve fiber guides the brain to targeted action—a deer with an eagle's eyes—together, mind and body obey the command of a cosmic force: the continuity of life. I glide unaware with feather-light movements through a cloud of bullets, to reach the unharvested golden wheat fields gently swaying in the wind. All around me hand grenades burst, bullets whistle with an insane fury. I run with the sensation that somehow my steps are in tune with Petros'—a comrade in our common struggle against a relentless pursuit. The dense wheat fields—our allies in the unequal battle—shield us from full view while we run left and right to avoid the torrent of enemy fire chasing us at every turn. If only we can enter the expanse of sky-high cornfields ahead, maybe...we can hide, maybe...wild hope. Every obstacle in the path of the expedition is swept aside. I offer myself to the altar of life for life.

The demonic fury gradually fades into the mountain serenity, confirming that we're no longer being pursued.

"Petro," I call out softly, still frightened, "how will we go back now?"

"We can take a shortcut down below, somewhere over there, I think." He takes a deep breath.

"We have to get back before the Germans reach Tranovalto." I pant.

"Yeah, our folks won't go into hiding without us."

I know that, of course. If we don't make it back in time, there'll be mayhem. That fear ignites both of us into action. We figure it should take us a couple of hours, but we're not sure, and we head toward the opposite mountain. After we scurry down the rugged mountainside and trudge uphill to reach the top, we discover another, taller, mountain ahead of us. The August sun burns like an inferno. The earth, so long without rain, is scorched. Not a drop of water anywhere. My mouth is parched. The low bushes constantly grip my only remaining good dress—white organdy with faint lilac violets and tiny pale chartreuse leaves—that buttons down the front, trimmed with a darker violet. It's too tight, but I still love it. I remember the first time I wore it before the war. I walked bent over to hide my hardly visible breasts and not be embarrassed. Now, all tattered from the thorns and brambles, it's shredding to bits and pieces.

Going uphill we approach a woodsy knoll but there, too, the fountains are dry.

"If we weren't in such a rush to get back, we could rest a little in the shade to cool off," Petros sighs.

"We have no time," I mumble, and I can feel my tongue sticking to the roof of my mouth.

We climb up in silence. The words have also run dry. Nearing the end of our climb, we scramble to the top, hoping to see the valley stretched out below, but no such luck. Another mountain up ahead rears its head.

"This is getting to be too much," Petro exclaims in exasperation.

"How long is this mountain range? When we started it looked like one mountain," I complain.

It's as though the land is playing tricks on us. Petros' uneasy glance mirrors mine—the fear that we try to hide from each other.

"Let's go, they're waiting for us," he urges in a dry voice.

Using the sun as a compass, we follow a zigzag path for a while, then descend toward what looks like a stream down below, hoping to find water. We head forward at a faster pace and pick up speed. Suddenly a crackling sound makes us both jump up.

"It's a rabbit; don't get scared, now." Petros, deathly pale, clears his throat.

"As long as it's not a wild wolf." I feign indifference, and he can't help letting out a laugh.

The noise is heard again more clearly and an old mangy shepherd dog comes out of the bushes followed by an aging goatherd.

"Whatcha doin' here?" he asks, coming up to level ground and leaning on his staff, ready to listen.

"We're dying of thirst," Petros says.

"Go over there, you'll find crystal clear, cool water." He points ahead.

Renewed hope spurs us on to find the spring. We scramble down the path, waving hurried thanks. Not a sign of it. *Will we ever find it?* I wonder, but keep the worry to myself. At last we discover the liquid treasure nestled in a shady grove and drink to our hearts' content. Refreshed, we reach the valley in about another hour, as the goatherd told us.

Not a soul is stirring in the middle of the swampland. A terrible, sunlit stillness envelops us. From time to time, the slowly moving air hisses through the green corn that sways with a lethargic motion; each movement changes the stick-like stalks into strange shapes. The murky bogs here absorb, there reflect the midday light. Further away we catch a glimpse of the hillside road leading to Mokro. Any minute now the German troops will be marching down there, heading straight toward us. From time to time I catch myself glancing in that direction. In the valley's vast expanse, danger walks side by side with us. The agony of every passing minute is an eternity. *Will we find our folks? Are they alive or dead?*

When we reach the outskirts of Tranovalto, I can feel my heart stuck in my parched throat. The cannons are booming in the mountains, and most of the people have already left. Here and there small clusters of villagers can be seen adjusting an animal's load and hurrying away. Some stop to put their weeping children on their back, and everyone runs to escape from the enemy's clutches.

Petros and I are immediately enlisted in the effort to escape. The donkey died some time ago, so we each have to make three separate trips carrying stuff to the shelter. The sun is setting behind the hills when, at long last, we settle down. Occasionally, a cannon burst is heard in the far away mountain. The little ones, thoroughly exhausted, eat a quick bite with their eyes half closed as their elders sit nearby on a tree stump or the bare ground. I look for a quiet corner to rest my weary feet, but before I have a chance, Ted and I are sent to the valley to fill the earthenware jugs. Darkness descends swiftly. When we reach the lake, the pale sliver of moonlight is reflected in the ochre-green water. Every now and then, it catches in its orbit the frogs jumping in midair, making their backs glisten before they plop and disappear in the water's silvery concentric circles. The flat, empty fields magnify every little sound of our heavy footsteps into a loud boom that sends a shiver up and down my spine. We dare not even whisper, fully aware that if there's a sudden surprise attack, we have nowhere to escape, nowhere to hide. The agony is unbearable, the road endless.

At last, we return to the eerie quiet of the campsite. I quickly put down the jugs and lie down to go to sleep. This chore was the last straw after the long day's trek. But sleep refuses to come. I feel a tormenting pain in what used to be my legs. What are left of them are two shriveled stumps attached to my body with searing pain. I lie there totally helpless. Immobilized. Thin, spider-woven wires that send waves of electric shock straight to my head now, connect these two dry sticks, disabled and useless to me. I watch part of my body dying before my very eyes, unable to do anything to save it. I start weeping. For the first and only time I shed bitter tears all night long, dreading that I will never be able to walk again in my life. The unbearable torture keeps me awake until the moon disappears in the nightmarish light of dawn. At daybreak the enemy guns resume their cannonade, resounding in the mountains. Heavy artillery fires repeated rounds of ammunition that sound closer and closer. Before long, hordes of German troops descend from the hills opposite us. Now and then bayonets reflect a steel-cold, piercing light, followed by heavy barrages of cannon fire that blast the land.

In this attack, the enemy uses tactics of lies and deceit to mislead the unsuspecting villagers with promises of goodwill and safety, provided all adult men show up when the Germans arrive. Otherwise everyone will be sent to the death squad. So the trusting country folk are convinced that the Germans are only after provisions, livestock and evidence that the able-bodied men have not joined the partisans. It's worth it, they think, in return for saving their lives, their homes, and their livestock. They have nothing to fear. They're safe, they think. The seventeen village elders agree to the plan and welcome the German troops with open arms, offering them food supplies from their latest crop. They bow down low, making submissive declarations that none of their townspeople have anything to do with the partisan army. Which is true. A few older women dart back and forth carrying eggs for them to create the impression of normal activity.

As soon as the Germans grab whatever the trusting villagers offer them, they ravage everything, living or not. Women who refuse to leave their homes are burned alive right in front of their menfolk, who watch in complete shock. As I enter the village, I see Stavroula, a hemiplegic woman who hobbled around leaning on her walking stick, slain like an animal lying dead in the middle of the street clutching her cane, hand carved by her older son.

Kiriaki, heavy with child, her belly running out ahead of her, tried escaping to the fields where she was disemboweled and died clinging to her yet unborn child. Many others were killed in the hills and the valley. All the homes, even the poor church, are burned.

The villagers who stay to welcome the enemy troops were all taken hostage and after an arduous march, were ordered to dig their own mass grave and stand there for hours awaiting execution. Everybody, save one, was shot down by Bren guns and dumped in the grave by their fellow villager, Niko. Then, Nikolena's husband was taken at gunpoint and used as a guide through the remote, winding mountain cliffs. Just as the Germans were about to reach the familiar, more heavily trafficked road leading to the highway, Niko sensed that he, too, would be shot now that he was of no further use to the enemy. Niko jumps from one cliff top to another and makes a hair raising escape under the steady bombardment of enemy gunfire.

"It was a miracle, how I escaped," he gasps, gulping mouthfuls of air. "Words can't tell what my eyes have seen."

From him we also learn that it was somebody from Paliocastro who had betrayed his own people.

"I was disgusted. The scum, didn't even deserve a dirty look," he says, spitting on the ground. "I recognized him, though, I've seen him around on market day. Shame on him, and he has two sons. What will they learn?" He fumes in anger.

"The Germans said they wouldn't burn our village or kill us. They tricked us."

We listen, speechless.

"We're ruined. Disaster hit our village. No men are left alive. They were caught in a vicious trap. The women..." he muffles a sob. "Who's left? Who'll mourn the dead?" he laments, choking back his tears. "I'm heading for the mountains to join the freedom fighters. I'm not staying here to be slaughtered like a sheep. May the memory of the dead last forever."

22   LOZIANI

It's mid September of 1943 and the hot midday sun still burns like a furnace. The frogs croak carefree, inviting with their monotonous call their chosen lady-frog who waits impatiently at the edge of the marsh to join in orgiastic love-making. We pass them by, indifferent to that passionate confession being displayed as we cross the swampy valley, after Tranovalto's total destruction, to find shelter elsewhere like modern-day wandering Jews.

We head for Loziani to seek a new homeland, not knowing what awaits us in that godforsaken place, a village high in the Hasia mountain crest. The uphill road adds to our burden.

We trudge forward, ignoring our fatigue, and stop only briefly to cool off in the shade of the pine trees lining the difficult, tortuous road, constantly worried about getting caught in a surprise enemy attack.

The twisting and turning along the dense, winding path seems endless until, all at once, we get a glimpse of Loziani, a charming, solitary village built on a steep mountainside. Strands upon strands of hanging gardens full of fruit-bearing trees cascade among the towering hemlocks like maypole garlands. Every turn brings into view more orchards and vineyards burgeoning with sun ripened fruit of all kinds: golden-hued peaches, oval-shaped, green and yellow plums, ruby-red apples. We devour them with our eyes and by the time we come close we can't take it any longer, and we snatch a fuzzy-skinned peach from the tree, greedily sinking our teeth into the juicy flesh. But, a bunch of sharp-witted village kids playing nearby starts yelling at the top of their lungs as soon as they spot us.

"Ma, ma, look, look," they yell, losing no time in broadcasting the news that strangers are looting their harvest. The womenfolk hurry outside to find out why the little rascals are shouting their heads off.

Caught in the act, my mother turns sideways, a little flustered. "Oh, well, come what may. Along with everything else." She drops the fruit pit from her hand but, luckily, we got away with it thanks to their kindness.

"Oh, so you're the refugees! Hungry, eh?" one of the boys' mothers laughs good-naturedly.

"Go on, take what you want," the other women tell us. They watch us with amazement devouring the fruit like a pack of summer locusts.

"Just look at them! Like they've never seen the stuff before in their lives!" Another woman laughs heartily.

The village hasn't been molested by enemy attacks yet, and the people seem so carefree.

In the village square, the partisan housing committee takes charge of arranging shelter for us. A local government, headed by members of the resistance movement who organized committees to help the villagers and refugees with their everyday needs, now carries out village activities. The committee soon finds a place for my mother, Tasio and me, Aunts Chrysie and Pelagia, and Petro and Ted to stay.

We all climb up to the next terraced elevation and reach Deligiorgo's house. To get inside we must first pass through the barn full of animals: goats, pigs, donkeys, chickens and a mule. Up above on the landing stand two well-built girls standing with eyes lowered, and further back three skinny boys cling to their mother, Giorgena. We go into our room that faces the densely shaded canyon surrounded by heavily laden chestnut and oak trees. We set up house with a half-burnt pot, a couple of badly scratched enamel dishes, a few spoons, and a crooked knife.

The wounds from the bloodbath of Tranovalto are still raw and painful. We weep bitterly for the senseless loss of so many people, but gradually the old suffering gives way to some serenity. At least we're saved from the attack that we were afraid was going to happen.

I figure this is a good time to broach again the subject of enlisting in the partisan army, but my mother is still adamant. She won't even hear of it, insisting that I'm too young.

"Not too young to be killed, though, huh? At least when you carry a gun on your shoulder, you can defend yourself. Like this you're at the mercy of getting killed or dying of starvation," I protest with the fervor of righteous indignation.

"I will not hear of it. Forget it," she answers, unbending.

In that case, I decide to join the emergency rescue squad that's being organized for the sick and wounded freedom fighters. On this point I won't relent. The partisans are giving their lives to defend our freedom, and we must help. It's the least we can do. She agrees provided I go only as far as the outskirts of town, but no farther. I take off with the thrill of victory to go to the training exercises, which for security reasons are always held at different locations. I sing with irrepressible enthusiasm as I climb the tall peaks, feeling a sensation of fullness and freedom each time I inhale deeply the fresh mountain air that fills my lungs to the bursting point. My singing gets louder and louder with each uphill step. There's no stopping me until I reach the top.

I spend most afternoons with the cultural arm of the youth liberation movement that asked me to teach the elementary school children the three R's. Ever since the Albanian war, they've had no classes because the local teacher was killed in the war, then the government kept delaying giving the necessary funds for a new one. Finally, the school closed down after the German occupation. It seems odd, at first, that I'm teaching young children when I haven't even finished sixth grade myself but, the minute I set eyes on those eager-looking, restless youngsters growing up unlettered, I'm sold on the idea.

A bunch of about twenty children gather around in a makeshift school where I go everyday after the training exercises. Books, pencils, note pads, even paper are unheard of, so we make do with a moth-eaten blackboard that could barely stand upright. Using poetry, stories, and songs, day by day the children start developing some sense of the chicken scratches we call letters. Before long their appetite is whetted, and they can't get enough. They put their noses to the grindstone and, proud as strutting peacocks, tell their parents they can read and write their own names. The darkness of illiteracy soon begins to give way to the light of achievement.

Besides the many and significant political goals, the cultural branch of the liberation movement begins to organize educational lectures, poetry recitations, theatrical sketches, folk songs and dances, even the traditional shadow play, Karagiozi—that character who bumbles his way through all sorts of improbable situations that give him a chance to display his inimitable flair for folk wisdom. These activities arouse not only the young generation, but also all the people who thirst for cultural enlightenment.

In these difficult times, the symbolic portrayal of the epic struggle for freedom, the Revolution of 1821 reveals its close ties to the present liberation movement. The older village youth are inspired to write a theatrical play about that glorious heritage that is a bold vision, especially keeping in mind that only a short while ago the peasant youth didn't even have an inkling about that period of our history. With single-minded devotion to the traditions and heroic feats of 1821, the young people create a vision of the past, using the knowledge they just acquired. They portray the brutal enslavement and oppression by the Turks, who occupied our land for close to four hundred fifty years, massacred our people, destroyed sacred churches, and erected foreign places of worship. These atrocities inspired Lord Byron to a fiery protest that stirred the consciousness of the entire world. In a patriotic battle cry against tyranny, the Greek people performed feats of inimitable valor and vowed then, as we are doing now, never to allow ourselves to be held in bondage by foreign oppressors. Never. Our ancestors raised high the banner of freedom and wrote new pages of glory and honor in the annals of our history, pages which have become part of our national inner voice and propelled us to greater heights.

The anniversary of the liberation movement of 1821 is anticipated with great excitement. We've been practicing for a special celebration with a program that includes poetry readings, a play and, of course, revolutionary songs.

The stage performance of the youth group resounds with the *klepht* songs of resistance that bring to life days of revolution and struggle by the unforgettable heroes and heroines of 1821: Papaflessas, the man of the cloth who brandished his sword in battle against the enemy, Karaiskakis, Bouboulina, Kolokotronis, Miaoulis, Rigas Feraios, among so many others. Those were the times when the unbowed Souliotisses women carrying their infants in their arms jumped to their death in the Zalongos dance, rather than be captured alive by the Turks, as they sang in one voice, with but a single heartbeat, a clarion call to freedom:

Fish live-not on land,
Nor flowers in sand,
Nor do the Souliotisses
Live without freedom.

Within such fervor of artistic creativity, I come to know and admire the words of the renowned poet Kosta Varnali, especially his poem "The Doomed."

"In the underground taverna....," begins Varnalis' poem. As I read it for the first time, it brings to life haunting images of the depth of human tragedies being played out in dark, dank, underground hovels—unknown to me until then. Standing tall and proud, I recite Varnalis' poem, and the crowd bursts into a rousing round of applause, showering me with feelings of love for our country that lift me to towering heights.

In the struggle for freedom from the oppression of the occupation, the words of the poet reflect his rich creative endowment as well as the drama of his times that his work symbolizes. He talks of the futile, wasted lives of the downtrodden—locked into hopelessness and futility—who desperately struggle to be released from the dark forces of inhumanity and social injustice. The poem expresses the deep-seated hope of people for a better, more just life for all.

Concluding that lively recitation of our country's history, I appear as mother Greece, my hands chained, my hair in two golden braids crowned with branches of myrtle, my gown a long, flowing, faded blue nightdress of my mother's that by chance survived until now. Taking slow, measured steps I come to center stage just as the partisans arrive to break the chains of bondage and liberate Greece. Triumphantly, the crowd bursts into song, chanting in unison the revolutionary hymn to Liberation.

> *Thunder in Olympos, lightning in Giona,*
> *cannons roar, the earth shakes.*
> *To arms, to arms, forward in battle*
> *for our precious freedom.*
> *Our fists are steel, our souls aflame...*

Those words echo from one corner to another, as young and old embrace in the midst of stifled cries and tearful eyes that nurture the flame of freedom in their hearts, and in their minds, the brave quest for the road to world peace and salvation.

Villagers from near and far—peasants wearing lice-infested, home-spun shepherd's wool capes—stand up in the hall as the *Ode to Freedom* echoes from one corner of that spit of land to the other, and emotion is written all over their wind-carved faces as the program ends with the National Anthem.

The people of this region embraced the liberation movement slowly, gradually, as they learned to cultivate and love their clod of earth: guarding it like a precious treasure that needs to be preserved and protected at all costs. After being trampled on and mercilessly killed by the Nazis, the peasants discover a newfound determination to break loose from their chains of bondage. Stirred out of their centuries-old conservatism, they mobilize solidly behind the freedom fighters, giving them their armed and unarmed support, providing them with food, shelter, and first aid for the wounded.

For a long time they stubbornly refused to face the new reality, believing the occupation was just another passing phase of the war, a midsummer thunderstorm that in time would clear up, like so many others before. They know from years of experience that human beings are unable to withstand for very long such an awesome force of nature and, eventually, depleted, they succumb to it. Tenaciously they held fast to their old beliefs, waiting patiently for things to change of their own accord. Their compromise with the familiar old world was finally shattered, their complacent false sense of security crushed when they saw with their own eyes the ominous danger that threatened them with extinction.

These villagers—who for generations have been linked to the cultivation of their land—are now offering their resources and their strength that for centuries has been nurtured by the earth. The hatred of the country folk for the oppressors was not born instantly. It matured slowly, with effort, out of their suffering. In time it was transformed into an active participation in the struggle for liberation that developed into an unshakable faith, an unquenchable fury for revenge. They learned first hand about the enemy's intent to deceive them, to use subterfuge to undermine the very fabric of their life, to extinguish the Greek people from the face of the earth. They join the revolutionary forces, fighting with courage and bravery in the front lines. Gone were their reservations, their doubts. Finally the fruition of the peasants' determination comes into its own.

Eventually what spurred them to action was when they realized that they must take their fate in their own hands. The seeds sown by Bishop Seraphim's words have taken root. They see with their own eyes that the partisans are spilling their own blood to save their country. They watch them coming down the mountains, hungry, feet bloodied by the holes in their tattered boots, sometimes injured, always dog tired after sleepless nights of constant fighting in ravines, on hilltops, in freezing cold or sweltering heat—yet they never complain. The freedom fighters' dedication and altruism spur the shepherds and country farmers to minister to them, to heal their wounds, to encourage them to continue their struggle against such an overpowering enemy, a battle between David and Goliath. But the soul soars high and hope is revived for a new beginning.

Here in Loziani we're completely cut off from the outside world and recent military developments since the radio, along with almost everything else, was destroyed during one of the attacks at Tranovalto. I remember the excitement when we heard the announcement in one of the last news reports from Moscow about the opening of the third front.

"At last! The third front is open," Mihalis, the tax collector shouted. "See, it wasn't so hard."

"So why did the Allies delay until now?" Kostis, the teacher asked, furrowing his thick, closely knit brows. "We've been suffering for no reason all this time."

Delirious, everybody caught up in the frenzy of the moment, tossed their hats in the air, danced around like crazy, gesticulating wildly, as ecstatic as though victory was staring them in the face. *"Zito, zito,"* they shouted, "Long live the Allies!"

"The end of the war is a matter of days, a week at the most," the optimists insisted, while the pessimists declared that "this war business will take years by the time the big wheels find an end to all the mess they stirred up." To many the obstacles seemed formidable.

"It doesn't look like it will end so fast. You'll see. That is, if we live that long," a villager called out bitterly.

Now, we have to wait for a passer-by to bring us some news that might just be gossip. It depends on who brings it and where he got it. Without a radio, reliable news is hard to come by.

Our everyday life faces another war—the war on lice. Lice are an indispensable part of the peasants' existence. They believe not only that they were born with them, but also that they're good for you and your health, especially for the circulation. "In the morning when you get up," they are fond of explaining, "you shake your homespun clothes you've been sleeping in two or three times to get rid of the itching. This wakes up your blood and your soul comes to its rightful place for the rest of the day," thanks to the beneficial effects of those little critters that squirmed all over your body the night before. This is what the locals also told the doctor from the health department some years back when he visited to investigate the typhoid fever epidemic that periodically decimated them. It was impossible for him to convince them otherwise.

Lice are the legacy that we have also inherited. It has become part and parcel of our everyday existence, a part we constantly try to be rid of, an onerous yoke we try to escape. We wage war on those tiny repulsive insects, fighting them with "fury and fire" every morning and every night. The same old tune from daybreak to sunset. Inspection and more inspection: a constant search for that minuscule enemy that always keeps us on the alert, in the woolen clothes because that's where they can easily weasel into, crawling between the warp and woof of the dense fabric, burrowing deftly in the seams of dresses, pants, everywhere—they don't discriminate. It's an unrelenting war to try and ferret them out. So much for the fury. As for the fire, that comes next. We throw them in the fireplace where they burst and crackle, pak, pak, pak, pak. We compete with our fellow-sufferers to see who will be the first to gain some relief from the maddening itching. Then comes the phase of mutual cooperation. We scratch like monkeys that spend endless hours grooming each other's skulls, mimicking our primate ancestors, poring over strands of hair until finally we're rid of them, for a little while at least. Soon enough though, the devilish critters repopulate us, selecting first the preferred area, the kinky hair covering our private parts. Then little by little they occupy every part of our bodies to the point where we're unable to sit still from the itching. The lice kingdom is re-established as though we have never been liberated from them at all, and warfare starts all over again.

Yet, when I wake up every morning with a song on my lips, I try to drown out the sorrows in the hum of a cheerful tune, to gaze upon the rose, avoiding the thorns. It's something that springs full-blown inside, like a ship in full sail. The village women love to listen. I open the window to air the bedclothes and there they are, with their suckling babies in their arms and their knitting so they won't sit idle. They take their post downstairs where they can hear better while all the time I'm busy sweeping and straightening up the room.

"Hey, what a daughter you have, she has a golden voice. Why don't you ever stop to listen to her?" they pause to ask my mother.

"Have I any time to listen to singing with all the worries in my head?" she replies, walking away.

The big war continues unrelenting, and the German attacks never stop. The aim of the invaders is to squeeze every last ounce of provisions from the already depleted land for their upkeep. As the war progresses without a decisive victory for them, they press on with greater ferocity, stocking up on cattle and food supplies not only for their own army but also for the legions of men hired from the other occupied countries that suffer under the Nazi-fascist helm. The enemy makes frequent expeditions into the hinterland, where they exterminate thousands upon thousands of innocent men, women and children who happen to be in their way.

Whenever the partisans engage them in battle to slow down the operation of their war machinery, echoes of the fighting reach us. A panting runner from the neighboring village crosses the mountain to bring us the urgent message that we are in danger of an enemy raid. The last time it happened, we immediately gathered our meager belongings, ready to leave at the crack of dawn when the enemy is expected to arrive in our village. We are so terrified; we stay up till daybreak, anxious that they could attack suddenly in the night. To our great relief they never come, maybe because of a heavy snow storm or for some other reason unknown to us It is only after we hear that there is no further danger that we begin moving around freely, but with heavy hearts because in nearby Deskati there was great suffering. Dozens of innocent people were butchered mercilessly, falling victims to raw atrocities, pillaging, fire, and violence that had never been seen before...

The battle-weary partisans trek in after the fierce fighting ends, carrying the dead and wounded on stretchers, on the backs of animals or on their shoulders, dragging their bleeding feet. Thin, pale, lips parched, eyes on fire, moaning in pain and fever, they languish in a makeshift first-aid station. You see beardless boys, well-built youths, and full-grown gray-haired men lying on a clump of straw like fallen oak trees. The first-aid station, the only one in the entire region, takes care of the injured and sick until they are well enough to be transported by stretcher to the surgery—a distance of four or five hours—where the doctor is stationed. The more lightly wounded are treated just long enough to get them back on their feet and then sent back to their units for combat duty. "They're good lads who never complain," say the old timers, proudly. "They're spilling their own blood to save us." The villagers can see that the *andartes* fight the Germans without respite in ravines, on mountaintops, in freezing cold or sweltering heat and they do whatever they can to help them. At such times, of course, the school has to close to provide all the possible help to those in need of nursing care and to deliver supplies to the partisans.

With the exception of bad weather that surely gives the impression of winter—the snowstorms, the freezing cold, the skeletons of trees silhouetted against the gray sky—days come and go unnoticed. Neither holidays nor festivities change the drab color of our life. We mark the passing of time by the growing meagerness of our food supply that can't be replenished with the new crop for a long while. Except for horse chestnuts, that are still plentiful. Petros, Ted and I gather them by the bucketful, and the pigs devour them in no time flat.

"Go on, try one," Petros urges me.

I decide to do just that to calm down my hunger pangs and satisfy my curiosity. *What have I got to lose? I'll take a bite and if I don't like it I'll spit it out. Simple.* So I try one, but it's not what I expect at all. I try in vain to rid myself of the awful taste, rapidly swallowing my own saliva to clear my mouth of the burn on my tongue, but it catches in my throat and won't go away.

That night everyone goes to bed early. Only I can't sleep. I twist and turn for a long time before quieting down. Suddenly, I jump up with a sharp bellyache, as though I've swallowed a live cobra and now it spirals around and around, biting my insides, spreading its poison in endless circles. The pain is killing me. In the middle of the frozen night I have to scurry down to the ravine since the houses have neither indoor nor outdoor toilet facilities. I hurry back to warm up but, before I have half a chance to lie down, another, more painful spasm, forces me to go outside again, although I can't stand the thought of that ferocious north wind blowing like a maniac. I hurry back and as soon as I open the door, the misty warm air of the manger smelling of the breath of animals penetrates my nostrils, and I feel comforted by the tender homeliness of the beasts lying about. I envy them, nestled in the straw and wish I could just lie by their side, but the pain won't leave me alone. Another trip to the edge of the ravine nearly gets me blown away by a gust of wind blowing at gale force. Back inside once more, I try to climb the stairs and break into a cold sweat. I barely manage to crouch doubled over on the bottom step and grit my teeth to muster enough courage to face the frozen canyon once more. I force myself to climb two more steps, biting my lips hard to make sure the others aren't awakened. *They can't help, so why disturb them? I may just as well go it alone.* That's what I figure until a dysentery attack hits me when I'm all by myself outside, too late to call anyone from so far away. Darkness surrounds me everywhere. Trapped in the marrow-numbing chill of the night, I drag myself to and from the accursed ravine countless times, without ever reaching the door. Forlorn and lonely, I wonder, *Why am I always so concerned about sparing others trouble at my own expense?* Now, ready to collapse, no one comes to my rescue.

I shiver all over, as much from the cold as from the fear that they'll find me in the ditch half naked, frozen to death. That terror makes me crawl back as a dull moon—cold, metallic in the steel-gray sky—fitfully appears between the clouds that are scattered by the harsh north wind. My body, crushed under the blows of the storm raging within, struggles to reach the icy, damp doorstep, like a weather-beaten ship on a frozen coast.

The instant I hit the ground floor, tormenting images plague me. They hound me, convulsing my limbs in the dismal darkness. Gigantic, windblown waves rise and fall from the black skies down to the dark depths of the sea where I reel all alone from dizziness with nothing to hold onto, wallowing in the mud among obscene writhing sharks that send their long fins to siphon off those last remaining drops of dried up, purple blood stuck in my veins. From afar, a vicious octopus spreads its huge tentacles to the end of the deep cliff that sways up and down, turning my stomach, drawing me to the bottom of the well that sucks me up in one single gulp, spewing a deep green bile that disgorges crooked, black burning corals. Cerberus leers satanically in the distance. Slowly the beast sinks under a purple rock bed and disappears into a vast nothingness.

"Hey, there." The landlady shakes me, rolling me over to put me on some dung-smelling straw that she gathers from within arm's reach. In a minute she returns with a heavy blanket and lifts my head to put a few drops of some potion on my parched lips. Shaking all over, I struggle to say something, but my voice is gone. I collapse on the ground looking at her with my mouth gaping wide open. I wonder if my eyes show her how gratefully I accept her offering or are they, also, too exhausted? Giorgena, with such great tenderness in her eyes, shows me that she understands everything and covers me to let me sleep. I can feel her warmth holding me close, lulling me to sleep.

The nightmarish dreams have ended.

23 STORMED BY NIGHT

A curious silence falls over the village square. Bishop Seraphim, the acclaimed spiritual leader of the liberation movement in northern Greece, emerges through the fog with a group of partisan chiefs, heading toward the first-aid station.

"Greetings, comrades and friends," the voice of Bishop Seraphim resounds, as a group of villagers and refugees rush over to welcome him.

His once tranquil brow is furrowed, accentuating the gaunt look from hunger and suffering on his face, which brings to mind one of the martyrs on a Byzantine icon more than the leader of modern-day mountain fighters. Only his eyes have retained their former brilliance, intensifying his piercing gaze. His looks clearly reveal his concern with the enormous responsibilities that he has assumed and the burdensome problems weighing him down every day, knowing their solution is largely beyond his control.

When he enters the first-aid station his presence is felt at once, and the sound of his voice arouses mortally wounded men.

"My sons," his still sonorous voice intones, "you are fighting for our freedom. You are defending one of the greatest virtues of life with your own. Your contribution is needed as much today as on the very first day you took up arms to save our troubled land that is struggling for survival under the most brutal tyranny in the world, the Nazi-

269

fascist Axis. We are awaiting your return to the front to fight by our side until we are victorious."

Bishop Seraphim greets them, asking every one a few questions before moving on to the next. He gives each man a handshake, and adds, "I wish you a speedy recovery. You are in good hands. Until we meet again," he says, and heads toward the village square.

Womenfolk and men, young and old come to hear him talk. His inspired words transform that small, insignificant corner of the earth to a fiery nucleus of revolutionary fervor and, for a moment, erase from the care-worn faces of those poor people the misery, the hunger, the illnesses, the troubles. They may not always understand every word he says, but the electrifying spark of his glance, his dynamic voice, fill them up with new energy that animates, that stirs them, urging them on to greater feats, to nobler ideals.

Joined by the *Iyoumenos* David who enlisted in the partisan army after the monastery of Zdani was burned down, Bishop Seraphim gladly accepts our invitation to share our evening meal. We have not seen the *Iyoumeno* since we left Tranovalto where he came periodically to visit us. His presence was always a welcome change from the drab refugee existence. He brought an occasional offering of food for the sick and the desperately needy, but most of all his smile and willingness to share his company with us for a while was something out of the ordinary, a small oasis in the sterile desert of the harrowing reality that undermined my mother's health worst of all.

For the guests we prepare some boiled potatoes and some beans saved from Tranovalto, the same food we have been eating for months now, and it's practically gone. What a wonderful surprise when our next door neighbor, Yiannis, a rather stocky man with curly brown hair and a long swirling mustache, brings us a piece of salted pork.

"A gift for the Bishop Seraphim," he says shyly to my mother, who hastens to add the offering to the pot of boiling food.

We haven't seen meat for months. And I more than the others because when my pet goat Malamo was killed—that's what my family did, no amount of talk that "she is sick and has to go," could have convinced me otherwise—I refused to put a single bite in my mouth, regardless of how starved I was. Their words were just a trick to fool me. Just the thought of eating made my insides churn.

"Go on, eat," they insisted. Their insensitivity had no bounds. "You'll starve to death if you carry on like this," they urged me, but I wouldn't hear of it.

I couldn't bear another word of deception. The longer I thought of that bitter hour when I heard Malamo's pitiful braying as they dragged her to be slain, the stronger my rage welled up inside me. She kept pulling on the rope and begged me with her eyes to save her. Even animals sense when their end is near.

I stood there, as much a victim as she. If I could, I would have gone far, far away where I couldn't see, I couldn't hear, I couldn't remember Malamo's haunting last glance.

Within days, another major enemy attack forced us to run into hiding from Tranovalto. Even when our lives were in danger, the vision of my loving, loyal, and beautiful pet Malamo followed me everywhere.

"Do you think we know if we'll survive?" Ted told me in a low voice, putting his arm over my shoulder. "For all we know, tomorrow will be our turn."

Somehow, his words softened the blow of my torment.

When our guests arrive that night in Loziani, as we do every night, we gather around the fireplace that casts the only light in the room. Our discussion with the Bishop Seraphim and the *Iyoumenos* David starts with the opening of the third front in 1943 and then moves on to other important developments in the European and African war efforts.

"I don't know, but to me the situation still looks very bad, Your Grace. How long do you think the war will continue?" my mother asks in a strained voice that lets her apprehension surface.

"What I can tell you in complete confidence, without going into specific details, of course, is that we are at the doorstep of new significant developments that will prove decisive for our anti-fascist struggle. Everything depends on our negotiations with representatives of the Allied troops. That will determine the outcome of the war effort. We face not one, but many enemies, including our own quislings who constantly threaten our every move, and we must exercise great caution," the Bishop says, stroking his beard.

"We heard that lately our partisans have been sabotaging many enemy installations," I say, firing a swift look at him.

"You see," the pensive *Iyoumenos* adds, "we're going through a transitional period, and it's obvious that outmoded social institutions are collapsing. Naturally, there is a great deal of instability, but the future belongs to us. I hope the young people will rebuild a new society on a better foundation."

We set the low *sofra* table and sit cross-legged on the floor around the hearth to enjoy this beautiful moment when from a distance the night air fills with the voice of the *telali*. The herald is making some vague sounds that remind us of Vangeli's melodious chanting in church, but our attention

272

is fixed on the fragrant food. The conversation continues as the town crier's voice drifts in louder and louder.

"Something about the other neighborhood caught my ear," Aunt Chrysie says, putting the last couple of stitches in the stocking she's mending before we start to eat.

We each take fork in hand, ready to pounce on the food. Our impatience is at its peak. The insistent droning of the *telali* continues. Then, almost under our window, the voice of Vangeli, the town crier and cantor, is heard clearly.

"The Germans are co-o-o-ming! Everyone must leave!" he bellows in a loud voice.

The *Iyoumenos* jumps straight up, like an arrow, helps the Bishop get on his feet, they say a hurried "good night" and leave. Their distinctive footsteps can be heard going downhill. The *telali* momentarily stops to exchange a few words with them, and then they disappear in the night.

"The partisans order everyone," the town crier continues, "to leave immediately."

The smell of the steaming hot food, still sitting in the blackened pot by the flickering light of the fireplace, penetrates our nostrils and we look at each other, holding our forks in midair.

"No one is allowed to stay in the village," the voice rings out and gets farther away.

"Open the window wide so we can find out what's going on," my mother calls out. "What's happened to you? Are you all numb?"

Petros runs downstairs and comes back panting to tell us that the partisans have issued an announcement that it is mandatory for everyone to leave town, without exception. They're afraid of another mass slaughter like the last one.

A special partisan unit will stay to guard the village from pillagers, he blurts out in one breath.

Only then do we force ourselves to get up, because our eyes are still glued to the pot and, reluctantly, we start gathering our bed covers, a little flour we have left, and a handful of salt. We head for the road leading to the mountains carrying the still-hot casserole by the handle, like holy myrrh.

The bad tidings spread like a shock wave and within minutes the whole town mobilizes for the mass exodus. Everyone hurries away carrying a blanket and a crust of bread.

The icy passage that leads to the mountain winds along a ravine covered with dense evergreens and follows a frozen stream that slows us down as much as the nagging thought of being deprived of a good meal whose smell worsens my hunger pangs. We march steadily in silence and arrive at a shepherd's hut late at night.

The huge bulging eyes of a grinning frozen donkey greet us at the entrance of a hut. We step over the up stretched legs of the carcass to get out of the bitter cold before we suffer a similar fate. Inside we find a fire that the shepherd started just before we arrived. This stately man leaning on his staff without saying a word bears a striking resemblance to freedom fighters of old as they are portrayed in the faded photos of my history book. Only he seems to belong here. The rest of us sit curled up around his dying fire, shut in by a fierce wilderness and the agony of imminent danger —with a grinning dead donkey that guards our doorstep—a mockery of our plight.

All, that is, except my mother who suffered another bout of malaria and sits bundled up in a thin blanket full of holes, getting fits of shaking one moment and, the next, burning hot as hell.

It's agonizing to watch her, knowing that, here in the middle of January in this brutal cold, there is precious little any of us can do for her. From time to time, I walk outside to catch a breath of air only to be greeted by the donkey's sardonic stare. Inside the hut, the air hangs heavy from fire and breath that smells of smoke and singed hay. Puffs of exhaled tobacco twirl in circles, forming round rings that rise slowly just above our heads and settle in a bluish-gray cloud over the smoldering open fire. An occasional flicker outlines the bent-over faces of that small circle of humanity.

At daybreak the last notes of a revolutionary song reach me from a distant group of partisans heading downhill toward the path that leads through the woods to the village. I escape the stifling air and stand momentarily at the hut's entrance. The thick forest soon muffles their brisk footsteps until they're gone, and I'm left there alone with only the frozen donkey's mocking grin for company. The thought that inside, my mother is suffering so, is agonizing because I know there's nothing I can do to comfort her. I feel trapped by the helpless feeling of being caught in the midst of danger with both hands tied behind my back.

A barrage of staccato machine-gun fire makes everyone jump.

"The smoke, the smoke," someone yells. "It's a target," a frightened voice calls out, and there's a mad grab for blankets that get tossed, cape-like, over the shoulder, and we leave as quickly as we can. Even my mother, in all her misery, musters every last bit of strength and gulps down two quinine pills without any water, then joins the procession.

We soon get swallowed up in the dense, forbidding Hasiot mountain range, frequented until now only by weather-hardened shepherds, and we take refuge in another mountain shack that they built as a refuge from bad weather. Like so many stray cattle, we drop down on the bare, deep-frozen ground.

"The bag of salt?" Aunt Chrysie lets out a loud cry before we even have a chance to catch our breath. "Who has it?"

Our search proves fruitless. In the panic nobody thought of it.

"I'll go fetch it," Petros cries out.

"Oh no you don't," she says, cutting him off short. He lowers his head and gives in without protest, sensing her firm will.

"At least let's have a bite to eat. Bring the pot over here," Aunt Chrysie instructs.

"Where is the pot with the meat and beans?" my mother asks in a tremulous voice, turning her head left and right. "Who has it? Oh, my God!" she groans.

No answer. We realize that in our rush to escape, we forgot the pot. No one speaks; it's too terrible for words.

All day, we stand around, famished and chilled.

"We'll freeze in this cold. Let's light a fire," Aunt Chrysie says, shivering.

"What about the smoke, won't it be a target?" my mother queries her.

"Oh, no. Don't worry. It's a cloudy day."

"Anyhow, I'd rather die quickly of a bullet than freeze to death slowly," Petros says.

I can hear my teeth chattering. "Come on, light the fire, before we freeze to death."

The others agree with me, and soon the fear of danger is forgotten in the welcome warmth.

"We might as we-e-e-ll...make so-o-o-me bread," Aunt Pelagia stammers, after thawing out for a while, and brings out a little bag of flour she keeps tucked in her bosom for extra safety.

"Without yeast and salt?" I ask. *What's the matter with her?* I wonder.

"Well, it's better than nothing." A wan smile creases my mother's parched lips. "How long can the poor children last on an empty stomach? They're ready to faint," she says with a sigh.

We stand around in a circle, chafing our arms for warmth, and watch Aunt Pelagia stir a mixture of melted snow with the fistful of flour that was saved for just this kind of hour, as though it was nothing unusual. Then, she puts the runny mixture on the hot stone to bake and it starts turning into a gray paste. Petros watches, wide-eyed in disbelief. Before the stuff is even half-baked, cannon rumblings can be heard in the distance and at once we put out the fire, thinking that the fire is a target again. Crouched around the still-warm embers, we're offered the 'bread,' an undone, unsalted, tasteless, grease-covered mush. And, yet, we devour it instantly, as though it's the most delicious food on earth. Which to us, it is.

"Mm-mm," I say, smacking my lips, "Americans should come here to find out how good cake can really taste," I whisper to my mother and a half-smile forms on her lips.

By nighttime, the cold weather becomes a deep freeze. A mind-numbing paralysis creeps inside me, turning my bloodstream into a river of icy stillness.

The weak and sick are suffering most and want to throw all caution to the wind and build another fire. My mother objects, saying how dangerous it is, but soon she's convinced that the risk of being spotted in the dense forest is not a threat. The shepherd, who didn't go along with the idea at first, changes his mind. As soon as the first sparks fly some people crawl out of the huts to get warmed up. My mother and brother, like most of the others, stay inside under cover. Petros and I, drawn away from the cold darkness, join those who are huddled around the fire and bask in front of the golden red glow of the flames jumping in mid-air, giving a wild, almost grotesque appearance to the bent-over faces seeking refuge from the cold. We sit on our haunches, next to a placid mare. I can feel her warm heavy breathing, probably tired out by the strife of life. No sooner do I start recovering than my mother calls out to me.

"Get over here, this instant!" her sudden command breaks the silence, but I have no intention of leaving.

The second time her voice is more insistent and, again, she orders me to get away.

"Now, this very minute." But I turn a deaf ear. How can I leave to go in that cold, poky little hovel?

"What's the matter with her?" I ask Petro.

"Yeah, leave the wedding feast, as the saying goes, to gather sticks?" He lets out a glum chuckle.

"I'm not dumb," I agree.

"Get over here, instantly!" I hear her call me for the third time, really infuriated now, and I leave whether I want to or not. I step inside the hut ready to complain that Petros was not called away. Why just me? I rehearse my objections, but my voice freezes in my throat at the sound of machine gun fire. Bullets burst out over my head like an unexpected hailstorm and, then, the barrage stops as abruptly as it had started.

I rush headlong outside to find out what happened to Petro, before anyone has a chance to object. My eyes, well accustomed to the dark, cut through the heavy veil of night and notice, in the pale shadow of the moon, several limp bodies scattered about on the ground and then, some people hidden behind trees. The fearless shepherd lies there with one hand outstretched toward the fire that he took a chance putting out by pushing a tub of snow over it with his wooden staff, to save the others. Like a macabre choreographed dance, his death eternalizes his last offering to life. Farther away, an emaciated boy lies dead, another victim who was probably too weak to run. A refugee from Paliocastro, who had been wasting away from alcoholism, lies sprawled on another corpse. At the spot where I had been warming myself, only moments ago, the poor, innocent beast of burden lies shuddering on the ground, giving up its last breath to the cold earth, as a thickening pool of blood falls drop by drop from its head into a round blackened hole that slowly melts the snow. I tremble.

Petros is nowhere to be seen. *How could he have disappeared just like that?* Sharp needles sting my spine. I must find him. I'm afraid something happened to him, but wouldn't he be somewhere around? I stand still, feeling my heart being torn into pieces from the muffled shrieks and cries all around me.

"What are you doing here?" He startles me. "You're supposed to be at the hut, like your mother told you," he says, standing near me, unharmed.

"Petro!" I shout with relief and our hands join for a moment, as though in silent prayer for the dead.

"Who has time to mourn?" he says. "The tears we shed for them now may dampen our own graves if we don't hurry," he adds, and we run to find our family in the hut.

The dead, buried in the snow, unsung, without a single votive candle to light their way to their last resting place, assume their final position on the stage of eternity's vast expanse. On the blood-stained earth, pain surrenders and the still damp ground sends roots deep within to nurture a love for life, wantonly lost.

Panic, like a contagious disease, pollutes the air, drawing into its orbit young and old, weary and strong. Unbridled terror governs the path we mindlessly take, one scared-out-of-his-wits person following the next, like cattle heading for the slaughterhouse. Maybe worse. When we come face-to-face with the frozen, sky-high, steep crag ominously towering above us, shrieks of despair explode in the air. To scale that precipice is to take our lives in our own hands. At the brink of what must be our last hour, my heart pounds to the breaking point. We start climbing, driven by our own madness. A mother carries her babe on her shoulders, another clutches her suckling newborn, limb-shaking, old men and women stagger along and last come the young and stronger, all intertwined into a serpent-like black knot, bound to the slippery cliff side, twisting, squirming, and pushing one another to get to the unattainable top. One body, one soul, one heartbeat, breath-upon-breath, ascending, steadily ascending. Below, an abyss.

A few, surely demented, who reach the top head farther up the mountain, toward the caves. The rest—at the limit of their endurance—collapse on a narrow ledge next to the crevasse. We sit side by side on the ice-covered ground, without covers, without a bite to eat, waiting for dawn to come, gripped by terror. All around, nature is an orgy of beauty. High in the sky, the full moon spreads a majestic glow over the all white, virgin snow; tall, statuesque cypresses make an offering to the star-shimmering sky; stalactites flicker playfully in the reflection of the light-festooned forest under the gently swaying pine trees. Unknowingly, the mind searches for a meaning to their existence, the sense of ours, struggling to understand the deeper meaning of our sun-drenched planet, which, millenia ago, was transformed with the eruption of energy-giving life that rhythmically pulses to the wavelength of each heartbeat. Mankind evolved, developed, became centered on an eternal, life-giving force that created our five senses and the intellect—that supreme achievement—to serve, enrich, and enlighten the human spirit. That spirit that always seeks a balance, that is in the forefront of the quest for the continuity of life—that supreme calling which unerringly has led us to this night, this moment.

I get up to stretch my legs and shake off the cold just as light dawns behind the dense evergreen trees, and the mighty, snow-capped mountain tops, diminishing in the distance beyond, come into view in the direction of the caves that from afar look like black specks. It is told in songs of the heroic feats of the revolution of 1821, that those dark caves were the secret hideouts of the *klepht* captains who ensnared the enemy that passed by. I want to see that place, steeped in mystery, to know it first hand. I head toward the caves and on the way, I stop to look at the razor-sharp cliff we climbed the night before. I need to be convinced in the light of day that it's truly there and not a fantasy that mocks me with illusions.

Looking down at the dizzying, steep frozen gorge is like staring at eternal darkness. Daybreak never did, nor ever will reach it. The thought of climbing it is madness. Either we were possessed by mass insanity or driven by a mysterious force that somehow propelled us upward. There can be no other explanation. To try going down is even more insane. More like suicide. *We'll be here till the ice melts, for sure,* I think to myself, with a shudder. I abandon the sight before I lose my mind. I head straight for the caves and enter the hollowed out rock, dimly lit by pine resin kindling, and instantly witness a mound of crouched bodies, mostly men, holding on tight to their knees. The smell of burnt pinewood mingles with the heavy odor of damp rock. A yellowish light fills the rear of the cavernous space, forming a backdrop that plays with the shadows of the slow breaths escaping from the closely pressed lips. Fascinated, I watch the amorphous shapes rising, twisting lethargically, mingling with the soft, foggy light that encircles the twinkling stalactites hanging from the moist stone and shedding slow teardrops. There's not a word.

I crawl out with my head bent. On the horizon, light fills the crisp winter day. Standing there, gazing at the mountain crests beyond, I face east and notice a path to the right that curves gently downhill. I follow it and climb up the first hill where a huddled group of partisans is talking in low voices with Nicholas, the schoolteacher from a nearby village.

"The Germans withdrew their troops, and left only a small rear guard in town," someone is saying.

He pauses to light a cigarette and another continues. "They're heading for neighboring towns—that means more attacks."

The teacher listens attentively, twisting his dark, bushy mustache between his thin fingers.

"Well, then," he says, leaving, "we can get away from this wilderness before hunger and cold devour us."

Just then he turns his head and notices me.

"What are you doing here all alone?" he asks, astonished.

"Just walking," I mumble, too chilled for words. "I don't know how we'll get back to the shepherd's hut. We'll get killed going down that cliff. It's solid ice. I feel desperate," I tell him. "Everybody's sitting on the ground, and I'm afraid we'll freeze to death."

"Let me show you a way out," he reassures me and accompanies me to the next hill to show me a path that avoids the frozen cliff. "Don't be afraid. If you want to, you can always find a better road," he says with a smile, "provided you're not governed by fear." He dashes away, hopping from one snow-covered rock to the next.

I run back to get the others before they turn into icicles.

"Hurry, we can get down another way." They look up at me, as if they're glancing at a warm ray of sunshine, and we take a gentler slope amidst the forest trees. We're so overjoyed to have found a way to escape; you'd think we're heading for a wedding. Later, Petros and I brave the danger and head for the shepherd's hut at the first encampment to get the little flour and the precious salt that we abandoned there. We find the overturned pot that had contained the stew we never got to eat, licked dry by the wild forest beasts. Tears come to my eyes, but it's senseless. Our life is at stake, and even though that food would have made a difference, this is no time for sorrow. We head back with the flour and salt that, luckily, had been tucked in between the twigs in the hut's ceiling.

Day in and day out we wait for an end to our suffering. Every night lasts a century. Groups of freedom fighters pass by from time to time, usually in the late afternoon after battling the enemy for endless days, bringing their wounded to the first-aid station situated at a nearby mountain. Barefoot stragglers drag their bleeding feet along in the snow, carrying their dead comrades on their back.

We suffer for ten days in the middle of winter, living in constant fear. At long last the partisans announce that the raid has ended and we can return to the village. They had fought grueling battles to free the village of the enemy, and they had to be absolutely sure that none of the Germans was lurking around, ready to spring another surprise attack. They were also on the lookout for ever-present looting by local pilferers.

The townspeople realized that they could no longer be deceived into thinking that the only purpose of the enemy troops was to make sure there was no partisan activity or that they were safe if they promised to obey their orders.

We find Loziani in ruins. Burned houses, destroyed property, barren trees that gape like skeletons line the roads that are strewn with boulders piled high in a mass of turned up earth. Housing is a nagging problem. We wander around homeless for two whole days looking for a corner to hide our head. At last we find a dank, windowless room with a packed dirt floor in a half-burned house at the edge of town, a room we share with a widow of the Albanian war and her five under-age children. Now she has nothing left. No food, no home, no husband, only five hungry mouths to feed. They sleep on one side of the fireplace, and we on the other. Twelve people living on a tiny clod of damp earth. We light a fire before daybreak to keep from freezing. The first sparks startle the children who rub their bleary eyes with their dirty fists and awaken crying out: "...I'm hu-u-u-ungry-y-y." Their howls get louder and louder, as they look at us with pitiful glances, pleading for help. Five pairs of piercing, black eyes nail us one by one, like red-hot steel arrows. Not a crumb to be found. Their woeful cries shatter every ounce of endurance.

Even water is scarce. The pipes have frozen, and we must go for a mile or more to get fresh water. To do a wash, I have to stand all day in my torn shoes to build a fire in the muddy yard, melt the snow in a huge old black pot, boil the clothes well to get rid of the dirt and the lice that are flourishing worse than ever, and then start all over again to rinse them. My mother lies sick and exhausted on the bare, cold floor. Tasio suffers from a nagging cough, his body weak and thin as a reed. My mother's health is going from bad to worse ever since the meager supply of quinine has run out. Her lips are dry from the constant fever and want of nourishment. We don't even have a drop of cool refreshment to offer her.

"I'm thirsty," she cries out, shaking all over, and my heart gets tied up in a knot when I see her in such poor shape. In that once lovely town full of fruit-bearing trees, isn't there even a handful of dried fruit left to make a soothing compote for my ailing mother? Torn by anguish, I drag myself from one ruined house to another, over the icy roads in threadbare shoes full of gaping holes to beg for a few sour plums. At least to get something to relieve her of her misery until the doctor arrives.

We wait for him from moment to moment. To no avail. The doctor never shows up. He's at the nearby village battling the typhus scourge.

"I'm exhausted. How long can I last like this?" My mother repeats over and over, agony etched in her face.

How can I soothe her pained glance? How can her troubled soul heal?

24 COLLAPSE

Desolation and ruins are everywhere. The village can no longer sustain us, and a new uprooting is unavoidable. But how can my mother survive another journey? She is worn out from malaria and starvation.

"Oh, I'm feeling weary. Why go somewhere else? Wherever we go, we'll find the same problems, if not worse," she says in a weak voice.

"If we stay here in this cold catacomb, either we'll die of the cold or hunger." Aunt Chrysie tries to persuade her, knowing how unyielding she can be.

After a heated exchange, my mother gazes pensively at the cavernous opening in the dark ceiling and nods her head sadly.

"Yes, sure, you're probably right. If we're going to leave, let's do it right away," she gives in, against her will, her heart in a knot. "Well, we won't have to worry about carrying a heavy load, thanks to those barbarians who burned the last of what we had left." Her lips part ever so slightly into a bitter laugh.

Despite her effort to put on a cheerful air, I understand that the mere thought of a lengthy trip in the middle of winter, in my mother's present condition, weighs heavily on Aunt Chrysie, but she tries to conceal her anxiety.

"She's just recovered a bit from those terrible chills and fever," she confides in me. "You had a hard time finding some quinine for her malaria, but now she's exhausted," she whispers, shaking her head.

"You're right," I answer.

"What else can we do, child? At least in Mokro, the doctor will be nearby, and Uncle Leonidas will be closer," she continues.

"I guess there's no other solution, but what worries me is that the village is so close to the main highway. In case of an unexpected enemy offensive, we'll be exposed to a greater risk," I say, ending the discussion, but secretly wonder what we're letting ourselves in for. The trip is not a short one; Mokro is at least five to six hours away on foot.

The caravan sets out for the downhill road, the same one we travelled to get here, full of hope. Now, we leave in a pitiful state.

Our first landlady, Giorgena, comes to see us off with a scrawny, reddish young chicken tucked in her armpit.

"So you can have a fresh egg to make you better," she calls out and hands the scared bird to my mother.

"Hey, aren't we refugees, too?" Rita, one of our former neighbors from Paliocastro, screeches. "Just doing favors for her, huh, what about us, don't we rate?" She carries on, green with envy.

"Shame on you, can't you see she's a sick woman? Are you out of your mind?" Giorgena shouts, and her round face turns red as a poppy.

"Never mind. How can we carry a chicken all that way? May you be well for thinking of me," my mother says to calm her down and put an end to the argument.

The released bird runs cackling to hide amidst the tumble down walls, probably afraid they'll change their mind and catch it again. Giorgena wipes her tear-filled eyes and waves with both hands until she is hidden from view. We trudge downhill, leaving Loziani behind, less than six months after we arrived.

Bitterness is written all over my mother's face.

The journey to Mokro is worse than we feared. It's almost the end of February, and a freezing wind stings us to the bone marrow.

To protect us from the stones lining the road, our feet are covered with raw pig's hide, but it gives no warmth and, without socks, our feet are turning purple and our teeth can't stop chattering. Tasios, who's still suffering from psoriasis, is covered from hand to foot with rags from a worn out shirt.

Aunt Pelagia moves slowly from pain and age, stopping often to catch her breath, and has difficulty bearing up under the strain.

My mother's plight is the most heartbreaking. Deathly pale, skin and bones, she has hardly any strength left. Her body's reactions are sluggish, as one foot follows the other involuntarily, and her dry hands mechanically unwrap a bundle to pull out a grayish worn cloth—I remember it white once with monogrammed embroidery—tied in a knot, and her wrinkled lips bend down to dip her whitened tongue in the grains of sugar. She lifts her head again, ties the knot as before, and holds on to it before putting it back in its little bundle. She stares at the infinite horizon with a blank look and seems to drag her body wherever the road takes her.

Farther along she hastens her footsteps, giving the impression that she's feeling a bit livelier. I sigh with relief, thinking that maybe eating more grains of sugar helped her recover some of her strength. I watch as she surveys the river's edge and beyond, past the lower snow-covered mountains toward the distant landscape. She finds the sight moving, I imagine. Truly, a wild beauty dominates the snow-covered scenery, as I have always supposed the Russian steppes must look. Unlimited acres of whiteness as far as the eye can see. My thoughts travel far, reaching those distant lands quickly, arriving at the destination like a swift arrow, so unlike walking in the crunchy snow that slows down the steps to an unwieldy pace. My mother swerves. She must want to break this awful monotony, similar to what must have weighed down those travelers through the steppes in the wintertime. *Maybe I should keep her company and help dispel the cloud of boredom and lighten her burden. She may be worried about a storm that threatens on the horizon.* I call to her, but my cry goes unanswered. I pause at the thought that she might have to answer a call of nature. In the steppes, I muse, how did they work out problems like that while crossing such vast distances, so many people traveling together—men, women, children, familiar and unfamiliar faces, all joined by a common pursuit? I hadn't taken into account that sort of thing before. Sometimes it's necessary to go through an experience to understand the problems others face. I cast another glance at her without figuring out what she's after. *Why is she so close-mouthed?* I wonder. The snow starts to come down fast in big, billowy tufts. I make out her silhouette veering off the regular path to make a hurried turn. The cold wind is blowing in my face. My eyes and nose run from the sting that gets sharper by the minute and quickly turns the droplets in my nostrils into tiny, tingling icicles. I'm forced to take my hand out of my armpit to wipe them off.

My attention is absorbed by that little detail, and suddenly I look around, and my mother has disappeared. *Where is she? What happened to her?* Like a lightning bolt, terror grips me, plunging its sharp arrow into my spine, numbing my limbs that stand there motionless, unable to respond to the insistent, gnawing alarm. The mind stops and hopelessly struggles to free itself from the paralyzing fear. Mounting anxiety holds me captive, until, by an enormous effort of will, my panic-gripped body responds to the command for action.

I run, galloping after her, pushing against the savage wind that suddenly starts blowing and beats against my bare legs. I reach her just short of the river's edge. She turns her head, and her heartbreaking voice mingles with the wailing wind.

"A-a-a-a...let me fall in and drown. Enough of this torture. I can't take it any more."

"No, mommy, no," I stammer, inarticulate with fear. "Don't, mommy, don't," I cry out.

She is trembling all over, and her face is distorted by pain.

"Oh! Oh! Why isn't the river deeper so I can fall in? What kind of a curse is this?"

Her despair overflows again....

"Anathema on you, husband. You went away, abandoning us, like lost birds, to lead this dark and cruel life. Is that why I endured the pain and hardship of living in a foreign land for so many years, to come back to my country and be worse than a serf? Even the cold stones weep for my pitiful state."

I take her by the hand, far from the hopelessness holding her hostage. Despite the freezing cold, I'm drenched in perspiration. As soon as the gale-force north wind dies down a little, I undo the knot in the handkerchief she still holds in her hand, and bring the sugar granules to her mouth to wash away the sorrow that creases her face. She drinks a few drops of water from the canteen, and bit-by-bit we get back to the main road. We walk side by side, speechless for a long time. I try to find her familiar courageous, patient self. This side of her is unknown to me.

The others, unaware, march along in the thick, blinding snow that falls by the bucketful. You can hardly see your own nose. We advance single file, one body following another, hands cupped over the mouth to keep the crazy wind from stealing our breath away. For me, the bad weather is a blessing. I have much to reflect upon. Keeping close behind my mother, my head bent low to cut into the wind, I monitor her steps, not letting her out of my sight for a single moment. Her words keep swirling around in my head, ebbing and flowing in a steady stream, unwilling to free me from their tight hold. They take me far away to the foreign land she anathematized.

There, in America, she struggled as a young woman, living in a strange environment, not knowing the language, missing the warmth of her mother's companionship, giving birth to her children without the comfort of hearing her own tongue, raising them, working shoulder to shoulder with her husband in his store, sewing, keeping house, adapting to a different world. In her letters—she was always prompt in her correspondence—her suffering pored out. "I spend my hours alone. Luckily I have my daughter to confide in." She wrote her mother, my *nene*.

"She's still too little to be your confidant." That's what my grandmother said in her wisdom. My *nene* understood it all, even though she had not traveled outside of her own village on the remote slopes of Mount Olympos. Her mind reached everywhere, judged everything with amazing accuracy. "Patience, daughter, wait a while until she grows up," my *nene* counseled my mother, with compassion.

It's no wonder the townspeople named her "The Holy Bible," and when she was about to die, they went to her one by one to hear a last word of wisdom from her mouth, to have and to hold as a guiding light, as a keepsake, after she was gone from this earth.

"What can I do?" my mother replied. "I need someone to tell my troubles to when their father leaves me alone to go to work. Especially now, it's harder because we're so far from Eftihia. When we lived with my sister in Philadelphia, she was my solace and comfort."

At night she went to help her husband in his ice cream parlor and took us along with her. In one corner of the cellar, she made hand-dipped chocolates, and a little further away she bathed us in an old tub, wiping the sweat from her forehead with one hand and with the other dipping the raisins and nuts in the huge black bowl full of melted chocolate, deftly twisting them with one sweeping motion of the hand and placing them row upon row on wax paper. Occasionally, she cast a glance toward us to make sure we were all right. In the morning she made ice cream, and while she cleaned the store, sat me at an empty table to practice my Greek letters—the *"phi"* gave me such a hard time, who knows why, I kept confusing it with *"psi"*—and I cast sidelong glances at the candy and comic magazines sitting on the display shelves, especially "Little Orphan Annie," "Tarzan" and "Tom Mix," who were my idols. Then she waited to get the few dollars my father grudgingly gave her, often a source of friction.

"Why don't we ever have enough money even though we work like slaves? Why did we have a child right away against my wishes, only I couldn't get rid of it? Why can't we go back to our home country?" she often exclaimed. "We'll lose our children in this chaos, can't you see what's going on? Youngsters get up and leave home without telling anyone, mothers don't know their own sons. In our homeland even the stones lining the street know who you

are, but here we're strangers among strangers, the very cement pavement attacks us." She burst out with deep longing for her homeland.

Why? Why? Why, the eternal question that vexed her
and aroused such anger.

I remember once it drove her to the point of pulling my
father's hair while she ran after him down the stairs—
squeezed there at the bend, the two of them tied in a Gor-
dian knot of discord.

Yet, she loved her husband.

"I adored him," she claimed. "And devoted? To the
nth degree. What's the use? He was still jealous of me...
maybe because I was so much younger than he. Who
knows? How could I have put up with it for so many years?
I left my country because of want. If my father had been
alive, he wouldn't have let me and my sister Eftihia marry
and go to a foreign land for a piece of bread. She wept
with her sister when they got together once a year and tried
to catch up with all the news and the sorrows that had befallen them. "Do you remember mother's words at the hour
of parting?" she asked her sister with a sigh, "when we
were going away *sta xena?*" This meant, not only going
to a foreign country but, being uprooted from their native
land, something akin to perdition.

My *nene* said, "now that my daughters are being taken
away from me to go to the accursed *xena,* I don't care if
they pour gold down my throat." That image affected me
deeply and left a lasting impression. *"Liquid gold."* My
child's imagination tried to grasp what it was like, what
the sensation of it, flowing down my throat, would be. Was
it cold or hot? Bitter or not? Would it choke you, making
you regret your greediness, your wanting it so badly? In

293

those days of my childhood, I could never quite figure out what was the true taste of that precious metal.

The memories I've been recalling for some time now as I'm walking behind my mother leave me, and my thoughts come back to the valley spread out before me. I realize that the snow has turned to freezing rain as soon as we change direction. We stop long enough to take a sip of water and hurry along before dark sets in. Out in the open field we march in bunches of two or three, some distance from each other.

The wind grows stronger, the sky darkens, it turns to a deep purple and, all at once, is pierced by millions of luminous sparks, as though daybreak is hovering in the horizon. The earth shakes, it groans, lights flare up again, and before we know it, a hail storm, thick and heavy, is pelting us with darts that sting like cold fire. We rush headlong, straight into the eye of the storm.

Six hours after we set out, we arrive in Mokro. We wander around like lost sheep before we find the villager who shows us where to stay, and we enter a bare, cold, unwelcoming room. An old dismantled aluminum stove gawks open-mouthed in one corner, and in another, two or three rusty pipes. Our first job is to set up the stove to get warm and dry. We're soaking wet, and we don't have a single change of clothes. My cousins and I tackle the job of joining the pipes that refuse to fit together after lying there for who knows how long. Every time we bend down to fix them, our chapped skin makes a loud crackling noise, like dried hide, which is just what it's become. Our legs look like overstuffed animal skins from the fierce wind that beat on us all day long.

"Go to hell and never return," Petros groans, trying to fit two pipes together.

"Hurry, my boy," Aunt Chrysie calls out in a plaintive voice, "it's getting colder, and I'm afraid we'll die of frostbite." She coughs and rubs her stiff hands together.

After spitting and cursing, Petros grits his teeth and in one final push gets the infernal beast hooked up. I feel it's a small triumph. When we go outside in the deserted town to collect some firewood, the clouds are black.

We light the stove with the damp logs. It sputters and dies out, belching clouds of so much smoke, we can't see each other. Only the dry coughs can be heard in the hollow space. My eyes are tearing like a faucet. I grope my way to the door to let in some air, and a blast of cold wind fills the room.

"When will we ever warm up?" cries out my mother, huddled in the corner next to the stove.

The villager who met us when we first arrived comes back.

"What's all this smoke? I thought the whole place was on fire," he gasps, and rushes out to bring some dry wood. When he returns he hands us a few boiled eggs and a bite of bone-dry bread for our supper. It's very thoughtful of him, but we're too embarrassed to say we have no salt and can hardly swallow the tasteless, dry food that sticks to the roof of the mouth. A sinking feeling plunges the mind into sleep which mercifully opens its escape route into a vast forgetfulness.

Within two weeks a new enemy assault heads our way. Numbed by the incessant blows, neither the body nor the mind reacts. There's no room either for bitterness, or grumbling, or fighting back. Without uttering a single word, we escape to the woods. About an hour outside town we run into a partisan unit that has set an ambush between two dry embankments, just below a well-concealed ridge. I envy their fighting spirit and their freedom of movement. What a difference from our bedraggled state.

"Yia sas," they greet us with a big "hello," and we strike up a conversation. One of them is from Thessaloniki, I soon find out.

"Markos." He offers me a swarthy hand with long ta-pered fingers, like a piano player's, reminding me of my pre-war piano teacher who struck the keyboard so melodi-ously. Listening to him turned my fancy to the visions I once had of becoming a concert pianist. What a glorious instrument! Perhaps Marko can play beautifully also, but I doubt if this is a time to find out.

"I also lived in that neighborhood near the synagogue on Syngrou Street," he tells me, excited. "My parents, luck-ily, caught a boat for Egypt, but I wanted to fight in the mountains. I wasn't about to let myself be taken by the filthy, blood-stained hands of those Hitlerites. Many of my people were misled, unfortunately, by the false promises of the Nazis..." his voice trails off.

"And now?" I ask after a long pause.

"Much later I heard from some friends of mine who also joined the partisans that one of our own, someone in author-ity, not to mention any names, urged people to board the trains, thinking it was for the better since they believed they would find work in Germany. Many didn't trust the Nazis, perhaps because they suspected deceit, but the leader of our people was persuasive, and they followed him, except for some of us who fled to the mountains or left Greece." He surveys the surroundings, listening for any suspicious ac-tivity. Total stillness prevails. "You can never be too sure." He looks at me again.

"Where are these people now? Thessaloniki had a large Jewish population before the war," I ask anxiously, sensing that something is troubling him.

"Haven't you heard?" he rivets me with a piercing glance, as his brown, almond-shaped eyes darken, and then turn inward. I feel I'm looking into the depths of his soul. "Concentration camps...horrible mass extermination." He stops, catching his breath. "Genocide..." His words, strained and distorted, struggle to escape through his choked up throat.

"What does it mean? How...?" I dare ask, with hesitation.

"How could you know...way up here...in this wilderness?" his voice rises. "What can I tell you? Mass extermination. Horrible. It staggers the mind. That's why I'm here, with people I trust. At least we're fighting."

Just then, his comrade-in-arms motions to him, and he leaves in a hurry.

"In that way you're lucky," I call out. "Until we meet again," I shout louder, sad to see him leave. I felt comforted and secure in his presence.

He turns his head, motioning vaguely, and is soon hidden behind the round hillock poised just below a rocky promontory.

It takes us another hour or so to reach what looks like a secluded flatland, hidden between some low rocks and a stream flowing fast, its riverbed filled with melting winter snow. Here and there a green sprig can be seen shooting up from the ground. Spring is around the corner, but the earth is still cold, showing no sign of flowers in bloom. I feel a sense of intense disturbance. My talk with Marko has left a deep imprint on my mind. I knew from his restless glance that no matter how much I tried to stretch my imagination, I could not fill the void left by the words he left unspoken. The little he did say sounds like an ominous warning of things to come, leaving me with a sense of dark foreboding.

"Mankind is confronted by problems which are endangering the very essence of world equilibrium, physically and mentally," Marko said. *What's happening? Where are we heading? Toward total decay and destruction?* I wanted him to tell me all he knew, to share his innermost thoughts of despair, to know whatever he did, but that was not to be. He went to fight.

The furor of machine-gun shooting reaches us from the distance. *Is Marko fighting there or has he been sent to set up another ambush elsewhere?* His pained expression concerns me. *What was he hiding behind that poignant look?*

As soon as there is a lull in the shooting, I get busy filling the water jugs from the nearby spring in case the front line moves closer and we can't circulate freely. On my way back, I find my mother all alone, leaning against the bare rock with her sweater unbuttoned. I'm frightened when I see her hair loose on her shoulders and her chest sunken deep inside her rib cage that sticks out, leaving a hollowness in the unfilled space as big as a fist. She's absorbed with religious devotion to de-lousing herself, and doesn't notice me. I backtrack a few steps, fearful of disturbing her. Such a moment of tranquility and solitude is so rare, I hesitate to intrude and gently rest the jugs on the ground, but I almost trip over a dead snake curled up like a piece of deadwood. What a curious, disgusting animal. You can't trust it. Supposedly, even after they die, you can see them moving, as though still alive. I lift it up high with a twig to convince myself with my own eyes.

"What are you fussing around there for?" My mother's voice takes me by surprise.

"Look what I found," I squeal, excited in the hope of amusing her. "Do you think..."

"Get out of my sight this very minute before I lift this rock and throw it right at your head," she cuts me short. Her words are hurled at me like a torrent.

I drop the dead snake and disappear as fast as I can. When I return, I nudge the snake with a stick and it starts its lethargic, serpentine movements. *It really moves! Such deception! It was only feigning death. How can that happen? Then what separates the living from the dead?*

Ted who doesn't concern himself with such queries, approaches, and we both laugh over my mother's fright.

"Hey, don't you remember when we were in grade school that even looking at pictures of weird animals disgusted her, and we teased her even harder?" I'd almost forgotten that.

"But what a silly fear," I blurt out, laughing.

"Yeah, because it's somebody else's. Let me see how brave you are." He goads me.

"O.K., show me," I eagerly offer.

"Oh, no, not now; another time when you don't expect it," he says, throwing me a sly look.

"Look," I call out, "look what I found in the grass," and pick up a transparent snake skin, as though the snake has just slithered clean out of it, leaving no trace of itself. It crackles ominously at the slightest touch, like a crow gone wild.

"Oh, you found a snake shirt!" he says, looking over my shoulder. He finds another one lying in the brush, and we each put one on a stick and run chasing the birds for hours, until dark.

We've been living in a makeshift hut for days now. It's the last thing my mother needs. The dampness and chill are bad for her, and she comes down with a nasty cold. As soon as the Germans leave, we return to the village, where her condition worsens.

"She probably has pneumonia," the women say. They quickly come to help, for they know her well and like her thoughtful ways and wise counsel.

"We better do something. We can't wait for the doctor," the women say. Rumor has it that he just left for an outpost to treat the men wounded in a decisive battle in the straits of Sarantaporo. "Who knows when he'll be back?" the women agree.

"What should we do? How about a couple of blood-suckers?" one of them says. Even in her feverish state, my mother absolutely refuses. She leans on her elbows to get up.

"I'm leaving," she gasps at the sight of the black leeches curling around in the bottom of the rusty old can, ready to suck blood.

I just want them to do something fast, and I kick up a fuss.

"Hurry up, what's the matter with you?" I start yelling, and finally they settle on giving her cups.

"O.K., O.K.," they hush me.

My blood starts to boil as I watch all this preparation that seems to take forever. They run around to get the glasses, to find some local *tsipouro* instead of alcohol, which is nonexistent, some cotton, and a few matches. Ready at last, my mother lies down on her stomach, and the women lift up her threadbare undershirt to her neck. Vaso places the flaming cotton inside the glass momentarily to burn off the oxygen and create a vacuum, and then she puts the cups on my mother's back, one at a time. Gradually the cups start sucking up the pale skin, forming a pink bubble under the glass, much like a peasant girl's robust cheeks. As each cup is removed it makes the sound of a dull thump and leaves a perfectly round, bright red mark where it was placed. Afterward Vaso rubs my mother's back well with the alcohol substitute, and by morning her fever is down.

My mother was deathly ill, and her recovery is slow. It's a wonder she survived. The illness completely exhausts her little remaining strength.

"Mmm, the poor thing, just looking at her makes you cry," Nikolena, who mostly takes care of her, says with compassion. "We've got our problems, too, what with the war, and being poor from way back, only now its worse— but somehow it's even harder for that star-crossed woman who saw better days in America. Now, she suffers so. It's hard to beg for your bread. That torments her; it eats her up, the hapless thing. What can you say? Her troubles are God-given. She has none of her folks here, and with your in-laws, what do you expect? Will they care about you? She's always an outsider." She sighs, bowing her head low as though she's signing someone's death sentence.

"What can she do about it? Nothing. With three mouths to feed," Theano says, and goes back to her knitting, shaking her head rhythmically until the motion lulls her to sleep.

Luckily, the enemy attack doesn't last very long, otherwise who knows what would have happened to my mother after the terrible illness she suffered. But her recovery is difficult. The least bit of effort tires her out, and she is constantly irritable. Her mood is gloomy, yet there are always chores and work to do.

I overhear her talking with Nikolena one day. "How can I get better after so many blows? One right after the other. What will become of us at this rate? My in-laws are fed up with us. How much longer will they feed us? I try hard, but I still get blamed for everything that goes wrong."

Nikolena offers her some friendly advice. "Why don't you get in touch with your relatives and let them take care of you for a while?"

"In today's times, you know what it's like to send a letter and expect a reply? It will take months."

"So, what's to be done?" Nikolena fixes a knowing, sharp gaze intently on my mother. She may be illiterate, but her keen mind instantly grasps all the subtle shades of meaning.

"How can we make a trip like that today? It's at least a two-day, dangerous journey to my hometown. One thing I know for sure, though: I can't stand this any longer. I've had it," my mother says decisively.

Her voice sounds determined, but I doubt if she's willing to take a chance on such a hazardous venture. In these perilous times, it's unsafe for a woman with two young children to travel such great distances through mountains and valleys. Part of me understands clearly what drove her to the decision to leave, but it's also difficult for me to grasp the innermost reasons that propelled her to find this solution.

My mother sends word by messenger to her relatives in her hometown that sooner or later we'll be there, provided, of course, we make it through the lethal "Dead Zone." Such arrangements are not easy. Once more, it's time to be uprooted from our temporary living quarters.

Most of the village youth have joined the freedom fighters, except Pantelis, the tall, proud lad, the *levendis* with the large, black eyes. He is still young, only seventeen, and has family responsibilities, but one day he declares his double intentions—to flee to the mountains and to marry. He doesn't want to leave Rinoula, his fifteen-year-old fiancé, "just engaged," as he says, because he is in a hurry to have a son, "to carry my name, in case I don't come back," he admits secretly to his favorite uncle.

The wedding takes place on Sunday, a week before we're scheduled to leave. The bride doesn't get all decked up with the customary metallic ribbons, the *"telia"*—she wears whatever is found hidden in the hope chest—nor does the groom don the traditional ribbons, the *"kordelia,"* but after the ceremony when the priest chants, "and they are joined as one body," the newlyweds secretly exchange passionate glances and the festivities catch fire. An old lantern, a tender shepherd and his flute, along with much singing, are enough to have a joyous celebration for a day, and let the world burn. The groom's lean-boned grandfather, despite his limp, jumps high up to the ceiling like a wound up jack-in-the-box and almost overturns the table in his outburst. The bride—eyes downcast, faithful to tradition— shakes in the middle of the dance floor, next to her man.

Kostaina, Panteli's mother, has taken a liking to me from the start. "Like my own daughter," she says when she sees me and now, for the wedding, insists on dressing me in native clothes. It's a small favor, and I actually like the outfit.

"I almost didn't recognize you," exclaims my mother. "You look like a real peasant girl. The outfit looks good on you," she says, genuinely pleased.

"Yeah, yeah, it's becoming on you," everyone agrees.

Kostaina proudly puffs out her chest and tries hard to convince my mother to let me stay with her for good.

"Stay, you'll be like my own, that daughter I would've had if I hadn't lost her. Poor me—what can I do? Such is my fate."

I feel sorry for her and help her as much as I can. The last week she insists I stay at her place. At night we all sleep in the one room still standing in her house. Only the bride and groom have their own separate *flokati* woolen blanket and can be heard tilling the earthen floor all night long amidst their moans and groans. The firmament shakes, but abandoned to the snores of the night, the rest pay no heed to what's going on.

Early in the morning Pantelis leaves to join the fifth partisan battalion stationed near the straits of Sarantaporo where it had been rumored enemy troops are amassing in very large numbers. The whole town comes out to send him on his way. The shepherd who played the flute on his wedding day, gives it to Pantelis as a going-away present. Rinoula is trying hard to hold back her tears, but his mother weeps copiously, and for a single moment holds on to his arm, struggling to resist the urge to restrain him.

The battle of Sarantaporo is acclaimed as a decisive turning point in the liberation war and becomes part of our land's legendary history. That good lad, the village's proud *"palikari"* Pantelis, fights with uncommon bravery that far surpasses his tender age, writing a new page in the annals of the freedom fighters' glorious achievements. He was killed, leaving Rinoula alone and sorrowful.

May his seed have taken.

25 DEAD ZONE

The hour of our secret meeting with the partisans draws near. To reach the highway, we must go through invincible passes plunged in deep ravines of remote mountains and from there cross the deserted valley that leads to the *'VER-BOTEN'* Dead Zone—the forbidden highway—where fear and terror rule. That is the only way to reach our destination.

The Nazi conquerors use the Dead Zone exclusively for the transport of troops, ammunition, and tanks. No one else is ever allowed to pass. Never! To cross it is to court death. On the spot! The vast network of sentry posts send frequent search-and-kill patrols that fire at everything—even your shadow. Risking such a dangerous expedition is our only choice, if we want to return to my mother's homeland.

In late February 1944 we get ready to leave. I can see that my mother is making a heroic effort to be stoic. Quietly, she sheds bitter tears, unable to express the anguish tearing at her insides. A woman refugee, in a lonely struggle that has brought her to the brink of despair.

"I'm exhausted. I can't take it any longer," my mother weeps. "This endless running from one strange place to another has worn me out. At least in my hometown I hope I can find some help from my relatives. I realize what a risky move this is. But what else can I do? I see no other solution before me," she tells her husband's kin gathered around, as we get ready to leave.

Uncle Leonidas sees us off with a show of emotion I've never seen before. An unfamiliar tremor quivers in his voice, childlike almost; his body trembles ever so slightly as he embraces us again and again.

"My children, my children," is all he can say between muffled sobs.

I'm eager to leave, but the urge to hold close to me this rare moment that I had been longing for—without even realizing what I was missing—is holding me back. And now, it slips right through my hands, like water spilling through loosely cupped fingers, as I hunger for new excitement to fill the void that I hardly realize existed. A feeling of deep anguish grips me. That face, so like my father's, makes an offering of affection—a parting gift?—something forgotten in the dimly lit solitude of my soul. A revealing moment, full of bright dreams of expectancy, curiously intertwined with a dense darkness that left in its path a strange shadow of mute memories.

At this moment, gazing at the wide-open, eastern horizon, I can't quite sort out the mixed feelings stirring within, shifting like a kaleioscope. I want time to become impaled at this very spot, while the sphere's orbit stops in its tracks, so I can catch my breath and find my way through this complicated Minoan maze. Fright at the thought that I may be lost, makes my mind spin. I have the feeling that I'm wandering around an endless succession of dark corridors that lead from one blind alley to another. In vain I try to figure out what's happening. How can I disentangle the myriad silk threads that complicate and hide the answers to the endless questions that have just emerged? Inarticulate cries stumble before this stranger who is curiously showing affection and tenderness at just this hour that swiftly goes by. Yet we must hurry to our appointment. The plan is to meet with the others who will be crossing the Dead Zone tonight at exactly a half hour before midnight. The hour is time-locked to the changing of the German patrol unit. We must be absolutely punctual and concealed because if the enemy suspects even the slightest disturbance, we're dead. No questions asked.

The anticipation of a new reality electrifies the air. I long to go and step forward, light-footed. Change, even when painful, is always better than standing still, I think. It breaks the monotony of the same sights, dulled by repetition, the dreary sounds that hold no hope.

"Let's not tarry," my mother calls out in a direct manner as she takes my brother Tasio by the hand, and we swiftly separate, leaving the others behind. "We have a long way to go," she adds without a backward glance, and we're off, following in the footsteps of the guide who leads the way and his sturdy mule.

I am fourteen years old, and I feel the surge of deep, hidden emotions, at once alluring and dangerous, pulling me. Each one of us, surrounded by our own inner space, does not dare disturb the tranquility of the moment. The mind travels far away. The faint candlelight that has lit our way until now is snuffed out. One footstep follows the next, and our footsteps steadily become enveloped by the transparent veil of rapidly approaching darkness. Beyond the horizon, a fine watercolor mark stretches across the mountains that lie just below the tiny tufts of constantly changing violet cloud-shapes that leap back and forth out of each other's path, dipping in and out of hues of rose and mauve—an ethereal game of hide and seek. Momentarily they disappear into fluff, only to return as migrating birds, in twos and threes and fours, that are whisked away again as rapidly as they enter. Gradually, the stones are drained of light, and almost visibly absorb hues of indigo blue that transform the massive rocks to steel gray statues. Tree shadows soon fall and surround us everywhere.

After a wide bend to the left, the road steadily goes uphill. Toward the right, the row of round-bottomed mountains hide behind each other and get smaller and smaller, then disappear in the distance until it's difficult to distinguish where they end and the sky begins. Soon the terrain becomes gravely underfoot, and just before a sharp curve in the road, we come upon a clearing that heads downhill. A succession of vertical bends and dips takes us to a secluded roadside fountain where we pause for a drink of water.

"Is it really so dangerous to take us across the Dead Zone?" I venture a chat with our closemouthed guide.

He shakes his head, pausing for a long time before answering.

"You haven't said a thing. It doesn't get any worse. Nothin' like it in the whole country." That's all he says before going back to his stillness. The unknown intrigues me. It's torture being kept in the dark, but he doesn't budge. He pays no attention to me. We march on in total silence. My brother Tasio has fallen asleep in his mother's arms, apparently lulled by the rocking motion of the steadfast mule.

Man and beast, teamed up, lead us through twists and turns, but it's too dark to see clearly. We reach level ground, and the valley absorbs the quiet sound of our footsteps. We wait at the edge of the first cluster of houses while the guide delivers the animal at someone's house, apparently according to some prearranged plan, and then rejoins us. My mother must have caught on to this without asking any questions, and she motions to us to follow him, so we continue our trek on foot.

In the stillness of the night, a faint ripple in the air signals our presence before we reach our secret meeting place. An indistinct murmur, like wisps of wind, spreads all around, and we move on cautiously, weaving in and out of pools of darkness cast by the heavily overgrown, untended fields. The figure of an *andartis,* a tall freedom fighter, appears, and he exchanges signals with our guide. The few trees lining the plot of land can be heard swaying in the soft breeze. Their sound mingles with the undertone of human voices as we enter the unreaped wheat fields that stand tall in densely packed clusters along the Elassona-Kozani highway. He makes a gesture to be silent, and we advance faster and even more cautiously, walking in carefully paced steps along the length of the Dead Zone. Someone parts the wheat stalks, bringing us in the presence of another *andarti.* He approaches, exchanges signals again, and lets us go a little farther. The people who came before us, a mute, buddhistically-seated group, are plunged in total silence. All human sound has ceased.

I look at the *andarti.* His manner has aroused my curiosity, and I begin having doubts. *Is he really one of our people, or is he a plant, someone who can't be trusted and is about to betray us?* There in the stillness of the black night, how can anyone find beginning or end? Some gestures catch my attention, then, a sense of movements nearby, a few halting whispers and what can you tell? *Are the others, seated on the ground, free of doubts? What have they surmised?* I drown my anxieties deep inside me as soon as the signal is given to get up. My turn comes to follow the night procession. Or death procession? Either way we're exposed. Nothing can change the situation now.

The clatter of German trucks can be heard clearly. The patrol must be getting ready to change any minute now. We come to a clearing—a thin strip that separates two fields. The weeds growing between them are gigantic. The fields are so close to the Dead Zone, the villagers didn't dare work their land, even in broad daylight.

"The Germans exterminated men and women who risked their lives to till their land," our guide told us on the way down. "Since then, they've been scared to death to get anywhere near them. Two years' worth of crop wasted, and people starving to death." He heaved a deep sigh. "From here on in, wherever you look," he said, "you see folks in such a sorry state it brings tears to your eyes."

Random shots accompany the military trucks rolling down the road. The sleeping countryside—bedded down early with fear—isn't stirring. The night grows more tense by the second, like a time bomb ticking louder the closer zero hour draws.

Our group of about fifteen people is led by three *andartes* who will each take five of us at intervals to the opposite side of the road. In the total stillness of the night, every shadow is suspect, every burst of gunfire a living terror. The air becomes more and more heavy. Fear stifles my breath. My heart, twisted in a knot, beats impatiently. A thousand and one images float before me, vacillating between visions of horrible failure and triumphant victory. Out of nowhere, shots echo nearby, raising a cloud of dust. We freeze in place. *They got wind of us* I think, with a shudder. I throw a quick glance toward the terrified lot to check if we're still intact. Without counting everybody one by one, I know we are all present.

We hold our breath, but no more shots are fired. We breathe a sigh of relief. A whisper from one cupped ear to another tells us that that was the signal for the changing of the guard. Soon we move on.

Time is ebbing. *Suppose we miss our cue and never make it across tonight? We're finished,* the thought races swiftly by. Within earshot of the road, there is no refuge.

An eternity of silent listening passes, but not another alarming sound is heard.

The starless night is cloaked in a black shroud. In a hush, the first group rises. *If they're caught, do we still have a chance to escape?* I try to dismiss the annoying idea buzzing in my head, like a mosquito. *What's gotten into me tonight? Maybe I'm on edge because I feel I must faithfully deliver all the letters and notes that so many people gave me for their folks. Most important is the secret message Bishop Seraphim entrusted to me for a top resistance leader in Thessaly.*

"I hope you're not stopped on your trip," the Bishop said, "but just in case, they may be less likely to search a little girl. As for crossing the Dead Zone, well, may God help you." He bid us farewell and now his words are ringing in my ears.

My four pockets garnished in red thread are full of tiny pieces of paper crammed with messages. My gray Eisenhower-style jacket, like the Allied soldiers are wearing, was made from a blanket found in a parachute drop in "free Greece" where we were living. The jacket and my overstuffed pockets make me look like an armored tank. And of course, I walk accordingly, as my new mail carrier occupation demands. Since there is no postal service, this is the only means of written communication, especially between far flung villages in western Macedonia and Thessaly, located on opposite sides of the abominable Dead Zone.

Abruptly, all movement ceases.

Stop! An *andartis* motions.

Someone immediately swerves in the direction the *andarti* guide signals, and the woman next to me jumps up, as though lightning struck her. Like an electric current running through our bodies, the rest of us shudder. Rooted to the ground, we hold our breath. Time is an eternity. One by one, the other groups leave and disappear among the wheat stalks. We can't see a thing and know even less. As long as the machine guns don't fire, there's hope. *When is our turn coming?* We're the last ones. I can no longer hold still.

In one swift, unexpected moment, it seems, we're walking into the den of Death that stands there with his mouth gaping wide-open, ready to devour us. At least death will come quickly, without questioning, searches, cross-examinations and agonizing thoughts about the outcome. Our bodies, riddled with bullets, wouldn't even need a *coup de grace. Will they find the letters and messages I'm carrying or not even pay any attention? Who will notice? One more cadaver to get rid of.*

The presence of the highway, straight as an arrow, dominates. In the distance, it disappears to the right and left. It receives us without partaking of our thoughts. As always, whether the road is irregular or smooth, it retains its neutrality. Only we, poised on the brink of annihilation, walk a tightrope across an abyss, face-to-face with a death squad that will fire straight at us. Plunged in our inner turmoil, we lean from one side of the scale to the other, constantly seeking a balance in our turbulent existence.

The Dead Zone is deserted. I hesitate to turn my head for fear of being noticed. *By whom?* Halfway across, a swiftly moving soundless mass of people secretly breaks the monotony of the asphalt road—a racing heartbeat skips a jump—then emptiness. The dark swallows our frightened footsteps. A mirage that appeared and is gone.

The fields on the other side give us temporary refuge. Not a word is spoken as we gather around again as before. We follow the *andartes* for a short distance, and each step lessens the tension. That can be even more dangerous. To be discovered now? Danger still lurks and there's a long way to go. The enemy's presence is always a threat, and we must be on the alert. We set out together for a while.

On the distant horizon, the gravely path is lit by a rising, pale moon. In the dim light, for the first time we see the faces of our group take form. What catches the eye is the terror of tyranny engraved deeply on everyone's face. Young women, prematurely old with hollow cheeks, sunken eye sockets, wrinkled faces, and the blank stare of children who had aged before their time in the cellars of fear and the harsh reality of the occupation. Now and then I catch a forlorn glance cast by the peasant-folk at the wheat that stands like jagged spears in the half-lit night. At the sight of those beautiful abandoned wheat stalks gone to seed, they bow their heads to the ground. Their once fertile crop will not contribute to the lessening of hunger, to the continuity of life. Nature has been ravished. It's painful to see it wasted.

The hour of parting has come. Some will head east, others south, without farewells, to get away as quickly as possible. Danger is still nearby. We only shake hands with the *andartes* who risked their lives for our sake. Silently, our eyes offer them our gratitude and admiration. Now they'll return alone to cross the Dead Zone once more and be tested in another trial by fire before they catch forty winks on some remote hillside until daybreak, when they can rejoin their unit.

The soft luminosity of the moon, shining through the slowly shifting clouds, guides our way, as we press ahead without stopping. Farther along, we pause and glance upward with reverence. Commanding the entire horizon to the north, Mount Olympos towers above, capturing our attention. The grand presence of the mountain looms larger than life—a symbol of godliness. The triumphant, legendary figure of old man Olympos, forever a fountainhead of patience amidst the storms and upheavals of fate, is something to behold. Olympos stands there, fearless, unshakable as ever, covered by thrice-eternal snow. The magnitude of the peaks conveys an idea of the sky-grazing grandeur. Looking up at it from this side of Elassona for the first time, its vast proportions are an awesome sight. At once, shattered hopes take wing, fortitude is revived. Footsteps become lighter, faster, almost running ahead toward the mountain beckoning beyond.

"How many of our ancestors have passed through these very same places... Some were killed, others pursued by foreign enemies. How horrible was that tyranny under the Turks...over 400 years...such a long time..." my mother's thoughts flow spontaneously. "In those days children, such as you, were not allowed to go to school and learn their own tongue. It was forbidden under penalty of death. So monks taught them secretly at night."

As I walk along the moonlit path, that image forms in my mind, as though it were happening now. It reminds me of the immortal poem which the illegal students recited on the way to the monks' hideaway school, during those endless nights of more than four centuries' bondage.

Moonlight bright,
Shine all night,
To go to school,
To read and write.

"Such sacrifices were needed. Those children went to the domed cellars hidden deep down in the bowels of the earth," my mother continues in a passionate tone, "to ensure the survival of our mother tongue. To be able to teach the classes until dawn, the monks carried chains attached to lead balls around their wrists. When they dozed off from weariness and fatigue, the heavy weights dropped to the ground with a crashing sound that startled them awake so they could go on with their lesson. Such was their devotion and dedication to hold onto and preserve our precious heritage."

Listening to her words that make our glorious past come alive, I can feel it stirring my conscience, becoming an inseparable part of me. "The grandeur of ancient heroes," she completes my thought, "moves me deeply." Her talk flows at an unhurried, effortless pace. My heart rejoices as I listen.

The same moon, as in those heroic days of old, shines on our path through the darkness.

26 FREEDOM

At the foot of Mount Olympos, near dawn, when the crowing roosters herald the start of a new day and the domed blue firmament awakens, fear slowly begins to fade as the threat of imminent danger and the gloom of night begin to disappear. But our anxiety has not left us. Weary after long hours of traveling, we're distressed by an agonizing thought. *Will we ever again see beloved places that still seem so far away?*

As we approach the mountainous country near Olympos, we're surrounded by devastated land. Everywhere, the aftermath of bombings, execution, and other cruelties have left their mark; killings, persecution, lamentation have taken their toll. The suffering has intensified and, along with it, the resolve to put an end to it. The fight for freedom has spread from one end of the land to the other and embraces the vast majority of people.

"Our liberation struggle must succeed," we hear villagers say, hush-hush, in the town squares.

"It's our only hope, our deliverance from this foreign domination," war-weary mothers whisper among themselves.

All at once, akin to a dream, my mother's birthplace, and home of the legendary freedom fighter of 1821, Georgakis Olympios, rises before us. The sun's rays are just bursting through the craggy saw-toothed peaks of the mountaintop, and its radiant brilliance absorbs the remaining trace of glow from the pale stars. We climb up the rocky terrain and hear from afar the church bells ringing. A shepherd wearing the traditional rough black wool cape over his shoulders stops whittling his staff with his pocketknife to wipe his long handlebar mustache with the back of his hand and gets up to cross himself. He's startled momentarily when he sees us approaching, but quickly recovers and bids us good morning.

"What are you doing here?" he asks.

"I'm going back to my hometown," my mother answers, heaving a deep sigh.

"What sort of news do you bring us?" he wants to know.

"The Allied troops have landed in Italy," my mother replies with a smile.

"That's good, the way I see it," he says, scratching his head. "It brings us some hope."

"At least one of the enemies was overthrown," my mother adds, with enthusiasm.

The shepherd nods, then goes back to carving his staff. We leave him to continue our uphill climb that shortly brings us to our beloved village. We feel deep sorrow, though, when we face so many ruined houses. More than half of the homes have been bombarded or burned down.

Before long cousin Yiorgos comes to greet us. We embrace with tears in our eyes, and I still find it hard to believe that we actually made it. After he tells us that all our relatives are well, he is eager to hear our news.

"Mussolini's government has fallen," my mother tells him. "One day maybe all the fascists will perish."

"Oh, yes. What happened in Italy is quite a story. But now is not the time to lessen our readiness to fight," cousin Yiorgos says. He looks a bit more weary than the last time I saw him, but otherwise unchanged.

"You're right," she sighs. "We must tighten our grip until these horrors are over." She clenches her fist with unusual liveliness.

"I realize you must be tired now. We'll talk about that and the other developments in a day or two after you've had a chance to rest a little from your long journey."

From the first days of our arrival, I can see that being back among her own people has renewed my mother's courage; it's like a balm for her soul that helps her stand tall again.

Of course, we knew for some time that the corrupt fascist regime was crumbling, and soon Mussolini, Il Duce himself, who, as everybody knew, was a mere puppet of Hitler, was overthrown by his own people. Not long after the Allies landed on the southern coast of Sicily, Italy made a secret truce with the Allies and surrendered in September of 1943. In our country, the German chief commander immediately announced that he would have full authority over Greece, including the sector that had been controlled by Italy. Their objective was clearly to capture the Italian troops along with their ammunition and military supplies before they had a chance to join the partisan forces fighting in the mountains. They issued a directive that if anyone was caught negotiating with the Italians for guns and artillery, they would be immediately sentenced to death. Despite these dire threats, both Italian soldiers and officers transferred enormous quantities of military supplies, motorcycles and blankets from their warehouses to the Greek partisan army and helped, not only to reinforce their meager supplies, but also to swell their ranks. Many Italian troops joined the partisans and fought alongside them against their former Axis ally, Germany. What they didn't give away, they sold for practically nothing to the Greek people, who hurried to their supply depots to snatch up all sorts of goods at bargain prices. Most of the Italians had a half-hearted interest in the war, and now they got rid of their war material and even their own weapons with zeal and panache. We also heard with sadness that in some parts of Greece that had been under Italian rule, the Nazi atrocities against their former allies were ferocious.

Yiorgo is constantly letting us know about the most recent developments in the war front, knowing how much good news encourages us to keep going. "We take heart that the Axis war machine suffered a big setback in the African front where Rommel, the 'desert fox,' was finally defeated after successive Allied battles had failed," he exclaims.

"What was even more amazing was the Russian victory in Stalingrad. The combination of the brutal winter in the Soviet steppes and the dogged determination and fighting of the Russian people led to a defeat of the seemingly invincible Nazi-fascist war machine," my mother adds.

The situation in the war front and in our country is still grim and scary. There is a long way to go before we reach our hoped-for goal. Like most of her fellow villagers, my mother wholeheartedly takes an active part in the liberation movement, now that her health is improving.

"Come on, let's amble along and do some fundraising to help the *andartes*. Idleness will get us nowhere." Efi, one of her girlhood neighbors, calls her when she arrives at our doorstep the first time.

Efi comes to pick her up in the afternoon after her husband and brothers return from the dairy farm, the *'strounga,'* as the locals call it. She's always freshly washed, and her clothes are spanking clean. Her round, expressive face shines with alertness, her brown eyes are bright and smiling, despite the fact that her husband was injured in the Albanian war and they have three young children to support.

"How are things with you, Efi?" my mother asks. "Is your family well?"

"What do you expect? Times are bad, and we have to make do, but for now we're well," Efi says, pausing on her way down the stairs. "Not that we had that much before, always poor, you know. I remember before the war me and my sisters came by your home to do some chores or dig for potatoes in the hills, and sometimes you were eating that deep red watermelon. It made my mouth water just to look at it. We'd sort of hang around, hoping to get a taste of it, even just a little bit of the pink near the peel. What could we do? Poor and needy, and your folks were well-to-do. That's life."

"True, true, but now you see we're all in the same boat. The war has leveled us all out. We're all poor. Nobody has any watermelon or much of anything." My mother laughs, and the two of them continue to chat amicably as they go down the steep rocky hill past the houses with the sloping gray slate roofs toward the St. Anaryiri church at the other end of town.

"Is anybody home?" they call out as they enter the courtyard.

In the battle for freedom, the youth are in the forefront. Swept up by this wave of resistance against the yoke of oppression, I too take an active part with renewed enthusiasm.

My mother offers no objection to my work in the village, but I run into difficulties when I ask her permission to join a cultural expedition that will travel to several neighboring towns—an hour or two away—to present a theatrical production and a series of lectures. Pleading, even begging, are useless. My mother is unyielding. The door is shut tight and double locked.

"We can't go without you. You're to have the lead role in our play, and we've spent so much time in rehearsals," declares Kimon, a soul full of zest and vitality in the struggle for a better world. "And as for the lectures, you've already done all this work, and we have a responsibility to tell our people how important our resistance movement is," he adds.

I can feel my face aflame with embarrassment to hear one of our leaders speak openly like that about me, but his words are heartwarming, and I'm pleased.

"I know we've said it over and over again," he continues, "but it can't be repeated often enough. Our life and our liberty are at stake. We have a sacred duty to defend them. By giving battle to the enemy, whether it's an ambush or a derailment of a train or a strike or some kind of industrial sabotage, we tie up more Germans in security operations, and they have fewer troops available for the battlefield."

"I know that my mother is putting us on the spot. The expedition has to go on, after so many weeks of preparation," I admit, "but my mother will not give in."

"Something must be done," Kimon says pensively. "You, Kosti, why don't you talk to her? She has a special affection and trust for you as one of her compatriots. Maybe you can convince her."

He gives me a long questioning look as his black eyes dart back and forth.

"Come now, you know how to talk her into it. She might listen to you. After all, you're our legal counsel," I add.

Kostis smiles, satisfied, as he heads for the door and leans his curly head on the doorframe, deep in thought.

"O.K., I'll go," he agrees. That same afternoon he approaches her without the least hesitation.

I eavesdrop on their conversation.

"Do us a favor, please, don't ruin our plans. You know our cause is sacred," he implores her in a low voice.

"Yes, my son, but the distance concerns me. If you run into an enemy patrol...?" she says and looks at him with an anxious glance, leaving her question unfinished.

After a short pause Kostis, who can express his thoughts with clarity and has a keen sense of timing, finds her weak spot.

"Don't worry at all. I take full responsibility for her safety. Trust me. After all, isn't your mother one of my great-aunts? We'll all return unharmed, I promise. Word of honor."

From a crack in the door, I can see Kostis is smiling to himself.

"She agreed," Kostis whispers quickly in my ear as he leaves. I'm thrilled beyond words.

High excitement, mounting to fever pitch, accompanies our rehearsals—in the half bombed out school building—for a play to celebrate the March 25 anniversary of the Greek revolution of 1821 against the Ottoman Empire. We are doing our part while our partisans are fighting bravely against the occupation forces, as our forefathers did in the war to liberate our homeland from the Turks more than one hundred years ago.

Out of the blue, thundering applause sends us running outside to find out what the commotion is all about. The townspeople, beside themselves, shout and run ecstatically through the streets to greet the arriving Bishop Seraphim, who is heading for the village square.

"Here glory marches alone, gazing upon the brilliant youth," he bellows, smiling proudly at the handsome young people hanging on his every word.

That evening the townspeople give a dinner to show their gratitude to him and his men. A bottle of homemade ouzo, *tsipouro,* and some wine materialize from nowhere, and soon enough the party gets going in full swing.

It happens now and again, when the *andartes* are away from their unit for some reason or after a long expedition when one battle follows another, when they find themselves in hospitable surroundings that offer a warm interlude in the midst of the constant danger and hardships they face. The civilians, too, need to escape, even for a few minutes, from the ordeals of the occupation, to unwind over a glass of wine, to chat about the burning issues they face.

Kapetan Zisis gets in the mood for song and dance, more than all the others in Seraphim's group of men. He suddenly jumps up and starts yelling at the top of his lungs,

"I want her, I want the beautiful girl," and before anyone knows what he's doing, he dashes outside and starts to run. As soon as Panos, the girl's cousin, sees him, he realizes that Zisis is after the black-eyed Xanthou, whom he met and fell madly in love with at the theatrical performance. He takes a shortcut through one of the narrow streets to her house, grabs Xanthou by the arm, covers her with a big woolen flokati blanket to make her look like a sheep, and quickly hides her at the back of the big fountain before Zisis appears.

"You idiot, don't you think Zisis will figure out what you're doing? He may be drunk, but he's not dumb," Stelios, one of the *andartes,* tells Pano and pulls him away.

"O.K., O.K., I'll think of something else," he says, freeing his arm.

Kapetan Zisis is staggering from house to house looking for the local beauty. There's no stopping him. A moment before Zisis' unsteady footsteps on the cobblestone street come close, Panos manages to hide her in a neighbor's house for safety.

"What's her name?" Zisis yells. "Tell me right away."

Panos, knowing Kapetan Zisis' dogged will and hot temper, immediately starts worrying that Xanthou is too close to her home, and Zisis might track her down. That will really get him in deep trouble with her family. Luckily her father is away, or else all hell would be breaking loose. They run downhill, holding her tightly by the arm.

"This way, this way," Panos whispers, flushed and perspiring.

Xanthou, all pale and shaken from the commotion, goes inside, and he stands guard in front of the house.

Panos' eyes gleam, and he turns to Stelios to exchange a few secret words. Stelios winks and leaves to rejoin the other partisans. Down the road he runs into Kapetan Zisis, who's ranting and raving.

"Where is she? Did you find her?" he stammers. "I'll marry her, don't worry," he says, nearly tripping over himself.

"Kapetan Zisi." Stelios sidles up to him. "I have an important message for you." They walk along talking and gesturing. "We just received an urgent mandate to go to Litohoro on a special mission," he tells him in confidence. "They need our immediate assistance," he says, looking Zisi straight in the eye.

"Let's go," Kapetan Zisis, answers, straightening his collar. "I'll find her when we return," he adds, in a calmer tone. The two men each light a cigarette and leave arm in arm.

When they reach the house where Seraphim is staying, Stelios levels with the captain.

"You rascal, you fooled me. We have to leave tonight in any case, but I won't forget her, mark my words," Kapetan Zisis declares, determined. "What beautiful eyes, what lips dripping honey, what a figure..." He walks alone into the night to light another cigarette.

The Bishop has no idea what's going on. He was very tired and left right after dinner to rest. The village women prepared his room and put a white *flokati* blanket on his bed from one of the chests hidden in the cellar. Next morning the villagers say farewell to him with tears in their eyes and return to their work. The women hang the *flokati* to air on the balcony, and what do they see? It's black! All covered with lice!

"Oh, well, what can he do? Lice don't care if he's a *despotis*. A bishop gets treated the same as the partisans," the housewives talk, laughing among themselves as they sweep the street in front of their houses until the cobblestones sparkle.

Our cultural expedition to the surrounding villages to give lectures and put on a play about the heroic resistance by a handful of Greeks against the vast Ottoman empire in 1821 was more than an act of defiance to the hordes of the Nazifascist oppressors of this small but valiant Balkan country. It also served to boost the people's morale and re-energize them to continue the fight for freedom. These activities turn out even better than we expect and accomplish our goal of recruiting more people from all walks of life into our liberation struggle.

The whole countryside is buzzing with excitement. Our triumphant songs of liberation and peace echo from one mountaintop to another and across the valley below.

We conquer our life by driving out fascism.
While we fight, we sing.
Full of pride and joy,
The youth always advance,
As if going to a dance.
Filled with passion, will and life
Our passage is a trail of light.

The next day Kostis greets me with a big smile as he bounds down the street and says that the executive board of the youth organization is pleased with our accomplishments. I glow with pride that our efforts were crowned with success.

This is truly a national uprising that I am proud to participate in, but the thirst for freedom and the fight against fascism is much more intense in the hearts of the young men and women. In the cities, the student body of the Universities of Athens and Thessaloniki and the Polytechnic School of Athens, the only higher education establishments, was the wellspring of initiative and inspiration to join the national resistance of our enslaved people.

Kostis, who was a student in the Law School of the University of Thessaloniki, told us at one of his recent visits that hundreds of students had died either fighting the occupation forces—gun in hand—in the resistance army, or in front of firing squads without a trial, or in concentration camps set up by the invaders in our country or in their countries. The enemy had occupied our country, but had not subdued it. We are determined never to let that happen.

Kimon stops me in the center of town one day. He leans against the plane tree, takes a puff of his cigarette and asks me to come to the next meeting of the youth executive board meeting.

When I get there, besides Kimon, I see Kosti leaning against the battered wall and Soula sitting on the window-sill. Kimon is pacing back and forth, stops short, and comes right to the point.

"We're impressed with your work and want you to become the educational and cultural director of a region in Thessaly." I'm taken completely by surprise and hardly know what to say. "As you know," Kimon continues, "our struggle must be intensified, if we are to win. And we must win."

"Of course," I readily agree, "but I wonder what made you choose me?"

"One of our greatest poets," Kostis picks up the thread, "wrote that 'the greatness in people is not measured in acres, but only by the glow of the heart and by blood.' We can see that that glow, the heart's passion, is what flames your being. We have all seen, unmistakably, that light reflected in your face and are sure that you can become a leader in the youth organization. I know you'll carry on the job you're entrusted with."

"We need your contribution and your enthusiasm to carry on our struggle," Soula adds.

"You'll be responsible for directing the work of about sixty villages. Your writing ability is good, and we urgently need someone to write articles for our newspaper, especially about issues that concern young women. Our youth has to be mobilized so everyone will take part in our antifascist resistance struggle by letting them know how much danger we're still facing from the Nazis. Hitler has no intention whatsoever of giving up unless he is thoroughly crushed. We also have a lot of work to do getting pamphlets written and distributed throughout the valley. You'll be constantly on the go, traveling from one village to the next and helping our other resistance fighters to organize meetings and cultural events with plays and poetry readings. What do you say?" Kimon asks.

"I must discuss it with my mother first, of course," I blurt out as I walk out.

Never in my dreams had I imagined such luck, but remembering how much my mother resisted the idea of my going on the cultural expedition, I feel anxious. I have a foreboding that she'll bring up all sorts of objections, like "what will the people say," or "you're too young for such dangerous work." Of course, I don't think of myself that way at all. After all the hardships I've lived through, and so many ways that I've come to understand myself and learn about other people—beyond what most 14 year olds experience—I believe there's nothing I can't do, or, at least, try to do. And one thing I do know for sure is that I don't give up. I keep on going. No matter what. Besides, with the help and guidance of the other resistance fighters, I'm sure I won't let them down. All the same, I wonder if I can persuade my mother.

I decide to ask Kosti to help me and, for yet another time, he comes to the rescue when I explain my concern to him about speaking to my mother.

"I have something important to tell you," he says to her. "I know that you have been imbued with the democratic spirit of the Franklin Delano Roosevelt era. Your daughter, as a member of the youth resistance executive board, will take upon herself, with the guidance of other fellow men and women partisans, the responsibility and the organization of lectures, theatrical performances, and the writing and distribution of leaflets in the villages of this province, to nurture and revitalize the antifascist spirit of the citizens. I know her dream—as is yours who are actively involved in the liberation struggle—is to leave a liberated, independent and democratic Hellas when all of you return to America at the end of the war."

To my surprise she agrees without a moment's hesitation and is glad to go. I realize how much it means to her to be free of obligations to others; this is a chance to find a way out and live on our own.

The *andartes* immediately arrange for our departure to Verdikousia, a distant village in the hinterlands of Thessaly, the seat of the Central Committee. We'll travel with an experienced guide, the shepherd *Barba* Lefteris, Efi's husband, who is familiar with crossing the Dead Zone. As soon as he finds out about the plans, he drops in to make the necessary arrangements.

"You know what this means?" *Barba* Lefteris says the minute he walks in. "I'm putting my head in the noose, sticking my head in the sack, like we say here, to take you through the Germans with their big guns and their patrols. It's a big job, not a joke." He heaves a sigh. "You don't escape from the Germans, even if you're God," he says. "I'll take you. Nobody knows the way like I do. I pray I'll come back alive to my wife and children," he adds, before leaving.

Feverish excitement precedes our preparations to go to the headquarters in Verdikousia. There's much work to be done, and I must be at my post promptly to take over my responsibilities.

We leave just as dark sets in. My mother helps Tasio climb the mule and our guide tells me to ride the donkey.

I'm excited at the thought of beginning a new adventure.

"We have a long way to go; it'll take us a couple of days to get there. What do you think?" *Barba* Lefteris directs his remarks to me, perhaps sensing my restlessness.

"I marvel at your bravery in setting out on such a dangerous mission," my mother tells him.

"It's what I know how to do. These days, though, you gotta be lucky. Anyhow, I think you must have a strong heart to travel such a long way. I hope we have a safe trip," he says, making the sign of the cross.

We head south toward Dolihi, the last town before the Dead Zone. The animals' hoofs sound hollow in the stillness of the dead of night. It makes me angry to hear them, as though they are to blame for the noise they make. We take our lives in our hands once again, and cross that hateful highway, there where a single shot is enough to remove us from the face of the earth. Next we travel toward Likoudi, and after, at Kefalovriso, we cross the river to arrive at the church of the Holy Ascension where we'll spend the night.

"Tomorrow we will set off before daybreak," our guide advises us, as we get ready to enter the church vestibule to rest for a while. "I'll be right outside with the livestock. If I hear a strange noise, I'll call out. Be on the alert to move fast if I give the word."

Before we even settle down on an old rug in the back of the church, *Barba* Lefteris' voice startles me.

"Time to go," he calls softly.

It feels as though it's been only five minutes, I think. Groping in the half-dark, we wash our faces at the nearby fountain, have a drink of cool water, and speed away.

As we move south before heading uphill toward the tall Kissavos mountain, the second highest in the country, *Barba* Lefteris tells us we have another day of travel before we reach our destination.

"Oh, we're going through bad times," he says, just as day breaks on the horizon. He swishes the mule's hindquarters.

"What hasn't this land of ours seen!" my mother says, almost as an aside.

"Look at the valley. This whole place, see how the enemies ruined it?" He points ahead. "They've done damage as far as the eye can see, not counting the other worse things." He pulls at the reins to keep the animal from sliding down the ditch. "How many brave lads were killed for nothing! You can't even count them. Do you suppose the living have it any better? Folk have no bread. They eat newspapers to stay alive. Newspapers!" He shakes his head.

"So much suffering." My mother sighs. "So much to tell, and so much not to." She wipes her brow before putting on her dark glasses that she managed to save by keeping them tucked in her bosom along with our citizenship papers. She always makes a point of saying how valuable they are because we can't return to America without our birth certificates and other papers. Then she wears her sunglasses that make her look odd in this deserted land.

"Now you look like one of them tourist ladies we saw before the war." *Barba* Lefteris laughs genially, and the gloom is lifted momentarily.

"Is this near the Sarantaporo straits where that big battle took place?" I ask, looking back toward the northwest.

"Oh, yeah, the Germans got what was coming to them," he says, rubbing his hands and hastening his pace. "They say the partisans received instructions from the British who were stationed in Egypt, I think. Anyhow, whoever told them, there were more than a hundred enemy dead and twice as many wounded, plus many trucks loaded with guns, ammunition, and gasoline that they captured," he concludes, raising his voice with evident pride.

"I also remember that battle well," my mother adds. "It got a lot of attention at the time since many of our local boys from Elassona, Katerini, and Olympos town were fighting there. In fact, one of the leaders was from my hometown, you know Alexis Laikos, don't you?" she asks without waiting for an answer, knowing the hero's widespread fame. "Who can forget the German reprisals against the villages that were near places where there were resistance attacks?" she adds in a mournful voice. "My God, those brutes were vicious!" she exclaims.

By and by we start heading uphill toward the tall Kamvounia mountains, like proud youth in their prime, and after another day's travel we reach Verdikousia, a mountain village girded by centuries old, towering evergreens—spruce and pine, mostly, and some oak trees. *Barba* Lefteris leads us to the small village square where the head of the youth movement is waiting for us.

"What can I tell you?" he tells my mother with deep emotion before leaving. "I've seen what you've been through. Now, who knows what will happen to you? Will you ever go back to America with your children, the way you want to?" he asks and wipes his eyes glistening with tears.

"Who knows what lies ahead? Pray for us to go back to America alive," she answers, and her eyes flutter with fear. "I can't thank you enough..." she murmurs through her muffled crying.

"Now I leave you in the hands of God." He waves goodbye and heads downhill.

Verdikousia is a picturesque village, perched high up on the mountain that has protected it from enemy troops and has spared it from the worst ravages of the war. Its remote location explains why it was chosen as the seat of the youth headquarters of Thessaly.

The few houses built of local mud bricks offer only the barest necessities. The functionary assigns us to a barren room in a half-broken-down house among poor but hospitable people who try in every way to make us comfortable. For the first time, after so many years, we're on our own. Freed of obligations to others for our daily bread, we can breathe easy. We're poor, living with many hardships, but we're independent. That means a lot, particularly to my mother.

"I'm tired of always being the victim of circumstance. Even now…but at least we're not a burden to others and we're not under someone else's command. I'm tired of hearing that we're eating their food. At least now, whatever I eat sticks to my ribs—even a piece of dry bread whenever we can get it," my mother says with a deep, liberating sigh.

My footsteps are synchronized with the new rhythm of fighting in the resistance movement. I work hard, and I'm constantly on the go. I visit one village after another, giving talks, editing and printing newspapers, distributing leaflets that were illegally handed out in Elassona and other German-occupied towns. It's a life full of unexpected perils. I'm always on the alert for dangers that may lie in wait at every turn, whether it's running into Nazi commandos or hunger—a constant menace—not to speak of bad weather and storms. As for the Dead Zone, it's become part of my regular routine. The old fear, which used to have such a spell on me, is long gone.

I start from the office of the central committee one day, carrying a hand-crafted shepherd's staff given to me as a gift by a local villager who saw me heading downhill on the dirt road toward the valley stretching for miles below.

"Take this, my girl, around here you need protection from the wild animals and wolves prowlin' around in this here wilderness."

His concern moves me deeply because I am so used to facing risky conditions on my own, without a supportive arm around my shoulder, that I have forgotten what it's like to have someone care about me.

"Thank you, *Barba*," I say, overjoyed, calling him "uncle" affectionately. "What's your name?" I ask.

"Yiankos." He flashes a broad, good-natured smile that reaches all the way to his ears.

"*Barba* Yianko, I wish a long life to you and your children and grandchildren," I add, beaming with pleasure at his kind gift.

"*Ainde,* may you go well." His soft brown eyes twinkle. "And remember to bring us peace." He waves, motioning to his watchdog to follow him.

"Have faith and it will come soon," I call out, lightly tripping downhill, holding onto my staff across my shoulders as I had seen shepherds do. Nothing can frighten me any longer.

Whenever I return to the seat of the executive board, I always find Tasio waiting for me, like the rising sun. He's the first one to spot me at the bend in the road, and by the time I get in town, he's stirred up the whole neighborhood with his gleeful shouts.

"There she is, she's coming, she's coming." His childish voice echoes across the hills as he runs to give me a big hug.

Who knows how strange my comings and goings to unknown places must seem to him. No matter how much I say or try to describe, it's still strange to him. Then again, I don't want to alarm him about the dangers I have to face. The time we spend together is special, partly because it's rare, usually only a few hours, though sometimes I stay overnight. I listen closely to his latest stories, as we walk home holding hands.

"Come, let's play hopscotch," he suggests.

"O.K.," I agree.

"No, I want to play hide-and-seek, I can play hopscotch by myself."

We run, chasing each other in the yard until it's time for me to have a bite to eat and leave.

"When are you coming back?" he asks me one day, casually kicking a stone along the road. Only his voice gives him away.

"Oh, in a few days. I have a lot of work to do down in the valley."

He avoids looking directly at me.

"And what will you do there?" he asks, holding on to me a moment longer. His looks far away with a pained look on his face.

"I have to write some articles because we're organizing a big meeting for women. We have to let people know that women have to fight even harder to win their freedom."

"Where are they coming from?" he asks.

"They'll come from all over…"

His little hand covers my mouth. "Can I come, too?"

We exchange a tender glance.

"Sure, why not. When there's another one near here. Maybe next time. Now it's too far for you."

I smile and kiss him good-bye.

He watches with a sorrowful expression until I make a sharp turn and take the familiar dirt path downhill.

These are hard times, and the struggle to survive is difficult for everyone, but for my colleagues in the movement, even more so. Nevertheless, the fact that I have assumed such a responsible position gives me the courage to face the most trying circumstances with courage and determination. Even my mother recognizes my contribution.

"Being dependent on others," she says one day, "has been one of the heaviest burdens to bear, one of the hardest blows of the occupation. Now, after all these years, that millstone has been lifted from my chest. And I owe it to you. You are supporting us, and through your work we'll be self-sufficient." A wan smile brightens her face.

The quiet, reflective hours with my colleagues are infrequent and perhaps for that reason alone are more precious. We chat over a meal, putting aside the most urgent needs and worries for a while to enjoy talking about each other's experiences and share the food amongst ourselves whenever the villagers have some to offer us, which is certainly not always the case. Ravenously hungry, we constantly scrounge for something to eat to stay our hunger pangs, no joking matter.

On the road, we try to make do with whatever happens our way, but the spirit of true friendliness is always there.

"Oh, never mind, Thomas, you eat it, I'm full," Nikolis insists, and his laughing brown eyes flicker mischievously, adding a singular brightness to his pale face.

"Yes, yes, I know. What year is this you're talking about?" Thomas's voice is hoarse from the nagging bronchitis that he suffers from.

He's constantly shaking off illnesses, and in the end he succumbs to T.B. in his twenty-first and last year of life.

"Well, whatever is left, we'll throw it to the chickens," Lena says, assuming one of her dramatic poses. She's always reminding us about the poor chickens.

"Oh, for heavens sake, drop it," we all cry out, but she just ignores us.

"Now, now, let's not forget the poor things, they've been practically exterminated." She mock-weeps for the pitiful birds.

"After we're liberated," I pipe up, "I'm going to eat for three days and nights without stopping." I sigh, and we all have a hearty laugh over my wistful fantasy.

We try to make light of our suffering and hardships. Our reward for our hard work is to know that the struggle for freedom marches on.

"Remember when you went to find Yianni?" Thomas asks me while we're chatting one evening, either leaning against the banister or seated cross-legged on the floor.

"Even I do, and my hair stands on end," Lena gushes.

"Oh, come now, let's not overdo it," I protest.

"So, will you tell us what happened or should I?" Nikolis insists, twisting his thin mustache with slender, tobacco-stained fingers. "Tell us. Go on, don't be shy." And before I have a chance, he starts.

"What I remember is that it was a difficult job. You had to deliver some urgent information to our people in Kardista about the demonstration. Right?" He pauses momentarily. "Your contact was to wait near the Dead Zone.

337

About an hour's time to reach the river, then heading directly east a little ways, and from there it would be just a short distance from the bottom of the mountain. By then the sky had cleared up after that rainfall..."

"You mean heavy downpour," Thomas abruptly cuts in.

"A torrent. Three days and nights, I thought it would never end..." Nikolis stops in the middle of the sentence, racked by an asthmatic cough, and bids me to continue.

"The river had overflowed completely. It was something else. I had never in my life seen such a raging force. I was nearly paralyzed with fear. But then again, there was no room for delay; Yiannis was waiting for me within earshot of the enemy sentry-box."

"He must have been counting the seconds," Nikolis speaks up softly, puffing at his cigarette.

"That was tormenting me. Well, to get to the point, I rush headlong into the freezing water, holding on tight to my walking stick. I thrust it in front of me with all my might, hoping it will break the force of the turbulent water long enough to give me a chance to touch solid ground before the fury of the river knocks me down."

"I know that treacherous river," Thomas interjects.

"I reach the opposite bank and run to find Yiannis before it's too late. I get there with my heart in my throat. I look around—not a trace of him. Only an eerie silence. I pause, move ahead an inch, and I see a shadow stir. Enemy or friend? I have to take my chances. I advance, and there he is! Ready to take off. I extend my hand—our prearranged signal—and we exchange a fleeting glance. That's it. We disappear, one heading east, the other west."

"How come the German sentries didn't get wind of you?" Nikolis muses to himself.

338

"I still can't figure it out. I could clearly hear them talking..." I shudder.

"Saved by a stroke of good luck," Lena whispers, and for a moment there is silence.

"Yiannis must have been startled to see you dripping wet from head to toe," Thomas blurts out.

"It never crossed my mind," I say, wiping my forehead.

"Yeah, and what happened to you, you daring creature?" Nikolis wants to know.

"I remember crawling noiselessly between the corn stalks, then making a beeline for the nearest town and knocking on the first door. Before I even open my mouth, the startled couple grabs me and pulls me inside. They wrap me up in one of those prickly goat's hair blankets, but I still can't stop shivering. Finally I tell them I have to go, but they refuse. So I give in and wait until dawn to head for my next assignment."

"Then again," Thomas picks up the thread of conversation after a while, "I remember when we were in a hurry to organize the regional congress. I had to visit so many villages."

"Yeah, and we were waiting for you in Moshohori to deliver the information we needed for printing the newspaper, *The Laokratia,*" I add, noticing a cloud pass across Thomas's face like a streak of lightning before he continues pensively.

"While we were talking at Kir Andonis' house, I hear a screeching sound. I thought the heavens had broken loose. I looked up and what did I see: three huge sheep dogs chasing poor Lena round and round the fence. The owner called them back just in time, otherwise...they would have torn her to pieces. What a close call. If you had seen those dogs when he whistled, they were comical. They put on their brakes so fast, you'd think their rear ends were peppered with a dose of salts," he says, and we all laugh.

"Never mind the dogs, I was petrified. The whistle scared me even more, and I took off like a maniac. Then I heard Thomas call me—'Lena, Lena, come back.' That's when I came to my senses a bit and turned back." She leans against the banister and wipes her flushed forehead.

"How did the dogs get outside?" I ask.

"Oh, well, the owner forgot that Lena was coming, and he let them out," Thomas explains.

"If you hadn't heard me, I would've been in real trouble." She smiles. "So many narrow escapes, it would take hours to tell all."

"What matters most is to carry on our struggle that I'm sure we will win, knowing the people are on our side. That's what keeps us going," Thomas says, and we part.

In this time of mass mobilization the women are an integral part of the titanic struggle, playing a decisive role in the fight for freedom—their own and the country's. Hundreds of women from all over the countryside participate in the congress, walking proudly, heads held high, determined along the way to their destination, confident of their position in the liberation movement, of their contribution to the world's vital concerns. Many *andartisses*—women freedom fighters in the partisan army—march forward, self-assured.

These very same women who two short years earlier didn't dare step outside their own houses to extend a simple greeting, mumbling between their teeth some inarticulate sound, the same ones who didn't know which way is up, now stand straight and tall, like fruit-bearing trees. Sharp-witted, eagle-eyed—real leaders—they give lectures and inspire younger women with courage. They stride to the podium to chronicle their long-standing suffering and oppression of the peasants who suffered exploitation, tyranny, and deprivation. The women recount their past and remember vividly years—no, centuries—of subjugation by the big landowners who terrorized their people into submission, forcing them to work the land under the most horrible conditions and then demanding that they hand over the crops they sweated all year long to produce.

"Nothing was left for us, save poverty, disease, and misery. Today we say NO to all that. The past is behind us." A fresh beginning beckons ahead.

"We have set ourselves new goals. This is an era of self-determination for people and for nations. We demand equality between men and women. We expect to move upward in the economic, political, and social spheres. Women constitute the unshakable, invincible support system in the world. We declare our human rights as women. They must be granted. Without pleas and begging. We want to share and to enjoy equally the fruit of our labor."

The tone is decisive, the message clear. "Mankind depends on us to raise, to educate our offspring—boys and girls—to solve their problems, to heal their wounds. We want to save and not send the children we bear to war, to their destruction. This is our new focus. It will be achieved only when our people are free in their own land."

Spontaneous outbursts of approval ring from shore to shore. "New life marches ahead...down with thrones and oppression," everyone sings with one voice, with but a single hope. Thousands of women and men chant, unified by a single vision.

If it is true, according to the teachings of Buddha, that you are what you live, that when you own a field, you only think of a field, you are an inseparable part of it and

341

become a field, then our only remaining possession is a flame, an outcry, a quest for freedom. All our belongings are destroyed, we are no longer preoccupied with material possessions, our personal concern over insignificant daily activities is a thing of the past that has left in its wake an unquenchable thirst, a divine Olympic torch to light our way, to lead to the eradication of oppression, to the declaration of freedom.

The closer the hour draws to the banishment of the machine-driven conquerors from our soil, the more bestial they become. The wounded monster sharpens its teeth before it dies. Sensing their end is near, the German invaders slay, torture, rape, burn, demolish with unparalleled fury and mania, even for them. Panic-driven as they are, they behave with ruthless, raw terrorism. As though the ravaging of our country for years is not enough, these last days of the occupation witness unequaled brutality and reprisals.

"If any attempts against us are made during our retreat," they warn, "we will turn Greece into a wasteland." They try to break down the morale of the people who suffered some of the bloodiest days the nation has ever seen. Bloody and glorious.

The *andartes,* in their continuous struggle, fire and are fired at in fierce battles against the barbaric Hitlerian fascists. The unconquerable people are not intimidated into submission. They mobilize into the most determined resistance force yet seen, unifying their resources, joining with the liberation army to wage the final triumphant battle to insure that the blue and white banner of liberty will once more wave above the sacred cliff of Acropolis. Only then will all the struggles and sacrifices be vindicated.

Liberation is celebrated in the land like the first lilting song of spring. Under an azure-blue sky, singing resounds with freedom, the sun embraces the earth with freedom, the air fills with the glorious light of freedom. On top of the tallest mountain, ecstatic with joy, I climb to freedom, to liberate my heart and soul in song.

"Free-ee-ee-dom, Free-ee-ee-dom, *Eleutheria-a-a-a,*" I shout. My voice, born anew, roars, echoing over and over, bouncing from one proud mountain crest to another, flying away and again returning through the ethereal light, blending with the lowing of sheep, resounding across to the far ends of the earth: sing, sing, sing to our thousand-times-blessed freedom.

Down below on the highway, the black anthill of the Nazi monster groans in an awful death rattle, taking to Hades the black reign of terror and horror they have inflicted on the land to deprive us of our liberty. Watching them go away, I feel that a terrible burden is lifted, and I am filled with a radiant excitement, akin to a child's first awakening to the light of day.

In village squares and city streets, people surge forward, dancing with flags and banners held high above their heads, with a flame in the heart, singing a hymn to this thrilling day of unrivaled joy. It fulfills the realization of a dream that stirs every heart—a fervent wish for peace among humankind.

27 THE RETURN

"A fresh breeze ushers in hope for a new and better life for all," newspaper headlines declare. *"Laokratia,* the rule of the people, shall prevail in this birthplace of democracy." We throw ourselves with youthful enthusiasm into the job of rebuilding our country from the ashes, redoubling our efforts to carry our message of peace and prosperity to every part of the land.

Now that we are fully liberated, the executive board of the youth organization decides to transfer our headquarters from Verdikousia down to the valley of Elassona. We can be within easier reach of the towns where we work and be able to coordinate our work more efficiently. In mid October we move to Magoula, a small nearby village, where we set up another temporary household to take care of our everyday needs. Our belongings are down to the bare necessities since we have nothing left. We follow the road toward creative rehabilitation. The needs are enormous, but we're ready to meet the challenge. A perfect unity reigns in our cloudless sky.

Soon I receive a message that I'm being transferred to Katerini. We stop on the way in Elassona. Exuberant outbursts fill the streets, and for three days we feast, as I had once dreamed!

The road is the same one we traveled before, yet how it has changed. The path of fear and death is now adorned with triumph and victory. Marching through untamed mountain cliffs, we go past hide-outs of proud freedom fighters of old that remind us of the heroic battles that brought us freedom. People pour into the road to greet each other, to bring together laughter with sorrow, tears with rejoicing.

Steadily, we head toward Thessaloniki, the starting point of our unforgettable journey.

Liberated Katerini is a sight to behold. Jubilation, dancing to the joyous rhythms of life, singing in the streets, fun-filled festivities, the proverbial *ylendi* with *kefi*—that almost indescribable *joie de vivre*—go on until all hours of the morning. The celebrations match and surpass everything we've seen until now. Enthusiasm, beauty, youth—the jewel and pride of our generation. Pent-up emotions spring loose and bubble to the surface like sparkling champagne, pouring out of the intoxicating bottle of happiness.

Side by side with this joy beyond belief, are memorials for the war dead, the resistance heroes and heroines, the countless victims of the occupation. The traitors are also remembered for dishonoring their country, for blemishing the good name of our people, for adding to the heavy burden of the occupation.

"Putana!" Whore! Stones are thrown at the clean-shaven heads of women collaborators seated facing the donkey's ass—the ultimate humiliation—while they are paraded around town. Throngs of people spit, hiss, and curse them for selling their bodies to the enemy.

The names of informers are made public, unleashing a fury from the victims' families.

"Traitors, traitors!" people cry out and hurl vicious epithets when the lists are posted in the town square. Phtoo! They grind their spittle into the dirt. "The scum, they deserve no pity!" Cries of outrage fill the streets. "The enemy was, after all, the enemy, but our own? They sold out to them. Innocent people were killed. So many sent to death camps."

New horror stories surface every day. So many people were betrayed by their own countrymen, as the Germans themselves admit—not the Nazi S.S. but hired mercenaries from occupied lands, showed the terrified captives drawers full of false accusations. "Your own townspeople brought them in," they declared. Those quislings are hated even more than the enemy.

"They have to pay for what they did. They deserve their punishment," the hue and cry is heard, as enemy collaborators are brought to trial for their heinous crimes.

Sometimes the pain goes deeper. Trying to bring justice backfires, and many families are plunged into despair when brother comes face to face with brother—one a freedom fighter, the other a traitor. The bloodshed continues...

Each home has its own lament; each grief brings a flood of tears. Among all our other losses, when we reach Katerini I find out that Aunt Fani passed away.

"It's all written in the books," she believed. She, too, suffered her full share of misery and sadness, enduring her unsmiling fate without complaining. There's no doubt that the hardships of the war stressed her to the limit and hastened her departure.

Thoughts of her surround me; I can almost hear her voice... I feel her presence that so often approached me in my dreams, yet I will never see her again to touch her silvery hair, to look at her sad face.

"Life is so strange," Aunt Anthoula says, tenderly holding my hand and caressing me with her soft brown eyes. "It bonds us with love, then fragments us with the pain of parting and sorrow."

We remain silent for a long time snuggled close to each other. I want to hold onto this moment before it's snatched away from me, knowing that very soon we must leave again.

After hours of waiting for a boat on the beach near Katerini, it's almost dark when we push and shove in the water to clamber on board. The ship takes off, but there are still many left behind. I suddenly realize that my mother, Tasio, and cousin Yiorgo are among them. I yell and scream, waving frantically, trying to tell the crew to let them on. I can't even be heard above the tumult in that wild mob scene. In vain I frantically wave my arms in the air.

The overcrowded boat sails full steam ahead, rocking unsteadily from the heavy load, so I resign myself to the inevitable.

I gaze toward the dim lights of Katerini rapidly disappearing on the horizon. A cool damp sea breeze gently brushes my cheek as the boat picks up speed and heads for Thessaloniki, bringing back vivid recollections of so much that has happened over the past years. Memories of the odyssey we've been through won't let go of me. I try to put them in a semblance of order. As I scan my recollections I keep asking myself: *What is this feeling that weighs on me, something indistinct and cloudy, like the bottom of a turbulent ocean?*

For a reason I can't explain, I'm unsettled by a thought that hounds me. It seems as if a shadow is following me, expecting an answer.

I can still feel a pair of gray eyes peering intently.

At this moment, going over in my mind the countless things that happened, I can't figure out why his glance was not at once familiar to me when I saw him in Magoula. Yet something told me I had seen him before. A memory held me prisoner, asking for recognition, but everywhere it was silent and dark. Instantly there was a change when a familiar voice asked to see the poster I was making, and I stretched out my hand to give it to him. He gave me a curious, almost frightened, look. I didn't know why. I never thought to ask.

I can see him standing before me now, slender, with a long, blondish beard, a wide forehead, and large, deep-set eyes that had such a pained expression, full of anticipation.

"Yianni," I called out, remembering where I had met him. A smile softened his serious face. He gave me his hand, as he had in that fleeting moment in the rainstorm when I brought him an important message, just steps away from an enemy patrol, at the doorstep of death.

Yiannis, his pseudonym from the days of the occupation, sidled up to me one day when I was working on a project, as though he wanted to say something to me, but he just went away and circled around aimlessly in the yard until I was ready to leave and he walked me home, as he did lately.

He started talking about our next newspaper edition.

"The articles made quite an impression on me, especially yours, better than the last one." Then out of the blue his expression changed. "From the first minute..." his voice sounded different, "I wanted to tell you...that...there's something special about you," he finally blurted out. "Whatever you do has its own style, a uniqueness which I like."

His words left me speechless. I had been doing things that seemed natural to me, spontaneously, and I saw no reason for praise. He continued in the same vein. My train of thought veered elsewhere. *He impresses with his plainness,* I said to myself. The essential meaning of that word was established forever by his presence, as though it was

with him in mind our ancestors thought it up. *So perfect.*
I forced myself to breathe out slowly.

"Love," I heard him say, "is based on affection, mutual respect, and consideration." In a severe tone he went on, "I want us to know each other better, to be able to understand each other without using words. Until then, neither a kiss nor an embrace. Silence. We will communicate only with our eyes. Love is a serious matter, not a game, as many believe."

I looked at him, dumbstruck. His words made a deep impression on me, perhaps because I had never before met anyone with such ideas about the philosophy of love. I was seized by strange feelings. Neither joy nor excitement—just something indescribable, as though I was suspended in midair.

I stayed awake all night, trying to decide if words, for sure, are needed for understanding each other, to figure out what it must be like to express thoughts without making a sound, just by looking. If so, could I do it?

Where did he get hold of such ideas anyhow? They're giving me a headache! I can't put up with him or with myself. In the morning I was feeling upset, and I left to work on the publication of our paper. We would talk again in a few days. Then came my transfer to Katerini.

I ran to find Yiannis, but he had disappeared. *What will happen to his questions? Will his love end before it even begins?* I went home depressed. At the last moment I saw a mutual acquaintance and asked him to give a message to Yianni.

"I don't know if I'll see him. You seem concerned. Don't mull things over too much. Take them as they come," he advised me and smiled.

I had a strange feeling, almost a premonition. We were parting without exchanging either a word or a glance. How would Yiannis explain that?

As I stand here at the ship's bow, many other thoughts come to mind, rekindling what we experienced these last years. Years that are deeply engraved in my memory, people and events that shall forever remain an inseparable part of me. Visions that are burned into my consciousness that I know, and have always been sure, if we survived, would become an indestructible force, a beacon of light guiding my life.

These true reminiscences are rooted in the wellsprings of life itself, possessing a vitality that surges from the innermost depths of this earth. They are carved out of the steep, craggy mountain rocks we climbed, shaped by the fierce winds and the rivers and valleys we crisscrossed before boarding this ship for our return.

Now, in the middle of the sea, surrounded by this small ocean of people, I feel a warm vibration joining together in a shared feeling of warmth, of knowing that we'll forever be part of each others' lifelines, linked together in a circle of friends who will not forget, whatever happens to separate us or cast us far away to distant lands. This bond, this attachment, will remain unsevered, unaltered. No one will ever be truly alone again. We're strangers, yet a single heartbeat unites us because we all struggled—each in our own way—to fulfill a common yearning and achieve a great victory by keeping alive the spirit of trust in humanity for these many years. We recognize in each other a part of humankind in all its multitude of names and faces, as infinite as human variability.

I stand alone on the prow, gazing at the past.

"I can somehow feel the weight of sixty years' experience on my shoulders," I confide to a woman standing by my side.

"Why sixty?" she asks.

"I don't know. For sure, I can't quite tell why," wondering myself at her question.

"You must feel tired," she interrupts my train of thought.

"Not tired or depleted. All I know is...it feels heavy. I've been through a lot..."

"What were you doing in Katerini?" she asks after a while.

"Oh, we just stopped to visit relatives, and now...we're going back..." I say, watching the dark clouds gather.

"How long have you been away?" she asks again.

"A long, long time, forever, it seems..." I pause, lost in reverie.

The sea begins to swell, pregnant with a mysterious churning. Soon near-gale winds raise strong waves that toss us from one side of the boat to the other. I feel seasick and try to hang on tight so I won't fall overboard. Huge waves send gallons of water cascading over my head, like it's the end of all creation.

It would be strange, I think, *if this is the way I'll go, after all we've been through.*

A young woman standing next to me helps me hold on to the boat long enough to steady myself. Then, in one swift motion, the boat changes direction and heads for the port of Thessaloniki where we'll be harbored from the rough seas.

Calm returns once more as daylight finds us ashore in Aretsou, a picturesque seaside area in the outskirts of Thessaloniki, where we often went before the war for all-day

351

excursions on a white ship, appropriately called *Lefki,* that glided through the waters of the Thermaic Gulf like a gleaming dolphin. We disembark by twos and threes, leaving footprints that quickly disappear under new ones in the sea-damp sand.

I realize I'm stranded out here all alone without transportation. I don't even have any way of contacting Aunt Vangelia. My mother has her address. All I know is that she made her way to the city after the burning of Paliocastro, but she's not expecting me since the boat made an unscheduled departure from Katerini, and she has no phone. I have no idea what to do or where to go.

"Come along, you're one of us." A woman standing near me takes my hand, like one of her own. "My name is Galatea." She glances warmly at me. "We've all been together in this struggle, so we're not really strangers," she adds.

"I don't know if I can tell you how I feel..." I answer, taking her arm.

"Come, my girl," she urges, whisking me away. We go to her house in Seih Sou, the woodland slope where my class went for springtime picnics in prewar days. Images of bright red poppies blooming on the hillside where we played, instantly come to mind. Her family welcomes me like their own child, extending a friendliness that breaks down all barriers.

I feel a deep stirring when I look at the Thermaic harbor of Thessaloniki stretched out before me in the full light of morning. The sea glistens, unwrinkled, taut from one end to the other, harboring the longing of so many years:

THE SEA
At last the sea has merged with my tears.

Oft-traveled sorrow,
Ocean-gazing grief.
Wails flood the forlorn shore.
Imploringly I seek
A gently swaying ship,
Thrice denied an infant
On a windswept coast.
I return to an earlier desolation.
A distant murmur silently glides,
Embracing me insatiably.
Life resurrects a tree.

Thessaloniki is as enchanting as ever, like a beautiful woman who shows the ravages of age and pain but still retains her mysterious, seductive hold on you.

On the day the city was liberated, the victorious entrance of Bishop Seraphim, accompanied by partisan leaders, was an epiphany. His proud stance, photographed under the Gallerian Arch on Egnatias Street, eternalized the moment of liberation for which he fought valiantly against such overpowering odds. Then he offered a solemn prayer for the thousands of brave priests and church dignitaries who were executed by the Nazis during the long struggle for freedom.

It's been four whole years since we left. Relatives—lost to time and place—begin to arrive one by one, all except those who shall never return...

"A profound change has taken place in the world. We're witnessing the end of one epoch and the beginning of a new one," Meteoritis says and smiles mysteriously as of old, his arms dangling at his sides.

Soon after I get back, he comes to greet me. We stroll along the waterfront, the *paralia,* and immediately get involved in a discussion, reminiscing and catching up with what happened over the years. He's been living here and working in the underground—a very different life from ours. We're both eager to hear stories of each other's adventures and bridge the gap of a long separation.

"Unfortunately, the new awakening could only have occurred after people experienced what they did, forcing them to see the stark reality through the prism of war and suffering," I suggest.

"Well, of course, that's a component of the mechanism of change," Meteoritis answers, raising his voice slightly. "And yet how many have remained aloof or, worse still, collaborated with the enemy, distinguishing themselves by their absence in the resistance movement? We've had our share of quislings," he adds, wiping his creased forehead. It seems as though each fold in his brow holds within it years of untold suffering.

I'm disturbed by what's happening, and I long to find out from him what he thinks of these developments. "Tell me," I say, "is the situation as explosive as it seems to me?"

"Oh, yes, and more," he pauses to take a deep breath and I wait. "You see, Athens, like Paris, was liberated by the resistance army, before the British arrived. An army of some 100,000 men strong laid down their lives to save our country from the nazi-fascist tyrants and now they're being asked to disarm and surrender to another foreign power. But the freedom fighters are also determined not to yield their weapons and have vowed to resist premier George Papandreous' request to disband by Christmas."

"Is he on the side of the British?" I ask.

"He's playing politics, as usual. He wants to stay in power, so he's trying to maneuver both sides to suit his aims. The ploy is to make the expatriate army that was stationed in Egypt the nucleus of the new Greek National Army," he stops in the middle of the street to light a cigarette.

"I heard that Stephanos Saraphis, the resistance leader, expressed strong opposition to that plan. He has the strength of his army and the will of the people behind him, so why doesn't he stand firm?" I wonder out loud.

"Well, of course he should. But you know, the Allies made a supposedly secret agreement that after the end of the war Greece would be under the British sphere of influence, so they have the upper hand now. Saraphis is worried that the monarcho-fascist forces will take advantage of that move to return the Royalist Army and use it as a means of bringing back King George."

"Greek King George Glucksburg who doesn't have a single drop of Greek blood in his veins," I add, and we both chuckle.

"I must go now," Meteoritis says, and lingers momentarily. "The resistance fighters, along with the majority of the Greek people, are vehemently opposed to restoring the rule of the king without a plebiscite. The people's vote should decide the king's fate," he adds at a clipped pace.

"We'll talk again soon." He dashes away with his hands thrust in the pockets of that same blue gabardine raincoat he wore in the underground. I let myself be drawn by the sight of his slightly bent-over frame that diminishes until all I can see is a small spot at the end of the street. Then I start walking back to Aunt Vangelia's house.

"Such an odyssey you went through!" exclaims Aunt Vangelia as she embraces my mother with tears in her eyes, as soon as she sees her arriving with Tasio from Katerini. "At least if we could have been together."

My cousin Katina, a mere slip of a girl when I last saw her, pops in. She greets me with a pretentious politeness I'm not accustomed to. A real city lady now, she offers me a limp hand and a quick peck on the cheek, her lips as cold as her hand. "Well, you came," she says in a dry voice.

"Yes, we came." *What else can I say? Can she understand?* I stand there astonished at her indifference about our years of suffering.

"Everything is heading toward normalcy now." She laughs flirtatiously.

"How did you figure that out?" my mother asks, slightly miffed by her disdainful air.

"Oh, haven't you read the paper? In Varkiza the royalists who just returned from Egypt..." She pulls out the newspaper from her handbag.

"Where they fled with the country's entire treasury to escape the war," my mother interjects.

"Never mind that, it's all over now. They reached an agreement. It's all settled, nothing to worry about." She flashes a gay, nonchalant smile.

"What have they agreed about?" I ask.

"Well, provided the partisans put down their arms and agree to cooperate, they will form a unified government with representation from all the parties. Isn't that wonderful?" She coquettishly strokes her blond curls.

"So, the king is being put back in power? Without elections to find out what the people want?" I inquire, hardly believing my own ears.

"Elections? What for? The British hold the reigns now. Who dares go against them?" Aunt Vangelia says, from the kitchen while she's stirring her famous garlic sauce.

"I certainly hope this will settle matters and keep all those different parties from arguing about who takes over which ministry," my mother calls out. "As though the occupation wasn't enough. Now we have more shootings over power struggles and the settling of old scores."

She turns off the flame, pouring the sauce over pieces of dry bread in a large communal bowl placed in the middle of the table, and the whole family gathers around.

I hurry through my meal to get together with Niko, who is coming over shortly to do our homework together. Like many other students who missed a lot of schooling during the war, we're studying hard to pass make-up exams that will allow us to skip the grades we missed.

"Well, let's get going," Nikos urges. "We have so much catching up to do. You couldn't go to school for three and a half years so you have a lot more ground to cover in a few months."

"Yeah, I know, but don't worry, we'll get it done in time," I reassure him.

Many times we have to go and wait in line on blustery cold mornings for the paltry handouts from UNRRA, the war relief organization. I put aside my studies and brave the fierce Vardari wind blowing right through the bone and shiver, as I stand on the sidewalk in a frayed old jacket and torn shoes full of holes. I feel like hiding in shame at the indignity of having rotten food thrown in our faces by the profiteers who steal what's intended for us.

Luckily, Aunt Vangelia is a source of strength and entertainment for all of us, but most of all for my mother, who often despairs.

"Nowadays long lines are in fashion." Aunt Vangelia flashes a black-stockinged ankle. "We *queue* for hours on end, and what do they dole out? Shoes for the left foot. What do they think we are, pigeon-toed or something?" she fumes in mock indignation.

"Imagine! Sometimes I spend a whole day and end up with a moldy bag of flour. Can they spare it?" my mother says, slumping in the chair. "Those black marketeers probably had a hand in that too. They'll poison us, but what do they care?" she exclaims.

"And besides, you don't get a thing without signing your name a thousand times. You can build a tower with all my signatures, Vangelia Mitropoulou," Aunt Vangelia goes on after a while. "Stacks of paper all the way up to there, touching the sky." She raises her hands, joining her fingertips in an inverted V to show us exactly how that high tower looks.

"Oh, my, you're too much," my mother laughs heartily. She dips her bread in the tomato and onion salad dressing, and the rest of us join in. "You have a knack for making light of hardship with your own inimitable sense of humor." She smiles at her sister with admiration. "I guess it's your passport to survival."

"Well, my heart only knows..." Aunt Vangelia whispers.

As more evidence of mass executions, jailings, and reprisals begins to come to the fore, it is clear that these are not isolated incidents of revenge carried out by reactionary thugs and hoodlums. Many of them are prominent officials who are known former Nazi collaborators. The crisis surges past the boiling point. Suddenly an explosive outburst is unleashed. It catapults an ultra-reactionary government to power against all odds, considering the fact that the resistance forces have on their side the vast majority of the popular sentiment and support. Political tensions, fueled by a growing spiral of terrorism and retaliatory vendettas, are running high.

Things take a turn for the worse when six ministers of the national liberation front withdraw from George Papandreous' government to protest the fact that they were only given secondary ministries in the coalition government, contrary to the terms of the Lebanon agreement reached by all the political parties that there would be equal representation.

A citywide strike is called in Athens that paralyzes all the public places.

Despite the Prime Minister's ban, thousands of demonstrators swarm Constitution Square and the Government Palace to oppose the return of the king. All of a sudden, British soldiers are firing shots into the crowd and the streets are covered with blood. In reprisal, the British Lieutenant General Scobie, acting on Churchill's orders, declares martial law.

It's like the occupation all over again. Spitfires strafe the Parthenon, and the Acropolis is swarming with British, instead of German troops. Scobie, who is stationed at the Hotel Grande Bretagne, has taken over command and set the British terms for an armistice: an immediate surrender of the freedom fighters' weapons. It is heartrending to see our country's liberators relinquish their arms with heads bowed down low in shame.

The latest developments are on everyone's mind. "What do you think of the bloodshed in Athens? Isn't it dreadful?" Aunt Vangelia asks my mother.

"*Aman,* isn't there an end to this strife in our country? It's an eternal curse," my mother bursts out.

"I tremble at the thought that we're next," her sister mumbles.

"We hardly enjoyed our Christmas this year. Once more the country is being plunged into a bloodbath. Imagine, brother killing brother, so close on the heels of the last war. It's a disgrace." My mother's voice sounds deflated, as though this is the last straw.

"Oh, they're just isolated reprisals. Probably a handful of fanatical hotheads acting up," our landlady, Despo, says.

"Well tell me, why did Churchill arrive in Athens on Christmas Eve to intervene in the civil war clash that's been raging for three weeks?" I shout in anger. "It's no secret that he hates the freedom fighters. Obviously he threw his weight against them, and his visit immediately opened the door for the return of the hated king and the establishment of a monarcho-fascist regime," I fume.

"Unfortunately," my mother adds, "the Greek resistance fighters failed to take advantage of that momentous occasion to negotiate better terms for a coalition government in which all the political parties are fairly represented, as they had agreed at the Lebanon Conference. Instead, they withdrew their ministers from the government in a huff, but still ended up surrendering their weapons. They'll pay dearly for that miscalculation."

"Well, one day those foreigners, the so-called big heads, will probably realize their folly, if any of them have any sense, instead of sawdust in their heads," Aunt Vangelia sighs.

"Who knows how many will be lost to the sword...?" My mother wipes a tear from her eye. "I hope we'll sleep in peace tonight."

Our time in Greece is drawing to a close. Soon, exactly when, we're not sure, we'll return to America. After more than two and a half years of separation, Kiki and I managed to send a couple of letters to each other that I saved as a keepsake, tangible evidence of our friendship. Maybe I didn't need it, but in the stark isolation of the occupation, a glance at her familiar handwriting gave me a thrill that I could not feel just thinking about her. Besides, there was never any time for more than that in the endless struggle for survival that dragged on one dreary day after another.

I wonder what will it be like now? Does she still care? Or are new friendships filling her life?

When Kiki and I meet on Egnatias Street, the two of us race wildly toward each other, stirring even the cold pavement that surely must sense the emotion pulling us together like a magnet.

We walk arm in arm for hours on end, talking, crying, and laughing, insatiably, without a pause.

Ever since then Kiki and I become inseparable and plunge into a whirlwind of activities, jumping on the tram that's teeming with people, attending gatherings and demonstrations, joining the thousands of people who stream into the streets from the woods of Seih Sou to the central thoroughfares in the busy market district to demand better living conditions and to declare our entitlement to human rights.

We go everywhere together, but there's one question she can't get out of her mind and never stops nagging me.

"When are you leaving for America? Did you get any news yet from the consulate?"

"No, I don't know yet," I tell her over and over and every time it wrenches my heart, and squeezes my forehead in a vise, pressing my temples tighter and tighter.

"There's so little time left for us to be together," Kiki whimpers before we part for the day. "You're going back to America...your father is sending for you...and I'll be left here all alone."

I put my arm around her shoulder, and then hurry away. Another separation. My life is a never-ending good-bye.

Her constant badgering is driving me crazy, until one day I explode.

"I can't stand this aggravation any more. We're ruining our fun, wasting our time in heartache. Don't you see grief doesn't get us anywhere? We're just losing the chance to enjoy the precious time we have together. These days will never come back. Let's forget about what will happen later."

She casts her melancholy azure gaze far away. The silence pounds my head like a sledgehammer.

"You don't care, you want to leave..."

"Stop. I just don't want to be left with gloomy memories. That's all," I protest.

"O.K., maybe you're right. Let's hold on to today. When we part we'll feel the bitterness of separation, but at least we'll have some happy moments to keep."

At night, after sundown, a harmonica plays a sweet melody under our living room window. "I'll take you away with me to another land, to other places." Bunches of youngsters saunter lazily back and forth along the narrow alley where we live. A few really young-looking kids dance and hop toward Egnatias Street, singing: "Youpi-ya-ya-youp, youpi ya." They prance around, and then fade into the crowd.

Once, a little before nightfall, a metallic noise interrupts the singing, and heavy footsteps are heard on the cobblestone street.

"What's going on?" our landlady, Despo, calls out, and we all crowd around the little window to find out what the commotion is all about.

And what do we see! The street is full of people. Men, women, and children—a whole village-full—bound in chains, are being dragged uphill.

As soon as we notice the police looking in our direction, we hide behind the frayed curtains before we get into trouble.

Where are they taking all those poor people? Despo whispers under her breath, astonished.

"I haven't got the faintest idea what this is all about. But, for sure, it doesn't smell right," my mother says, shaking her head.

"Where are they dragging all those chained people?" I think, baffled.

The following day more people bound in chains are herded past our window in the dark of night.

"It's like a mass evacuation of the countryside," my mother says.

"Meteoritis hasn't been here in days. He can probably tell us what this is all about, but it's definitely not a good sign," I say. "Surely something sneaky is going on, and I don't like it," I add, deeply disturbed.

Meteoritis often flirts with Kiki, who's provocative and pretty. He laughs, clenching his teeth, the way he always does, then takes off just as suddenly as he appeared, seemingly out of nowhere.

Once I step out of the kitchen and overhear Meteoritis, who is on his way out, talking privately to my mother about me with real admiration.

"My, I'm impressed with how much your daughter has changed! She has become so mature," he says, clenching his teeth in a smile.

What I don't know is that Kiki is just coming in and overhears the exchange.

"Oh, so you just flirt with me, but you think nothing of me." She darts in front of them, screeching at the top of her lungs. "I want no part of you anymore." She scoots past him in a big huff.

"I do enjoy talking to your daughter," Meteoritis goes on without paying attention to Kiki's outburst. "I really admire her."

That comment stirs up all kinds of doubts. I loved hearing what he said to my mother, but deep down, compared to Kiki, I don't think I have a chance so I try not seeing him to avoid getting disappointed.

In a few days, after a chance encounter on Egnatias Street, Meteoritis and I stroll down to the harbor side by side. "This is all too reminiscent," he says, "of another assault on our fragile republic, a coup that triggered a bloody three-year dictatorship in 1936, under Ioannis Metaxas who was trained in Germany by the Nazis. Will they bathe the nation again in bloodshed?" he wonders out loud, digging his hands deep into his coat pockets.

"Do you suppose that can really happen?" I ask.

"There's a grave danger that a *clique* of military diehards and foreign powers will bury the democracy we fought so hard to win," he murmurs as he walks along with stooped shoulders.

"Oh, no, Roosevelt won't let that happen. Can't you see everyone is waving American flags? Have you heard anyone support the British?" I answer with confidence, and then study his furrowed brow that seems to reflect his doubts.

"Maybe..." he pauses, abruptly.

"I think some influential members of the old reactionary oligarchy are teaming up with foreign interventionists to crush the people's movement," I suggest.

"It's all part of the imperialist games." A sharp note of sarcasm creeps into his voice. "They're about to install a rightist monarcho-fascist government under the aegis of the British troops who are occupying our country. Isn't that obviously their ploy?" he concludes in anger.

"One more point." He stops in the middle of the street and turns to face me. "You must realize that Churchill was determined to contain a takeover in Greece by the left wing liberation forces at all costs. Communism was anathema to him, and he distorted the purpose of the liberation movement, that was to elect a democratic government of all the people. He became embroiled in a life and death struggle with communism and dreaded what he thought of as a left wing takeover, supported by the Soviet Union. In order to achieve his goal, he made a deal with Russia to offer her a free hand in Rumania with its rich oil fields in return for control over Greece. That was a sure fire prescription for further conflict. It left the people who fought in the liberation movement exposed to attacks from the British who could, and did, use their military force to crush them."

"What about the Americans? How did they see these machinations?" I ask.

"Right after the war, Americans were in favor of supporting the will of the Greek people for a democratic regime and against the return of the king without a popular vote."

"After all, they don't have one. That's why people the world over love the American pro democracy stand," I say.

"Well, that's so, but despite the initial opposition of the US to dividing Europe into spheres of influence, the US succumbed to the British pressure and its stand gradually changed. That coincided with the eventual decline in American popularity here and in other parts of the world. Now, this political polarization is bringing us to a head-on collision course. Things can only get worse," he adds, lowering his head.

As though he's still living in the underground, Meteoritis makes occasional unexpected visits in the same gabardine coat. When there's time, we chat for a while. He has a fierce loyalty to doing everything he can to improve the lot of the poor and to defend human rights. Besides, he knows so much about poetry, music, and philosophy. Talking to him opens up new vistas for me. Then he disappears, and again we lose track of his whereabouts, until one day he resurfaces.

Insatiably, carefree late summer afternoon hours are sucked in like luscious nectar, awakening sensations of eager anticipation in my crowd of friends. Sunburned bodies drawn by the force of an inward light, head for the sea, propelled by an urge to become steeped in the glow of the brilliant sun that beckons to us with a promise of eternal vitality. Our whole group of fellows and girls heads toward Kalamaraki for a dip in the cool refreshing water.

"Let's go farther out," Meteoritis calls to me.

"But I can't swim," I blurt out, feeling my face turning red.

"Don't worry, it's not deep," he urges, and I doggie-paddle, trailing behind the others who can all swim like fish. In deep water, a few feet farther out, he lets go of me.

"O.K., you're on your own," Meteoritis laughs and moves away. Beyond his reach, it's either sink or swim. I could drown him, not so much for anything else, but for his laughter. Amusing himself at my expense. But it's a challenge, and besides, what's the choice?

"See?" I call out in a few minutes. "I can go wherever I want, free as a bird or a fish," and it's my turn to laugh. He swims swiftly toward me, gripping me in a tight embrace. I'm still burning mad at him and protest, but it's no use. His lips cover mine, and the intoxication of the wine-dark sea engulfs us both. Just then the others approach, and we all head for shore. Meteoritis has left me something to remember him by whenever I go swimming.

Now each time we get together someone else is missing from our midst. We dare not ask. We already know the answer. Only too soon we also find out that some, secretly executed, will never return. Others are being sent to the concentration camps on the barren islands of the Aegean Sea where torture and death are daily rations.

28 BETRAYAL

Throngs of people pour into the main thoroughfares shouting slogans, like "Bread and Jobs!" Often there are fierce clashes with British soldiers who frequent the dance halls at night where they run into the couples dancing cheek-to-cheek, repeating an indifferent, "sorry, sorry," and in the daytime they drive their noisy jeeps around like maniacs. The fear and terror they spread is a menace. You never know from which direction danger will hit you; it's almost as bad as the occupation. Their intimidating tactics have no limits. One day walking down King Konstantine Street in the busiest part of the city, British soldiers shoot a man in cold blood right before my eyes. His brains go flying through the air and hit a marble column, then splash in my face like so much bloody confetti. The stunned crowd runs over to see what happened. The British menace us with their bayonets. They stop us dead in our tracks, and order us to leave.

"Go away or you'll be next," our own collaborators yell at the crowd.

No one moves an inch, riveted in place by fear, paralyzed by the sight of the horrible crime.

"An innocent man!" someone cries out.

"He was standing in front of a clothing store and…and I heard a gunshot...the next thing I know he's dead," a horrified passerby says.

"They're stifling the will of the people!" yells a middle-aged man in a frayed blue suit that hangs on his back like rags on a scarecrow.

Unrest has become part of our daily ration.

Hundreds of eyewitnesses and thousands of sympathizers attend the funeral procession, marching in step with the mournful dirge for the latest victim, the people's new hero. The cortege advances slowly on Panepistimiou Street, filing past the gray stone university building where hundreds of students swell the ranks. Amid the wails of the angry crowd, I hear a voice saying my name. I turn left and right to see who's calling me and thread my way across the street to the municipal hospital where I see the disabled veterans of the *andart* resistance army—fierce, ascetic faces—following the procession from afar with heads bowed. All except one. He looks straight at me. He's balding slightly at the temples and unshaven, his left leg is missing below the knee. I go past a knot of people and feel the sting of his glance burning right through me. Our eyes meet and my vision dims in a flood of tears.

"Marko, you here?" I stammer and slowly approach the railing. He leans on one crutch to offer his hand between the iron fence spikes.

"See what's become of us? The heroes of the resistance movement. Our hopes and dreams are gone. Wasted sacrifices. We've been betrayed. Betrayed!"

His unswerving glance nails me. "Now the powers that be are massacring us like sheep," he says, enraged. "Killing us at the doorstep of our own home. What did we fight for? What was the use...? To end up here, scorned?"

With great difficulty I bring before me the sight of Marko fighting courageously next to his proud comrades-in-arms in the mountains for the liberation of our homeland. The vision quickly fades.

"I'll come to visit you. How long will you be here?" I ask.

"Who knows?" He leans his furrowed brow on the rusty railing. "I'm in ward 407. Ask for Michel Venetin, that's my name." He takes a deep breath.

"What can I bring you?" I ask, in anguish. I can't bear this any longer.

"Cigarettes." A crooked smile forms on his lips. "I'll be waiting for you. You'll come, won't you?" he repeats, as I am drawn into the sea of mourners heading toward the cemetery.

"Yes, tomorrow or the day after, for sure." I turn my head away to hide the tears streaming down my face.

On my way home, the sight of Marko won't let me rest. How can a free spirit be trapped so unjustly like that? *It's unbelievable, tormenting,* I think, full of rage as I cross the threshold to enter my house.

A strange rattling cry is heard from the roof. It stirs my curiosity and I run upstairs through the narrow passageway to find out what it's all about. Leaning against the wall I see a living cadaver staring me in the face. His breath smells of death, his bones are covered with dry, shiny skin, his eyes sunken in an abyss. The living-dead person turns his hairless head and lets out a muffled sound. From some mumbled words I learn his name, his persecution by the SS and finally his incarceration in the death camps where dying and desolation were his constant companions.

"How did I survive?" the skeletal being says, reading my mind.

I can't tell if his presence or mine is a delusion. How improbable is it to be here in front of him, witnessing the untold pain that I saw in Marko's eyes that day I met him in free Greece, fighting with the partisans in the mountains. He spoke briefly of the horrifying death camps. What meaning can his words have, conveyed to me when even now, at this very moment, I'm unable to believe in my senses. I feel my own eyes must be deceiving me.

The young man—or is he aged?—goes on talking. His mind has retained unerringly everything that has disappeared from his withered flesh. The longer I listen, the more I begin to sway, to lose my balance. The hollow echo of his words shocks me.

"I reached the bottom of the pit. I was starving to death...among living corpses feeding upon each other...a desperate effort..."

His words ring in my ears. I lean on the wall for support.

Somehow, he swallowed tar that gave him a black lung, a fatal illness, and the SS abandoned him on a dirt road, near death.

His mind has retained whatever he lost in physical stature. He knows who he is, his number, engraved on a yellow star, symbol of genocide at Dachau and Belsen and Auschwitz for now and forever and ever and ever in an eternity of raw human barbarism. The unburied dead man goes away to continue living his own terrible freedom.

I stay impaled there, the prisoner of a monstrous inhumanity.

I have to search for a long time to find Marko's room when I go to visit him at the hospital the next day.

"I must get used to calling him Michel," I think to myself, but it bothers me. I'm upset. I wonder if the number Marko gave me was correct. *Did I hear him right? Did he give me the wrong one?* I go in circles down corridors, searching one hallway after another in the age-old hospital, walking past wounded and sick patients who look at me with a forlorn curiosity. They're lying on unpainted iron beds covered with tattered graying sheets, staring ahead with an expression of gloom on their pale faces.

What is that horrible odor that hits me? I wonder, opening one door after another to find him. It seems like a smell of iodine, urine, and tobacco smoke that hangs in the air. I open and close the doors in a hurry and move on. I get in a sweat searching in vain for Marko, *no, Michel. I must learn.* Times have changed. I run around and, at last, find ward 407 staring straight at me. I enter an enormous room with a high, old-fashioned ceiling, crumbling walls, and windows stuffed with rags to keep out the cold winter wind. Michel sees me the instant I open the door and greets me with a poignant smile. I approach, happy to see him. He introduces me to his friends, sharing around the cigarettes and a few homemade sweets I have brought.

Pavlos, a young man with curly black hair, is lying in bed with swollen glands and looks miserable from the pain. His bloated face is red from the fever and almost grotesque. Yet he can't stop talking with an intense liveliness that makes his eyes glow.

"You know, don't you, that returning *andartes* are shot before they even cross the threshold of their homes. That's not manly, it's underhanded and dishonest." He complains bitterly and the others nod in agreement.

"Are you telling me?" Demos, a big, burly man, limps in and joins the small circle seated around Pavlos' bed. "Mountain freedom fighters who served their country honorably are ambushed at night, the minute they lay down their arms, in compliance with the notorious Varkiza agreement. That was some agreement! It was our downfall. And now we're paying for it with our own blood. We expected a fair deal, not a trap," he fumes, blowing thick smoke at every pause.

"Supposedly they're killed by strangers, while everyone knows," insists Theodoros, farther away, leaning on the peeling wall. "Everyone knows very well"—he takes hold of his crutches to get a little closer—"that the perpetrators are former Nazi collaborators."

"What do you think?" asks Grigoris who has not yet spoken up. He's a thin, balding man whose face is in a permanent frown as he tries to light a cigarette with his mangled hand. "The quislings are being rewarded while thousands of fighters and heroes of the liberation movement are dying a slow death or tortured, yes, tortured in the concentration camps on barren islands."

"In Makronisi instead of Dachau," Michel cuts in, "the cream of our youth languishes. Oh," he groans with pain, not only from his wounded leg but also from a crushed heart. "And not just a few. Thousands. Countless."

"Our mistake was to trust that bloody Varkiza document and surrender our weapons. We were a trained army! Who ever heard of giving up power just like that?" Pavlos objects, leaning his good looking body on the rusty bed rail. "Without any guarantees for our life, without any certainty of preserving the ideals for which we fought and lost good men by the thousands," Pavlos protests, and the others shake their heads.

"We were deceived by the foreign powers. Those self-serving bastards who follow the age-old saying: 'divide and conquer' to keep us subjugated." Demos defends his point, gesticulating with his callused hands in the smoke-filled air.

"The storm has hit us for good. The blowing wind has changed course before our very eyes, setting in motion a catastrophic tornado that threatens to eclipse the sun from the face of the earth," Michel starts talking again, putting out one cigarette after another. The thick cloud of smoke streams upward toward the cavernous ceiling. His eyes look wild.

373

"It's cost us an arm and a leg," Pavlos murmurs in a tired voice.

"Proud people don't give in." Theodoros taps his crutch on the floor in a cold fury, inviting angry dirty looks from some of the patients lying in bed, too feeble to join the conversation.

"At least we're alive. We answer 'present' at the roll call," I say as I get up from the rickety chair to leave. "Regardless of what we suffered, we continue. Our struggle has not ended…" I say, and leave Marko with a warm handshake, catching his quizzical glance momentarily before we part at the door.

On my way out I have no difficulty locating the exit. My thoughts race to the day I first met Marko, the valiant brave fighter. He's no longer Marko. It's different now. We're not fighting for freedom in the mountains. Liberation is here, but where is freedom?

Hunger, poverty, and unemployment send people by the thousands to the streets. In 1945, as conditions worsen, the demonstrations turn into a true groundswell. Each new protest march is more impressive, more gigantic than the other. The last street killing has stirred up more incidents.

One day, as I'm getting off the tram on my way to a youth movement demonstration, I notice my long lost friend Avyoula, lively and pretty as ever in a crisp floral print dress that looks smashing on her petite, svelte figure. I still call her by her nickname, "little devil," for her mischievous smile and run to catch up with her at the corner where she's waiting to cross the street. I push my way through the crowd, calling out, "Avyoula, wait," but I can't be heard in the uproar. Just as I reach her, two cops arrest me and grab the leaflets out of my hand. I can only see her brown hair waving in the air as she disappears from

374

view. I give up motioning, to keep Avyoula out of trouble. They would have no hesitation accusing her of being my accomplice.

"Where are you taking those shitty papers? Who gave them to you?" the cop with the crew cut and twisted mouth swears at me.

"Speak up, you dirty pig, before I bust your head. That'll teach you a lesson." The other one yanks me by the sleeve. I struggle to free my arm.

"Hey, who d'ya think you're makin' a fool out of? Dirty bitch," barks the first one, shoving me along.

I soon realize they're heading for the jail near our house, and it shakes me up. I slink along to keep from being seen.

The hell with going to jail, I think. *As long as my family doesn't see me. That's all I need.*

After a barrage of rapid-fire questions by a couple of disgusting brutes, they send me to the dungeon. I walk through a dark, dank, foul-smelling corridor reeking of urine and feces. Inside the crypt is hidden a living horror. Prisoners thrown on top of each other in a heap, under horrible conditions, swelter in the infernal heat. Now I see with my own eyes where they brought all those people who were marched in chains under our window every night. I crouch down next to them, listening to their lament.

"Is this what we get for everything we did for our country's liberation?" they moan.

A long time passes—I'm in a stupor from the heat and the shock. Finally the hideous voice of a hoodlum calls me back.

"Get lost, you scum. And don't let us catch you at this again. You'll be sent to rot in the dungeon like the others and nobody will ever hear from you again, you filthy American," he spits, exposing a row of black decaying teeth in a twisted grimace that stretches the thick skin around his depraved-looking mouth all the way to his ears.

When I return home, Despo is in a turmoil. "What's the matter with you? What happened?" I implore her to talk to me.

"Don't ask, don't ask."

"What is it? Tell me, before I go crazy," I insist, but she acts as though she's deaf.

At last, in a flood of tears, she says, "Meteoritis was sent to a concentration camp."

"Where? When? How did you find out?"

"Where? To hell. They'll kill him. You know that, don't you? Like so many others." Despo is beside herself.

One worry on top of another. I start shaking. I remember when Meteoritis taught me to swim. Now, he languishes in exile. He is gone, and one by one, many in our crowd of friends are disappearing. I just found out about Yianni. Jailed in Larissa. Lena, too, is rotting in prison.

"Despo, I feel miserable. Wait till you hear what I have to tell you."

"What? What is it, my girl, tell me. Tell me what's troubling you." She comes to my side and puts her arm around my shoulder.

"Oh, many others are imprisoned. You don't know them. Friends. We worked together. Who knows where they'll send them. I fear the worst," I confess. "Everything's happening too fast and hitting too hard."

"This is too much. A never-ending grief. Don't fret, my sweet. Come over here; let me make you a cup of coffee. I'll read your fortune, too," she offers, trying to cheer me up. Her concern moves me.

"What will that cup show when we can see what's happening all around us, before our very eyes? Anyhow, maybe you'll find something good to tell me." I follow her to the kitchen to keep her company.

"Sit." She slides a chair in my direction.

"Oh, for heaven's sake, I can help myself. Tell me, what else is on your mind?" I ask.

"Oh, my, I don't want to dump it on you all at once." She straightens the hairpin in her bun with nervous fingers.

I watch her, a beautiful buxom woman with glistening chestnut brown hair, her eyes limpid pools of autumn light. Most of all, she can charm you with her sweet disposition. A true Smyrna type of woman who loves to sing *amanedes* with her husband Andreas: those plaintive, sometimes almost mournful, songs from her land.

"A while ago, the *Iyoumenos* David from the Zdani monastery came over." She pushes in her hairpin. "To visit. He's been transferred near here. Well, he got to telling me and your mother about Bishop Seraphim." She looks steadily at me, not moving an eyelash. I sit wordless, glued to my seat, clutching my cup. "He's also being hounded. Imagine a man of the church being followed like a common criminal. It's all because of his ideas and what he did up in those mountains. Now look at him."

My mother rushes in from the clinic with Tasio, who's been getting radiation therapy for his malnutrition. The treatment leaves him bald, so he has to wear a beret to hide his shiny head that makes him look prematurely old. He shies away from all his playmates and hangs around only with his cousin Anesti, to avoid being teased and hurt by their cruel remarks.

377

"I'm shocked, absolutely shocked." She comes back in time to hear the last news and joins the conversation. "Only time will tell if the powers that be will go to extremes and harm him," she adds, dejected. "Now," she says with a sigh, "I must write to your father to let him know what our news is."

Thessaloniki 8/4/45

Dear Petro,

After three whole years I take pen in hand to etch this letter. It is completely impossible to describe our suffering and ordeals that we went through for four entire years. I see the children alive and I make the sign of the Cross that we were saved from so may dangers!

We arrived here four months ago in miserable condition and thanks to two or three friends of mine who took pity on us and helped us with clothes etc., we passed the first few months. Since February the Consulate has been giving us a little money, and in the state we are in we can't even buy a length of cloth, and a pair of shoes costs 8,000 drachmas. Since we came here we wrote you many cards and ten days ago I sent you a telegram because I could not do so sooner, so I was comforted a little because I can imagine your anxiety with all you have heard, but really you can't possibly imagine what's happened in this war. Through the Red Cross every now and then I received a letter from you while we were trapped and pursued by the Germans. We ran from one village to another in mountains and valleys and I couldn't write to you for twenty months.

I thank God we were saved.

We are waiting for money every day, you know how necessary it is.

Because of our hardships I have to take Tasio for radiotherapy. I did everything I could to save the children; God gave me a lot of strength to struggle like a beast. I had the responsibility of being a Mother, but also a Father.

Imagine Petro how happy you will feel when you see us in front of you!

What a moment it will be when you embrace your beloved children, grown now and mature.

I leave with an embittedered feeling before Despo "reads" my coffee cup. The writing is clearly on the wall. Nothing can save us.

Bishop Seraphim joins the thousands of others—clergy and laity alike—who are persecuted. The final blow is his demotion from his position as Bishop of Kozani and Paliocastro in Macedonia. Stripped of his ecclesiastic authority, he is placed under house arrest and threatened with imprisonment if he tries to escape or disobey the restrictions imposed on him.

In my halting English I've written my father two cards. How can five and a half years be squeezed into such a tiny space? What to say and how much to leave out? All I know is that it's time to part. Separation uproots, it's what eats out your heart, turning it into ashes. *The hour of parting is approaching,* I think. I can't get that agonizing thought out of my mind.

We embrace, relatives and friends in tears, and in November 1945, board the Red Cross ship *Gripsholm* that will take us to America. We face a new strange world—clean, to an obsessive degree, organized according to a regular

379

schedule, comfortable and aseptically sterile. The smiling crew greets us with flawless Scandinavian politeness. Dinner has an unfamiliar, tasteless quality about it, but is plentiful and filling.

It's the middle of the winter, and I have no coat. I wear a heavy gray blanket that the Red Cross gave us over my shoulders. It's so big it follows me around like a long furry tail. At night, leaning on the ship's bow rail, I look out at the twinkling lights engulfing the harbor of Thessaloniki in the distance. A dense fog separates us.

Early in the morning I go back to the railing to gaze at the harbor, to gather a few wildflowers of nostalgia for reminiscence on the long voyage. I hear familiar warm voices calling. "Here, here!"

I look in their direction and my heart pounds. A cry freezes on the mast. "Come, come back." They're my friends, all of them, as before, before the killings, the jailing and extermination in the death camps on barren islands that eat away the spirit and flesh of the flower of our youth. They've come in a rowboat to say farewell for one more time. They're standing with arms upraised, wind blowing through their unruly hair, stretching their fingers to the sky. Wild, untamable voices echoing from stem to stern, cry out within. "Go back, don't go away."

The wish *'Until we meet again' is for now, it exists, don't forget it,* a voice within me quivers.

The small boat next to the huge ship is not strong enough to hold me even though it runs on a true course. I want to land here, using the boat's old rusty anchor.

In the distance, the rowboat recedes, growing smaller and smaller. The beloved faces rise to gigantic heights, reaching closer to me, coming alive, waving frantically in the dim, gray dawn of a new day.